A Collectors Identification and Value Guide

COLLECTING TOYS

By Richard O'Brien

BOOKS AMERICANA
INC.

ISBN 0-89689-002-3

To
Mary Marek Zeman
and
Julie Marek Chivers

ACKNOWLEDGMENTS

Although I'd like to say I did it all myself, I certainly didn't.

First, to Jim Harmon, a longtime friend, for his article and advice on toy premiums. Next, to an even longer-term friend (since 1943), Bill Kaufman, for all his photos, and to Alan Levine and Al Rizzolo of the Red Pony for allowing us to photograph their toys. Thanks, too, to another good and generous friend, Ray Funk, for his articles, photos, and listings on Doepke and Smitty, and to C. B. C. Lee for his articles on vehicles, photos, and listings and prices on Tootsietoys. Gramercy to Barbara and Jonathan Newman, for their article and help on paper toys, and to their son Jonathan A. Newman, for his photographs. Equally appreciated are Charles W. Best's article, photos, and additional help on the Guns section, Thomas W. Sefton's list, advice, and prices on pre-1932 Buddy "L" toys, and Albert W. McCollough's background information on Buddy "L".

Much has been unearthed on American toy soldiers that was previously unknown and ignored, and for this I wish to thank former Auburn Rubber employees Floyd Link and Charles (Mike) Hornett, and former Barclay Mfg. Co. employees Harry Bogaty, George Fall, Gloria Mary Zulumian, Frank Terminini, Sally Newman and Lawrence McDonough, as well as Bob Wilkens, Joseph A. Tighe and George Thorne. Thanks too to Sandra Malik of Donsco and Karl Zipple for virtually all of the information on Grey Iron. Astounded thanks to Don Pielin for generously allowing me to use many of the pictures in his "American Dimestore Soldiers, Volume 1", and my appreciation to new friend Ed Poole for photographing most of the Auburn soldiers in this book, as well as to Karl Zipple again, for his photographs of all the Greyklip soldiers. Still in the photos department, thanks to Virginia Barber of Garth's Auctions Inc. and David Redin, Jay Remer and Pamela S. Brown of PB 84, a division of Sotheby Parke Bernet, Inc. My gratitude also for the help of George H. Merritt and Barbara Gemme of MB Communications (Milton Bradley), Judith H. Sussman of Gabriel Industries Inc. (Hubley), Robert M. Gray of the Ohio Art Company, George Fink of Buddy L, Ted Ericson of the Toy Mfrs. of America, and to collector and friend Dave Weiss for his advice.

For much of the research and some of the illustrations in this book, I am indebted to Playthings Magazine and its editor Penny Gill for the extensive use of their files, as well as to the employees of the New

York Public Library for their helpfulness as I checked through scores of toy trade magazines back issues. Finally, to my great agent Albert Zuckerman, for finding me the outlet for this work, and to Books Americana Inc. publisher Dan Alexander for his courtesy, friendliness, and helpfulness.

After all this, it's hard to believe I've forgotten anyone, but I probably have. So to him, her or them, I can only offer my apologies and sincerely state that I did appreciate their efforts.

INTRODUCTION

Although this book is intended primarily as a price guide, it is my hope that it will prove to be more than that; that it will provide enjoyment and information for all those who are interested in toys. For this reason I have enlisted a number of experts to assist with the book, and it is my hope in future editions to add more. It would be quixotic to attempt to list each of the virtually countless toys produced in the U.S. since the 1700s, but I am quixotic enough to hope to eventually come much closer than I have with this book, as sizeable as it is. For these reasons, and since it is the publisher's plan to present an updated version at regular intervals, perhaps even annually, I would like to hear from any collectors or dealers with well-researched background information, photos, and lists on companies and categories not already comprehensively dealt with in this volume. Corrections would also be very much appreciated.

The prices shown alongside each toy were determined by my going through thousands of items on hundreds of sales lists, by poring through auction results, by strolling through flea markets and toy conventions, and by checking with knowledgable collectors and dealers and then, where possible, averaging out the prices. These figures, however, can serve only as a guide, as prices range widely on many items, and on scores of others, only one example emerged as being bought, advertised, or sold. Furthermore, in addition to the often great range of dealer's prices, auction prices can fluctuate widely, even in the course of the same auction, as interest can be feverish and monied, or totally spent-out, disinterested or uninformed. Thus there is a need for a book of this sort, and as the years and editions roll on, perhaps it can help serve as a stabilizing force, to the benefit of buyer and seller alike.

In my conversations with collectors and dealers about the idea of this book, the one point stressed over and over was condition, and the impact it has on the price of a toy. For this reason, since some readers will be turning to only one section of this book, and also since types of condition can vary with the different kind of toys, I have included several paragraphs on condition in each of the categories with which this book deals.

As much information as possible is given on the items listed. Where information is skimpy, it is because it was all I had. Sizes are noted wherever possible, and when just the number of inches is given, without specifying whether it is length or height, it is because that information did not appear in the list I received. Any words in quotes indicate the words are found on the toy. "Litho" is an abbreviation for a toy that is lithographed.

At this time the prevalent feeling in the collectible toys field is that despite an uncertain economy, there has been no slackening of interest, and prices continue to rise. However, for those who wish to consider this field as an investment, and it can be a good one, it should be stressed that mint or near-mint condition provides considerably more financial safety than any of the other conditions, as this is the only condition sure to attract all collectors and dealers of any particular toy. Furthermore, World War II still seems to be the utmost cut-off point for most serious collectors, and investments in any toys produced after 1940 or 1941 are much more speculative.

The publisher has asked that I also give an opinion as to future collectible toys. I really don't have that kind of prescience, but for the record, toys based on something tend to have added attraction. Thus, future collectibles might include any toys based on "Star Wars", "Star Trek", the Beatles, on comic strips like "Pogo" and "Peanuts", or on television series and historical events, such as space flights. G. I. Joes, particularly the foreign soldiers, and some of the other well-made jointed figures, such as the Captain Action series of the 1960s, seem to be already attracting collectors, although so far only to a small extent. Toys with esthetic appeal often interest collectors. Many plastic toys have this characteristic, and perhaps generations raised on this material will find it as attractive as today's collectors find cast iron, but this of course is problematic.

Richard O'Brien
February, 1978

TABLE OF CONTENTS

VEHICLES
(see also Tin Wind-Up)

CAST IRON AUTOMOTIVE TOYS
by C. B. C. LEE

The manufacture of cast iron toys began shortly after the Civil War and had about reached its zenith by the beginning of the twentieth century. The first toy automobiles began to appear soon after their real life prototypes began chugging along the horse-carriage roads, by which time some of the great 19th century toy makers had already gone out of business. Among those that continued into the automotive era were Hubley, Dent, Wilkins, and Kenton. During the first three decades of this century, others came to the forefront, such as Arcade, Kilgore, A. C. Williams, and Champion. Others also made toy cars and trucks in smaller numbers or for a short period of time, such as Grey Iron, Freidag, and North and Judd. Many of these firms made no identifying marks on their toys, and it has only been in recent years that many very familiar toys have been correctly attributed, as catalogues, patents, and old advertisements have gradually come to light. Probably the greatest American toymaker of all was Ives, but this firm is thought to have made only one toy car, a clockwork driven horseless carriage runabout with figure, measuring 6½" long and 6" to the top of the jockey-cap on the driver. This is a rare toy today, and one in excellent condition commands a considerable price (about $1600 as of this writing.) But other similar vehicles and varying smaller sizes by Hubley, Dent, Wilkens, etc. vary in value from around $20 to $300.

Value does not have much relationship to either age or size, however, having more to do with scarcity, complexity and nicety of design, detail, and "desirability". As with anything else in a free market, it is simply the rule of supply and demand.

C. B. C. LEE is the pen-name of a New England doctor whose hobby is collecting, researching, and writing about toys. He began collecting as a boy in the 1930s, and was lucky enough to have a mother who saved his collection while he was disinterested, serving in the Army, getting his education, and getting started in practice. It was still safely in her attic when second childhood set in prematurely 17 years ago, and he has been busily enslaved by the hobby ever since. He has contributed to books and magazines on the subject, published not only in the U.S.A., but also in England, France, Italy, New Zealand, Australia, and Japan. He is in touch with collectors on five continents, and enthusiastically recommends the hobby as "escape therapy" and an antidote for the pressures, anxieties, frustrations, and insults of life in the real world.

Demand and "desirability" are affected by a number of factors. One of these is nostalgia, and the current market seems to have most of that hooked into the period from mid 1920s through the mid 1930s. In automotive toys, quality also peaked during this decade, but then, so did the squeeze of the Great Depression. The latter event shrunk Santa Claus's budget, depressed sales, and eventually resulted in a down-grading of quality. It also resulted in these most desirable of toys being the most scarce today.

As a general guide to factors affecting desirability, there are a few broad easy clues, however. Accuracy of scale and proportion, the use of many different cast parts, cast-in or decal logos and details, hand-painting (by the original maker, but NOT by some later child or collector!!), etc. all enhance value. In most cases, a 4-inch roadster with a separate chassis, separate nickel-plated radiator and headlights, and a separate cast figure will be worth much more than a two-piece one with the halves riveted together. The Hubley Packard is a complex assembly of nearly 20 parts, with opening front doors, hinged hoods, plated radiator and motor, license plate, seats, and driver. It is a handsome toy, and was relatively expensive when originally marketed. A mint example today can sell for more than $5000. Nearly as complex, but much less scarce, the Kilgore Stutz roadster will sell for up to $700. Of similar value are the Arcade Buicks, Reo, Checker cab (with separate nickeled radiator) and several large buses. Because of scarcity, certain pieces of similar quality demand higher prices: White panel truck or moving van, $1000 plus; White A.C.F., and Mack buses, about $2000. The very rare Brinks Armored truck by Arcade is worth even more. These high prices are due to extreme scarcity, many of these pieces being in fewer than ten known collections, and some having only 2 or 3 examples known in the country. For this reason, the market is very shallow, and only a few more coming on the market could drop the values dramatically. If someone found a case of twelve Brink's trucks in an old warehouse, he might sell the first one for $3000, but would have trouble getting $500 for the twelfth one. An example of this is the handsome Arcade Andy Gump 348 roadster. This was approaching $1000 in the inflating market a few years ago, but several have sold recently for under $250.

In small cars, around 4" long, the vast majority are currently worth between $10 and $40, but a few scarce ones, such as Arcade Nashes, Dent LaSalles, Kenton Pontiacs and other nickeled radiator members of this set, 4-casting nickeled-radiator cars by A. C. Williams and Champion, go for $100 or more.

Other special cases inclued some small trucks with logo publicity on them: Borden's Milk truck, a LIFE-SAVERS truck the size and shape of a roll of the candy, etc. can sell for more than $300.

But these values are very volatile, both up and down, and may be badly obsolete even by the time this is printed. The lawyers long ago defined the "fair market value" as that price paid by a (knowledge-able)willing buyer to a (knowledgeable) willing seller.

TOOTSIETOYS, DIE-CAST, AND SLUSH
by C. B. C. LEE

Die-casting was an outgrowth of the invention of the Linotype machine, introduced at the Columbian Exposition at Chicago in 1893. A trade-journal publisher in that city named Samuel Dowst began to adapt the type-casting machine to making small promotional minatures, collar buttons, and so on related to the Laundry Journal he also published. By the turn of the century, however, the die-casting business had become his principal business, and he was producing a myriad of small party favors, candy premiums, political items, and penny jewelry. Amongst these were several charms and miniatures of automotive, trains, and aircraft. By 1911, he produced a small 47mm. limousine with free-turning wheels. By 1914 a 77 mm. Ford touring car was marketed, and a matching pick-up truck was made two years later. All three of these stayed in the catalouge until the late 20s, and the truck as late as 1932. In 1922 a line of doll furniture was developed, and was trade-named Tootsietoy after the daughter of the company's president at that time, Tootsie Dowst. The name later was used to identify nearly all of the toys the company sold. However, it continued to make items for other buyers, and still makes the metal marker pieces used in the deluxe Monopoly game. Tootsietoys continue to be made today, the present name of the Company being the Strombecker Corporation.

As with other collectibles, the value of obsolete toys today is not greatly related to age. The oldest Tootsietoys were made in such large numbers and for so long a period that they are not hard to find today. Others, some of which were unpopular in their day, were not sold in great numbers and are rare today. The 1932 Funnies series of six pieces drawn from the contemporary comic strips is an example of this. These were made in a boxed set of 6, having cams on the axles, which imparted action to the figures as the toy was pushed along the floor, and having details and figures hand-painted in up to seven different colors. This boxed set sold for $1.00. The six pieces were also made in simpler non-action versions with simple paint and sold for 10ᵉ each. For reasons hard to understand today, these toys were not popular. Consequently they are very hard to find, and are more valuable. Some of the individual pieces must have been better liked by their owners and were played to death or lost, making them even scarcer. So, though all were made in about equal numbers, some are rarer than others. Uncle Walt Wallet in a roadster is the most valuable, often selling for more than $100. Uncle Willie and Mamie in a boat is at the other end, worth about half as much.

In regular production cars, LaSalles and a sort of pseudo-Lincoln have the greatest value, up to about $75, while other Fords, Yellow Cabs, and early Mack trucks are seldom above $25. Graham automobiles are presently worth about $35 except for the roadster and town car, worth about $45. A 1925 panel delivery truck, often called "Federal" by collectors, was made in stock versions having legends on the side panels saying: MILK, MARKET, LAUNDRY, GROCERY, BAKERY, and FLORIST. Their rarity is in about that order, MILK being worth about $20 up to FLORIST at about $100. This same line of small trucks were also made in small numbers with custom private liveries, and over a dozen such versions with store names on the sides are presently known to exist. There were probably more. These, too, vary in value according to scarcity, the commonest, HOCHSCHILD KOHN & CO., presently being worth about $100. One which had the J. C. Penny logo on the side is worth twice that, and a few might fing a buyer at even higher prices.

Other manufacturers also made die-cast toys, and a few of these are desirable enough to have some value. Barclay made a small series of separate body/chassis vehicles in the late 1930s, and a west coast firm TIP-TOP Toys, which are of fair value. So are a few of the finer die-cast Manoils and ERIEs. Many others are in little demand, such as JANE FRANCIS, GOODIE, METAL MASTERS, IT'S A BEAUT, and certain Hubleys. Post-War items, including most of the Hubley, Tootsietoy, Midgetoy, Manoil, etc. output seldom sell for more than $2.00

Slush casting was a process simple enough to be done in tiny factories, and even in home-industries during the depression. A few large manufacturers made toys in this way, most notably Barclay, Manoil, Savoye, Kansas toy and Novelty, and others, but many were made by anonymous small unidentifiable and local operations, using molds made and marketed by a few firms. Many slush-cast toys are of very little value today, but there are exceptions. Foremost among these were dealer promotional replicas of real cars, made by Banthrico and National Products. These can sell for up to $200. Other very accurate and detailed slush models, similar in size and scale to the contemporary Tootsietoys, can be worth up to $50, most notable among these being certain nicely cast models of the Reo Victoria, Cord, Packard, Chrysler Imperial, and early Buick.

As with other toys, condition is very important. The values quoted here are for those in like-new condition. Paint-wear can drop the value to half, and broken or missing parts can drop it to nearly nothing. Repairing can occasionally partially rescue an exceptionally rare piece, but more often depresses the value. Reproductions are beginning to appear on the market, and will also tend to depress the values of the real thing. As with anything else in a free market, cost is largely a matter of supply and demand, both of which can wax and wane cyclicly. Let the buyer beware.

CONDITION OF A TOY
AND ITS RELATION TO PRICE

The price of a toy depends not only on its desirability, but on its condition. A toy in mint condition is generally worth twice what that same toy would bring in good condition, with "very good" falling about equally in between good and mint.

"Mint" means just that; the condition in which it was originally issued—perfect, regardless of age, not the slightest blemish. Needless to say this is a fairly rare state of affairs, but enough toys exist in mint condition to make it an employable term. Many people hoping to dispose of toys are tempted to call an item "mint" when it is really "near mint", "very good", or sometimes just "good". Inevitably this can result in unhappiness all around, and not infrequently, a cancelled sale.

"Good" signals a toy that has seen considerable wear, shows it age, but is basically sound. A collector will collect it, but will often not be wholly satisfied with it as an example of his collection, and thus prices are often drastically below that which the same item in mint can command.

Condition below good result in another drastic drop in price, and toys with missing parts, although otherwise in excellent condition, will usually fall into this lower-priced category. Rust, even small spots of it, can seriously lower the price of a toy. "Near-Mint", "Very Fine", "Fine" and similar terms often found in sellers' descriptions denote conditions between Mint and Very Good, and are priced accordingly.

The key to grading is to avoid wishful thinking. Grading can sometimes be a problem for the uninitiated, but common sense will usually prevail, and when possible, a consultation with an expert in the field can often clear up lingering doubts. A toy in its original box is worth up to 10 to 20% more if the box is in mint condition, with the price dropping as its condition lessens.

VEHICLES

	G	VG	M
A. C. WILLIAMS four-casting nickeled-radiator car, approx. 4" long	50.00	75.00	100.00
A.C. WILLIAMS Touring Car, cast iron 9½" long	250.00	375.00	500.00
AMERICAN NATIONAL COMPANY "Juvenile Auto" dump truck pedal car, red and yellow tin, 57" long	75.00	112.50	150.00
AMERICAN NATIONAL Packard car, 1920s coupe	100.00	150.00	200.00
AMERICAN NATIONAL Velie, child's pedal car, circa 1918	100.00	150.00	200.00
ARCADE A.C.F. Bus	750.00	1125.00	1500.00
ARCADE Allis-Chalmers Tractor with Bottom Leader, approx. 12" long, circa 1937	60.00	90.00	120.00
ARCADE Ambulance, 6" long	20.00	30.00	40.00
ARCADE Andy Gump car, No. 348 on license plate	125.00	187.50	250.00
ARCADE Anthony Company Dump Truck, reads "Anthony Company Inc., Streater, Illinois" in raised gold embossed letters on tailgate	250.00	375.00	500.00

See page 32   See page 34

The handsome and complex Hubley Packard sedan (285 mm.) and Kilgore Stutz roadster (260 mm.) are made up of 15 and 13 separate castings, respectively. Both highly sought after, greater rarity causes the Packard to be worth about eight Stutzes.
Caption and Photo by C.B.C Lee

	G	VG	M
ARCADE auto, looks like 1933 Plymouth, white rubber tires, approx. 4¾" long..	22.00	33.00	44.00
ARCADE auto, four-door hard top, 6" long	100.00	150.00	200.00
ARCADE Avery Tractor circa 1920s, 4¾" long	50.00	75.00	100.00
ARCADE Brinks Armored Truck	1250.00	1875.00	2500.00
ARCADE Buick, two-door circa 1928, 8" long, spare tire on rear	350.00	525.00	700.00
ARCADE Bus, 8" long, seven side windows, circa 1930	60.00	90.00	120.00
ARCADE Bus, circa 1940, 8¾" long....	30.00	45.00	60.00
ARCADE Bus, 9" long, circa 1949	25.00	37.50	50.00

See page 8   See page 9

See page 10
Arcade Chevrolets, rear is 1924 series (170 mm.) and 1928 series (205 mm.), the older one is rarer and worth somewhat more than the handsomer later series. The reverse is true of the Fords, front, where the Model T series (165 mm.) is commoner and less valuable than the Model A series (170 mm.)
Caption and Photo by C.B.C. Lee

	G	VG	M
ARCADE Bus, with driver, cast iron, 13" long	220.00	330.00	440.00
ARCADE No. 316x bus, double-decker coach, 1932, rear stairway to top 8¼" long	120.00	180.00	240.00

7

	G	VG	M
ARCADE Bus, double-decker, rear stairway to top, circa 1938, 8" long......	80.00	120.00	160.00
ARCADE "Catepillar Tractor", No. 268x, 1932, chain caterpillar treads, approx. 5½" long.................	35.00	52.50	70.00
ARCADE Caterpillar Tractor, large yellow version.....................	60.00	90.00	120.00
ARCADE No. 311 bus, 1920s, approx. 6" long	25.00	37.50	50.00
ARCADE No. 269 very early Caterpillar tractor	200.00	300.00	400.00
ARCADE Century of Progress Greyhound bus, 10" long, circa 1940.......	25.00	37.50	50.00
ARCADE Century of Progress Greyhound bus, 12" long, circa 1940.......	16.00	24.00	32.00
ARCADE Chevrolet utility coupe, 1924, rubber tires, black with gold belt line, silver headlights, 6¾" long, with chauffuer........................	80.00	120.00	160.00

Arcade Yellow cabs. The commoner older series, rear (200 & 205 mm.) are worth less than the later ones, front, (205 & 200 mm.), the G.M. cab at left and a late variation of the older Yellow cab on the right. Demand for the banks drives their value up, being competed for also by the bank collecting fraternity. Also made in a larger scale. See page 13

Caption and Photo by C.B.C. Lee

Yellow cabs made by other manufacturers, Hubley, Dent and Kenton (all 210 mm.), are scarcer and fetch more than the similar Arcades. Arcades are so marked underneath. Most other makes are not.

Caption and Photo by C.B.C. Lee

The big Arcade buses (range from 290 to 330 mm.) vary widely in scarcity and value. Ascending value from left to right: Fageol (about $100), Yellow Coach (about $700) (A double-deck open top version of this one is about the same value), A.C.F. (about $1200), White (about $2000), and Mack (about $3000). Other makes are generally quite a bit less, as are smaller sizes.

Caption and Photo by C.B.C. Lee

	G	VG	M
ARCADE Cherolet Coupe 1928, 8" long white rubber tires, spare tire on rear................................	120.00	180.00	240.00
ARCADE Coupe, 5" long, 1920s two side windows.....................	50.00	75.00	100.00
ARCADE Coupe, 5" long, 1920s, two side window.....................	60.00	90.00	120.00
ARCADE Coupe (Ford?), 6½" long, one side window, 1920s................	60.00	90.00	120.00
ARCADE Coupe, 6¾" long, two side windows, early 1920s..............	60.00	90.00	120.00
ARCADE Coupe, 9" long, circa 1920s, spare tire on rear, two windows on side............................	150.00	225.00	300.00
ARCADE Coast to Coast bus, 10" long...	35.00	52.50	70.00

9

	G	VG	M
ARCADE corn cutter and binder.......	25.00	37.50	50.00
ARCADE corn planter...............	8.00	12.00	16.00
ARCADE No. 116 coupe with working rumble seat, 1920s, approx. 5" long...	25.00	37.50	50.00
ARCADE disk harrow..............	7.00	10.50	14.00
ARCADE double-decker bus, open, 18 tin seats on roof, dual wheels on rear, "Made by ARCADE MRG. CO. FREEPORT, ILL." on each side, 13¾" long, circa 1930s......................	350.00	525.00	700.00
ARCADE dump hay rake, 5"..........	22.00	33.00	44.00
ARCADE dump hay rake, 7"..........	40.00	60.00	80.00
ARCADE dump truck, 6" long, circa 1927..........................	40.00	60.00	80.00
ARCADE dump truck, open cab, 8" long, early 1920s.....................	80.00	120.00	160.00
ARCADE dump truck with driver, 10½" long	150.00	225.00	300.00
ARCADE dump truck, Red Baby, 11" long, 1920s.....................	90.00	135.00	180.00
ARCADE Fageol Coach (bus), circa 1932, 6" long..........................	50.00	75.00	100.00
ARCADE Fageol bus, 12½" long, dual wheels, circa 1930s...............	90.00	135.00	180.00
ARCADE Farm Mower..............	15.00	22.50	30.00
ARCADE Farmal Tractor, Model B.....	160.00	240.00	320.00
ARCADE Fire Engine, 9" long, 1930s...	40.00	60.00	80.00
ARCADE Fire Truck, circa 1936, 13½" long, rubber tires, removeable hose reel, bell, six firemen in blue coats, steam boiler......................	50.00	75.00	100.00
ARCADE Ford coupe with rumble seat No. 106........................	22.00	33.00	44.00
ARCADE Ford coupe with rumble seat No. 116........................	40.00	60.00	80.00
ARCADE Ford gondola, 13" long, circa 1927..........................	150.00	225.00	300.00
ARCADE Ford stake truck, 7" long.....	40.00	60.00	80.00
ARCARDE Ford touring Model T with driver..........................	40.00	60.00	80.00

	G	VG	M
ARCADE Fordson tractor with driver, cast iron 5¾"......................	30.00	40.00	60.00
ARCADE "Gasoline" truck circa 1930s, 13" long.........................	150.00	225.00	300.00
ARCADE Ice Truck, 6½" long.........	50.00	75.00	100.00
ARCADE Ice Truck, circa 1930s........	30.00	45.00	60.00
ARCADE Industrial Derrick...........	350.00	525.00	700.00
ARCADE International Harvester Caterpillar tractor......................	80.00	120.00	160.00
ARCADE International Harvester Caterpillar tractor, large.................	200.00	300.00	400.00
ARCADE International Harvester dump truck, white rubber tires, circa 1929...	100.00	150.00	200.00
ARCADE John Deere thresher, mid-1930s	75.00	112.50	150.00
ARCADE John Deere tractor...........	16.00	24.00	32.00
ARCADE limousine (or bus), circa 1920s, 12½" long.......................	100.00	150.00	200.00
ARCADE Mack "American Oil Co.", circa 1928, 10½" long..............	150.00	225.00	300.00
ARCADE Mack bus..................	1500.00	2250.00	3000.00
ARCADE Mack Truck, circa 1928, 8½" long	100.00	150.00	200.00
ARCADE Mack Truck with dump body, driver, body cranks up and dumps, 1920s, 8½" long..................	100.00	150.00	200.00
ARCADE Mack "Gasoline" truck, 5" long	25.00	37.50	50.00
ARCADE McCormick-Deering combine, 10", cast iron.....................	60.00	90.00	120.00
ARCADE 10-20 McCormick-Deering Farm Tractor.....................	30.00	45.00	60.00
ARCADE "McCormick-Deering", manure spreader with shaft.................	60.00	90.00	120.00
ARCADE No. 450x McCormick-Deering thresher, 9½" long, 1932............	70.00	105.00	140.00
ARCADE Model A Ford 6½" long, circa 1928, with driver...................	100.00	150.00	200.00
ARCADE Model A truck, stake sides.....	12.50	18.75	25.00
ARCADE Model A wrecker, circa 1929, 11" long..........................	150.00	225.00	300.00

	G	VG	M
ARCADE Model T Ford coupe, driver, two side windows, 6½" long, circa 1922	80.00	120.00	160.00
ARCADE Model T Ford sedan with door in middle	40.00	60.00	80.00
ARCADE Model T Ford sedan, two-door, with driver, 6¼" long	75.00	112.50	150.00
ARCADE Model T Ford four-door car, 6"	22.00	33.00	44.00
ARCADE Nash, approx. 4" long	50.00	75.00	100.00
ARCADE New York World's Fair bus, 10½" long	21.00	31.50	42.00
ARCADE No. 1 Farm Tractor	18.00	27.00	36.00
ARCADE Oliver Tractor, black rubber wheels	15.00	22.50	30.00
ARCADE plow, one-gang, with black rubber tires	3.00	4.50	6.00
ARCADE plow, two-gang	4.00	6.00	8.00
ARCADE Railroad spike driver, cast with small wheels, upright lever	40.00	60.00	80.00
ARCADE Rumble coupe with driver, 6¾"	120.00	180.00	240.00
ARCADE Sedan circa 1937, cast iron, 8" long	60.00	90.00	120.00
ARCADE semi-truck, cast iron, 1920s, blue	22.00	33.00	44.00
ARCADE sickle bar mower	5.00	7.50	10.00
ARCADE stake truck, cast iron, blue, 7" long	40.00	60.00	80.00
ARCADE stake truck, 1920s, 7½" long	80.00	120.00	160.00
ARCADE tank No. 3960, 1930s, 3" long, spring-firing cannon	12.00	18.00	24.00
ARCADE taxi, four-door with driver, red, white and black, 7¾"	60.00	90.00	120.00
ARCADE threshing machine	37.50	56.25	75.00
ARCADE thresher machine, circa 1930	30.00	45.00	60.00
ARCADE tractor 273	25.00	37.50	50.00
ARCADE tractor with white rubber wheels	10.00	15.00	20.00
ARCADE transport service semi-truck	160.00	240.00	320.00

	G	VG	M
ARCADE truck, black rubber tires, 1930s	18.00	27.00	36.00
ARCADE red baby truck, with driver, open back, 11" long...............	90.00	135.00	180.00
ARCADE White bus.................	1000.00	1500.00	2000.00
ARCADE White dump truck, circa 1920s	300.00	450.00	600.00
ARCADE White moving van...........	500.00	750.00	1000.00
ARCADE White panel truck..........	500.00	750.00	1000.00
ARCADE wrecker, circa 1930s, 6" long..	30.00	45.00	60.00
ARCADE wrecker with driver and hard rubber wheels, 11" long.............	100.00	150.00	200.00
ARCADE wrecker with driver, 11½" long............................	70.00	105.00	140.00
ARCADE No. 3, small Yellow cab.......	22.00	33.00	44.00
ARCADE "Yellow Cab", 1920s, 7¾" long............................	170.00	255.00	340.00
ARCADE "Yellow CAb", No. 155, 1930s, actually orange and black, 8-1/8" long, nickel-plated driver, white rubber tires, lead cowl lights...................	50.00	75.00	100.00
ARCADE Yellow Cab with driver, 9" long, circa 1927...................	150.00	225.00	300.00
ARCADE Yellow Cab 15" long, circa 1924............................	150.00	225.00	300.00

Demand for comic toys is greater due to added competition from comic art buffs, but supply in recent years has driven the sale price of the Andy Gump car down to less than one third of what it was bringing five years ago. Arcade make the Andy Gump (185 mm.). Hubley made the Popeyes, the big cycle (212 mm.) still beilng rare in prime condition. The smaller cycle (140 mm.) and standing figures (85 mm.) are not quite as tough, but almost.

Caption and Photo by C.B.C. Lee

Examples of small iron pieces (cars in this size are generally between 90 and 120 mm.) which are of relatively high value ($75 and up) because of scarcity and features, noted in text.

Caption and Photo by C.B.C. Lee

	G	VG	M
ARCADE Yellow coach bus............	350.00	525.00	700.00
ARCADE Yellow coach bus, double-decker............................	350.00	525.00	700.00
Army Truck, pressed steel, cloth top, black wooden wheels, approx. 10" long	10.00	15.00	20.00
Army Truck, "USA", rubber, covered with impregnated canvas, white rubber tires, dual wheels, circa 1938.........	4.00	6.00	8.00
AUBURN RUBBER ambulance, white or khaki, circa 1938..................	3.00	4.50	6.00
AUBURN Cord automobile (first car produced by Auburn) circa 1936......	3.00	4.50	6.00
AUBURN Ford coupe, circa 1937.......	3.00	4.50	6.00
AUBURN Ford sedan, circa 1937.......	3.00	4.50	6.00
AUBURN midget car, 10½" long.......	8.00	12.00	16.00
AUBURN milk truck, 4" long, circa 1940............................	3.00	4.50	6.00
AUBURN Oldsmobile, circa 1940.......	3.00	4.50	6.00
AUBURN Plymouth sedan, circa 1940...	3.00	4.50	6.00
AUBURN racing car, approx. 6½" long, circa 1939........................	4.00	6.00	8.00
AUBURN tank, approx. 3" long........	2.00	3.00	4.00
AUBURN tank, approx. 4½" long......	3.00	4.50	6.00

	G	**VG**	**M**
AUBURN tractor with driver, circa 1938	4.00	6.00	8.00
AUBURN truck, open bed, 4" long, green, circa 1940	2.00	3.00	4.00
AUBURN truck, open bed, 5¼" long, circa 1940, marked USA, khaki	3.00	4.50	6.00
"Austin", cast iron, early 1930s	20.00	30.00	40.00
Austin car, cast iron, red	16.00	24.00	32.00
Austin car carrier, truck with three cars, circa 1920s	100.00	150.00	200.00
"Austin" stakebody, 3¾" long, 1920s, cast iron	25.00	37.50	50.00
"Austin" wrecker, 4" long, 1920s, cast iron	30.00	45.00	60.00
Auto, raked cab, cast iron, early 1930s, approx. 4" long	18.00	27.00	36.00
Auto Trailer, 12½" long, carries three cars, all two-door, circa 1932	150.00	225.00	300.00
Auto Trailer, 1920s, 22" long, with coupe, two-door sedan, and four-door sedan on trailer	80.00	120.00	160.00
Auto with trailer, circa 938, 2½" long, both auto and trailer very streamlined .	30.00	45.00	60.00
BARCLAY Ambulance, circa 1938	4.00	6.00	8.00

Small iron pieces of intermediate value ($30 to $70)
Caption and Photo by C.B.C. Lee

	G	VG	M
BARCLAY Anti-aircraft truck, no driver, man firing AA gun, double-barrel, circa 1940......................	3.00	4.50	6.00
BARCLAY Anti-aircraft gun vehicle, post WW II, black rubber tires...........	2.00	3.00	4.00
BARCLAY Armored car, black rubber tires, circa 1937, two protruding weapons.........................	5.00	7.50	10.00
BARCLAY Armored car, streamlined, one protruding cannon, white rubber tires.	5.00	7.50	10.00
BARCLAY Cannon truck, white rubber tires, single figure, circa 1940........	6.00	9.00	12.00
BARCLAY Cannon truck, white rubber tires, driver and rider on back, circa 1940............................	6.00	9.00	12.00
BARCLAY Cannon truck, white rubber tires, driver, man firing cannon, circa 1940............................	4.00	6.00	8.00
BARCLAY Cannon truck, driver, man firing cannon, slightly lower and longer than similar model, comes with white rubber tires or metal wheels (Metal wheeled version about $1 cheaper in Very Good)......................	3.50	5.25	7.00
BARCLAY Police Car No. 317, slush mold, approx. 3¾" long, circa 1930s..	5.00	7.50	10.00
BARCLAY Renault Tank, circa 1938....	7.00	10.50	14.00
BARCLAY Searchlight Truck, white rubber tires, circa 1940.................	7.00	10.50	14.00
BARCLAY Tank "4562"...............	9.00;	13.50	18.00
BARCLAY Tank, soldier's head out of turret, post WW II....................	4.00	6.00	8.00
BARCLAY Tractor, circa 1940.........	4.00	6.00	8.00
BARCLAY "U.S. Army" truck, white rubber tires......................	5.00	7.50	10.00
BARCLAY Truck, "U.S. Motor Unit", circa 1940, white rubber tires........	6.00	9.00	12.00
"Bell Telephone" cast iron truck, white rubber tires, cast iron, 1930s.........	30.00	45.00	60.00
Bell Ring Toy, cast iron, pierced wheels..	600.00	900.00	1200.00

Some small pieces of relatively low value ($5 to $30)
Caption and Photo by C.B.C. Lee

	G	VG	M
BIG BANG carbide armored car, cast iron, 9½" long....................	30.00	45.00	60.00
BIG BANG motor tank, 9" long, circa 1933............................	9.00	13.50	18.00
Boattail Speedster, cast iron, 5" long, blue with nickel wheels, driver, circa 1920s............................	30.00	45.00	60.00

BUDDY "L"—Buddy "L" toys were first manufactured by the Moline Pressed Steel Company, Moline, Illinois, in 1921, and were named after the son of the owner, Fred Lundahl. Lundahl had started the company about eight years earlier, manufacturing auto and truck parts (fenders, etc.). The toys were originally made as special items for his son, but as Buddy Lundahl's playmates began to clamor for similar toys of their own and their fathers began asking Lundahl senior to make duplicate toys for their sons, Lundahl went into the toy business. Buddy "L" toys were large, typically 21 to 24 or more inches long for trucks and fire engines. Construction was of very heavy steel, strong enough to support a man's weight. These were made until the early 1930s, when the line was modified and lighter-weight materials were employed. Before this time, Fred Lundahl had died, having already lost control of the company. The company has changed names several times, being known as the Buddy "L" Corp., Buddy "L" Toy Co., etc., in recent years dropping the quotes around the L. Continuing to make toys till the present day, the company even put out a few wooden toys during World War II, when its main plant made nothing but war-related toys. The early Buddy "L" trains are also popular, and tend to be worth even more than the vehicles. Buddy "L" material from the pre-1932 period is almost indestructible and as a consequence, 50% of the pieces found are either very rusty or have been repainted at some point. The basic metal seems to hold up forever, but repainting and rust drops the price well below "good".

Following is a list of pre-1932 Buddy "L" toys compiled by Thomas W. Sefton:

Large Trucks			G	VG	M
BUDDY L	200	Express Truck 1921-31	50.00	75.00	100.00
BUDDY L	201	Dump Truck (ratchet) 1921-30	50.00	75.00	100.00
BUDDY L	201A	Hydraulic Dump Truck 1926-31	66.00	99.00	132.00
BUDDY L	202	Coal Truck 1926-31	66.00	99.00	132.00
BUDDY L	202A	Sand & Gravel Truck 1926-31	66.00	99.00	132.00
BUDDY L	203	Stake Truck 1921-24, 1926-28	50.00	75.00	100.00
BUDDY L	203A	Lumber Truck 1925-30	50.00	75.00	100.00
BUDDY L	203B	Baggage Truck 1929-31	66.00	99.00	132.00
BUDDY L	204	Moving Van 1924-30	66.00	99.00	132.00
BUDDY L	204A	Railway Express 1926-31	66.00	99.00	132.00
BUDDY L	206, 206B	Street Sprinkler Truck 1924-31	83.00	124.50	166.00
BUDDY L	206A	Oil Truck 1925-30	66.00	99.00	132.00
BUDDY L	207	Ice Truck 1926-31	83.00	124.50	132.00
BUDDY L	208	Coach 1928-31 (Lt. Green Motorbus)	83.00	124.50	132.00
BUDDY L	209	Auto Wrecker 1928-31 (Tow Truck)	66.00	99.00	132.00

Fire Trucks			G	VG	M
BUDDY L	205	Hook & Ladder 1924-31	50.00	75.00	100.00
BUDDY L	205A	Pumper 1925-30	50.00	75.00	100.00
BUDDY L	205AB	(Working) Pumper 1930-1931	100.00	150.00	200.00

			G	VG	M
BUDDY L	205B	Aerial Ladder 1926-30	50.00	75.00	100.00
BUDDY L	205C	Insurance Patrol 1926-30	66.00	99.00	132.00
BUDDY L	205D	Water Tower Truck (Working) 1930-31	134.00	201.00	268.00

Model T Series

			G	VG	M
BUDDY L	210	Flivver Truck 1925-30	50.00	75.00	100.00
BUDDY L	210A	Flivver Roadster 1925-27	66.00	99.00	132.00
BUDDY L	210B	Flivver Coupe 1925-30	66.00	99.00	132.00
BUDDY L	211	Ford Dump Cart 1926-30	100.00	150.00	200.00
BUDDY L	211A	Ford Dump Truck 1926-30	100.00	150.00	200.00
BUDDY L	212	Ford Express Truck 1929-30	100.00	150.00	200.00
BUDDY L	212A	One-Ton Ford Delivery Truck 1929-30	100.00	150.00	200.00

Construction Equipment

			G	VG	M
BUDDY L	220	Steam Shovel 1921-31	34.00	51.00	68.00
BUDDY L	220A	Heavy Steam Shovel 1929-30	66.00	99.00	132.00
BUDDY L	220 AB	Heavy Shovel (on Treads) 1929-30	83.00	124.50	166.00
BUDDY L	230	Sand Loader 1925-31	50.00	75.00	100.00
BUDDY L	240	Small Derrick 1922-31	24.00	36.00	48.00
BUDDY L	241	Large Derrick 1922-31	40.00	60.00	80.00
BUDDY L	250	Overhead Crane 1924-27	200.00	300.00	400.00
BUDDY L	250A	Traveling Crane 1928-30	200.00	300.00	400.00
BUDDY L	260	Pile Driver 1926-28	100.00	150.00	200.00
BUDDY L	270	Dredge (Clamshell) 1926-30	100.00	150.00	200.00
BUDDY L	270A	Tractor Dredge (on Treads) 1929-30	118.00	177.00	236.00
BUDDY L	280	Concrete Mixer 1926-30	50.00	75.00	100.00
BUDDY L	280A	Mixer (on Treads) 1929-31	66.00	99.00	132.00
BUDDY L	290	Road Roller 1929-31	134.00	201.00	268.00
BUDDY L	300	Sand Screener 1929-30	66.00	99.00	132.00
BUDDY L	350	Hoisting Tower 1929-31	166.00	249.00	332.00
BUDDY L	360	Aerial Tramway 1929-30	166.00	249.00	332.00
BUDDY L	400	Trencher 1928-31	100.00	150.00	200.00

End listing by Thomas W. Sefton

	G	VG	M
BUDDY L Robotoy Dump Truck, with driver, operates on remote control....	50.00	75.00	100.00

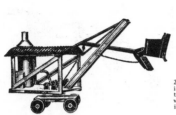

No. 205-AB—Buddy "L" Pumping Fire Engine. Length 23½ inches, width 8½ inches, height 10¾ inches. Finished in red enamel. Fill the boiler with water, replace the cap and a few strokes of the air pump will send the water through the hose more than 30 feet. Packed one in a carton. Weight 12 lbs. _____ See page 18

No. 220—Buddy "L" Steam Shovel. Length 20 inches, height 15 inches, width 8 inches. Roof finished in yellow, wheels and shovel finished in black, balance in red. Packed one in a carton_____ See page 19

No. 201-A—Buddy "L" Hydraulic Dump Truck. Length 25 inches, width 8½ inches, height 9 inches, height with body raised 13 inches. Hydraulic unit has cylinder 5½ x1 inch and will raise a load of 12 lbs. Packed one in a carton. Weight 9 lbs._____ See page 18

No. 203-B—Buddy "L" Baggage Truck. Length 26½ inches, width 8½ inches, height 12½ inches. Equipment includes truck, skid and three empty steel containers. Fitted with spoked disc wheels, solid rubber tires, dual wheels in the rear, headlights, bumpers and enclosed cab. Packed one in a carton. Weight 15 lbs.___ See page 18

No. 205—Buddy "L" Fire Truck. Length 27 inches, height 12 inches, width 8½ inches. Equipment includes two extension type steel ladders, brass fire gong and hose reel with 20 feet of sash cord hose. Packed one in a carton. Weight 10½ lbs._____ See page 18

No. 230—Buddy "L" Sand Loader. Length 21 inches, width 9½ inches, height 18 inches. The buckets mounted on an endless chain operated by a crank scoop up the sand, and elevate it to the top, where it is dumped into a chute. Double chain type elevator with twelve steel buckets. Packed one in a carton. Weight 12 lbs.
--- See page 18

29"

21'

No. 209—Buddy "L" Auto Wrecker. Length 26½ inches, width 8½ inches, height 13½ inches. Equipped with latest automotive type crane, with 7½ inch boom swinging in an 18 inch circle. Fitted with spoked disc wheels, solid rubber tires, dual wheels in rear, headlights, bumpers. Packed one in a carton. Weight 15¼ lbs. ------------------------------------ See page 18

No. 300—Buddy "L" Sand Screener. Length 29 inches, height 21 inches, width 18 inches. The elevator is double endless chain type with adjustable boxings and 14 steel buckets. A complete sand and gravel plant consisting of truck, elevator, chute, screen, measuring bin and hopper. Packed one in a carton. Weight 22 lbs. ---------------------------------- See page 19

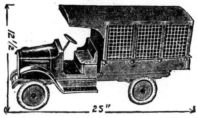

12½

25"

No. 204-A—Buddy "L" Railway Express Truck. Length 25 inches, width 8½ inches, height 12½ inches. Box finished in green enamel, chassis in black and wheels in red. Packed one in a carton. Weight 12 lbs. See page 18

No. 207—Buddy "L" Ice Truck. Length 26½ inches, width 8½ inches, height 12½ inches. Equipment includes pair of steel ice tongs and three pieces of glass imitation ice. Fitted with spoked disc wheels, solid rubber tires, dual wheels in the rear, headlights, bumpers and enclosed cab. Packed one in a carton. Weight 10 lbs. ------------------------------ See page 18

No. 205-B—Buddy "L" Hydraulic Aerial Truck. Length 39 inches, width 8½ inches, height 10 inches, height with ladder extended 56 inches. The ladder unit is a sectional type, 2 inches wide with ⅜ inch rounds, made of steel and can be extended to approximately 4½ feet. It is mounted on a 5½ inch turntable. Packed one in a carton. Weight 15 lbs.------------------- See page 19

AMERICAN NATIONAL COMPANY "Juvenile Auto" Dump Truck Pedal Car, red and yellow, 57"
long. (see page 6)   Photo Courtesy PB84

	G	VG	M
BUDDY L Station Wagon, wood........	15.00	22.50	30.00
Buick, cast iron, two-door with driver, hard rubber tires, 8½" long..........	900.00	1350.00	1800.00
Bus, 1930s, 15½" long, aluminum......	60.00	90.00	120.00
Bus, late 1920s, 23½" long, six side windows.............................	50.00	75.00	100.00
Bus, cast iron, 4" long.................	12.50	18.75	25.00
Bus, cast iron, 4½" long, five side windows, circa 1928...................	20.00	30.00	40.00
Bus, cast iron, 4¾" long, circa 1920s....	8.00	12.00	16.00
Bus, cast iron, with driver, rubber tires, 13" long.........................	175.00	262.50	350.00
Bus, double-decker, cast iron, four figures, 8" long....................	70.00	105.00	140.00
Bus, cast iron, double-decker, 9½" long..	140.00	210.00	280.00
"C2 TO C Co." semi-trailer, cast iron steel wheels, small.................	8.00	12.00	16.00
"C. W. Brand Coffee" Dump Truck, approx. 11¼" long, 1930s.............	40.00	60.00	80.00
Cabriolet with rumble seat, cast iron, circa 1920s........................	45.00	67.50	90.00
"Cannonball Express" child's pedal car, red-painted, 37" long...............	150.00	225.00	300.00
Car, cast iron, 4" long...............	12.00	18.00	24.00

22

	G	VG	M
Car, cast iron, with people, 3" long......	20.00	30.00	40.00
Caterpillar tractor, cast iron, red, with driver..........................	12.50	18.75	25.00
CHAMPION Gas and Motor Oil truck, 8" long, cast iron, circa 1930s...........	30.00	45.00	60.00
CHAMPION four-casting nickeled radiator car, approx. 4" long.............	40.00	60.00	80.00
CHAMPION race car, 9" long, circa 1930s.........................	35.00	52.50	70.00
"Champion" motorcycle and rider, 4½" long, cast iron...................	15.00	22.50	30.00
Checker Cab, circa 1920s, with driver, thin white rubber tires, with rear tire..	300.00	450.00	600.00
CHEIN Army Truck, circa 1918, tin.....	12.50	18.75	25.00
CHEIN "Hercules" moving truck, Mack, circa 1920s......................	20.00	30.00	40.00
Child's car, battery-operated, red-painted, 44" long.................	60.00	90.00	120.00
Child's car, battery-powered, 60" long...	90.00	135.00	180.00
Chrysler Airflow, cast iron, 4½" long, 1930s..........................	30.00	45.00	60.00
CLARK friction auto, manufactured from 1899-1909	160.00	240.00	320.00
CLARK friction auto, circa 1901, wood body covered with steel.............	180.00	270.00	360.00
CLARK 9" long friction duck being driven by small girl on its back, circa 1910	90.00	135.00	180.00
Convertible, futuristic, 1930s, with large streamlined fenders, black wooden wheels, heavy pressed steel, large size..	3.00	4.50	6.00
COR-COR dump truck, dumps back or side to side, 23" long..............	50.00	75.00	100.00
Cord, supercharged, 1930s, rubber, black rubber tires.....................	4.00	6.00	8.00
Coupe, cast iron, red................	20.00	30.00	40.00
Coupe, cast iron, with rumble seat, blue, circa 1920s......................	10.00	15.00	20.00
Coupe, tin friction, 17½" long.........	24.00	36.00	48.00

TOLEDO Metal Wheel Co. Fire Pumper Pedal Car, Red-Painted. 59" long. (see page 47)
Photo Courtesy PB84

	G	VG	M
Coupe, two-door, modern, tin, battery-powered, electric side lamps, 9" long..	20.00	30.00	40.00
DAYTON open touring car, dated 1909, friction motor, driver...............	110.00	165.00	220.00
DAYTON touring car, 13½" long, friction motor.......................	120.00	180.00	240.00
DAYTON touring car, 13½" long, unpowered..........................	90.00	135.00	180.00
Delivery Truck, 3½" long, cast iron.....	40.00	60.00	80.00
Delivery Truck, 10½" long, with driver, friction..........................	40.00	60.00	80.00
DENT aluminum bus, sample..........	80.00	120.00	160.00
DENT aluminum bus, 7½" long, sample.	30.00	45.00	60.00
DENT bus, cast iron, sample, 6¼" long	50.00	75.00	100.00
DENT fire truck, cast iron, 7" long, sample	40.00	60.00	80.00
DENT fire ladder truck, 8½" long, with driver........................	25.00	37.50	50.00

	G	VG	M
DENT fire truck with ladder and men, cast iron, 18" long, sample..........	200.00	300.00	400.00
DENT hose reeler with men, cast iron, large...........................	150.00	225.00	300.00
DENT ladder truck, 10" long, two drivers.......................	20.00	30.00	40.00
DENT "Patrol", 6½" long, circa 1920s..	80.00	120.00	160.00
DENT Steam Roller, cast iron, 6" long...	40.00	60.00	80.00
DENT fire pumper, cast iron, sample, 7" long..........................	50.00	75.00	100.00
DENT LaSalle, approx. 4" long.......	50.00	75.00	100.00

DOEPKE "MODEL TOYS"

by Ray Funk

Doepke "Model Toys" advertised their toys as outlasting all others 3 to 1. The company's full title was the "Charles Wm. Doepke Mfg. Co., Inc." of Rossmoyne, Ohio. Each toy was an authorized replica of the actual thing and the decals and coloring were exactly as upon the real equipment or trucks, with the exception of the manufacturer having his own, in this case "Model Toys".

At the end of the Second World War, the Doepke Corp. hit the market with five models, first in a line of heavy duty metal operating replicas, employing metal tread or authentic miniature tires, either Goodyear or Firestone, with authentic tread and name and tire sizes, exactly as on the real tires. This, to the best of my knowledge, has never been done so perfectly, even in the model kits of today.

These toys all had rubber smoke stacks, and received the approval of Parents Magazine, P.T.A., Boy's Life Magazine, and all other experts and advocates of good toys at that period. The first five numbers were 2000, 2001, 2002, 2006, 2007. Why not 3, 4 and 5, I cannot say. Perhaps Doepke had toys planned for these numbers that fell through. Following is a listing of the Doepke vehicles.

RAY FUNK is a leading collector and authority on trains and other toys, as well as a collector and authority on comic books and Western literature.

No. 2000, Wooldridge H. D. earth hauler, bright yellow, four hugh tires, 25" long, and weighing 10 lbs. The actual manufacturer's address is listed as Sunnyvale, Calif. I'm sure most of you have seen the John Wayne movie, "The Fighting Seabees", which used several of these, along with caterpillar bulldozers and road graders. These Wooldridge's caught my eye with their maneuvering ability, and could traverse the roughest terrain easily. Two long doors, the length of the bottom of the dirt-hauling area, could be released to deposit a load. Price was $14.75 new in 1945.

No. 2001, Barber-Greene high-capacity bucket loader, 13" high, 10 lbs., dark green, all steel and rolling on steel tread, was designed as a toy to load earth haulers. Handcrank operated, operated exactly as the real thing. Price $14.75.

No. 2002, Jaeger concrete mixer, bright yellow, 15" long, 8 lbs., on four wheels, steerable via draw bar (all model toys sterred exactly like the real thing), though perhaps the best-detailed, was the poorest-sellng toy, as although you could, it wasn't feasible to really mix concrete in them, due to small amount received versus cleaning time. This toy was priced at $10.75 to $13.75.

No. 2006, Adams diesel road grader, dark orange, 26" long, 14 lbs., all six wheels, three axles, and blade adjustable to all angles, exactly like the real thing, steerable via steering wheel, priced at $14.75.

No. 2007, Unit Mobile Crane, dark orange, 11½" long, 19½" boom, eight lbs. and eight ounces, adjustable side jacks, steered via a drawbar, with block and tackle, and removable operating clam shell as standard accessory. Priced at $14.75.

No number 2008, as the next year, No. 2009 was released and No. 2000 dropped. No. 2009 was a Euclid earth-hauler truck, with uncoupling four-wheel tractor to use to tow other toys. 27" long, 11 lbs., Euclid green, or light road-grader orange, the trailer dumped in the same way as the Wooldridge. Priced $14.75.

No. 2010, American-LaFrance pumper fire truck, 18" long, 7 lbs., bright red with chrome trim, ladder, bell, fire extinguisher, hoses and nozzle, a reservoir that held water for hand-operated pressure pump. A beautiful toy at $16.75.

No. 2011, Heiliner earth scraper, 29" long, 13 lbs., bright dark red, loaded and dumped and operated on four wheels as the Wooldridge did. Priced at $16.75.

No. 2012, Caterpillar D6 tractor and bulldozer, caterpillar yellow, 15" long, 7 lbs., with real bulldozer treads for sharp realistic turning (removable only by using punch and hammer to remove connecting pin from between two of the pads) and adjustable bulldozer blade, plus heavy draw bar. Truly a beautiful toy at $13.75. Diesel motor was cast metal.

No. 2013 eliminat ed and replaced No. 2001. No. 2013, Barber-Green mobile high-capacity bucket loader, 22" long, 12" high, 10 lbs., buckets on chains and rubber conveyor belt, adjustable and steered by steering wheel, priced at $19.75.

No. 2014, American La-France aerial ladder fire truck, 23" long, 42" extended ladder height, 11 lbs., bright red and chrome, bell, red light, adjustable side jacks, single unit truck steered by steering wheel, priced at $20.75.

This ends the listing of Doepke "Model Toys", doomed to extinction by its lower-priced, lighter-constructed imitators of lesser quality, some of which were started in the 1920s, and others that came into being in the 1950s, several of which are still around today, but none ever containing, before or after, the heavy-duty constructed realism and operating qualities as had the one and only "Model Toys".

	G	VG	M
DOEPKE No. 2000 Wooldridge H. D. Earth Hauler, 25" long..............	10.00	15.00	20.00
DOEPKE No. 2001 Barber-Greene high capacity bucket loader, 13" high......	10.00	15.00	20.00
DOEPKE No. 2002 Jaeger Concrete Mixer, 15" long...................	6.00	9.00	12.00
DOEPKE No. 2006 Adams Diesel Road Grader, 26" long...................	12.00	18.75	24.00
DOEPKE No. 2007 Unit Mobile Crane, 11½" long......................	7.50	11.25	15.00
DOEPKE No. 2009 Euclid Earth Hauler Truck, 27" long...................	10.00	15.00	20.00
DOEPKE No. 2010 American-LaFrance pumper fire truck, 18" long..........	7.50	11.25	15.00
DOEPKE No. 2011 Heiliner Earth Scraper, 29" long.................	12.50	18.75	25.00
DOEPKE No. 2012 Caterpillar D6 tractor and bulldozer, 15" long.............	12.50	18.75	25.00
DOEPKE No. 2013 Barber-Green mobile high-capacity bucket loader 22" long..	10.00	15.00	20.00
DOEPKE No. 2014 American-LaFrance aerial ladder fire truck, 23" long......	12.50	18.75	25.00
Dual Road Race crossover track, 1/32 0-27, per track.....................	2.50	3.75	5.00
"Dugan Brothers" ride-on van, metal....	30.00	45.00	60.00
Dump Truck, 7" long, cast iron, driver..	25.00	37.50	50.00

	G	VG	M
Dump Truck (Beck), steers via horn on top of cab, late 1940s, large..........	7.50	11.25	15.00
DRUDGE "Hyster" lumber carrier......	40.00	60.00	80.00
EAGLE bell toy, gong bell, East Hampton, Conn........................	250.00	375.00	500.00
Electric car, cast iron, 3¾" long........	60.00	90.00	120.00
"Electric Powered Rider Convertible", lithographed tin, circa 1950, 29" long, riding toy........................	15.00	22.50	30.00
ERIE streamlined auto with tail fin, tail fin has taillight mounted in it, approx. 4¼" long.................	5.00	7.50	10.00
ERIE super-charged streamline auto, looks like Cord, circa 1930s..........	4.00	6.00	8.00
Farm truck, "Speed", with driver, 7" cast iron........................	54.00	81.00	108.00
Fire Engine Pumper, friction, gear shift lever, with drivers.................	90.00	135.00	180.00
Fire Pumper, early wind-up, metal, 11"..	90.00	135.00	180.00
Fire Truck, cast iron, 7" long..........	17.50	26.25	35.00
Fire Truck, friction, with driver, metal and wood........................	54.00	81.00	108.00
Fire Truck, pressed steel friction toy, 12" long........................	30.00	45.00	60.00
Ford coupe, 4" long, 1924.............	20.00	30.00	40.00
Ford coupe, blue, chrome wheels, 5" long............................	42.00	63.00	84.00
Ford coupe, cast iron, black, chrome wheels, circa 1920s, 5" long..........	35.00	52.50	70.00
Ford coupe, rubber, 1935.............	2.50	3.75	5.00

"Electric Powered Rider Convertible" 29" long circa 1950   (see this page)
Photo Courtesy PB84'

	G	VG	M
"Fordson" tractor with driver, cast iron, 5¾" long	44.00	66.00	88.00
Fordson tractor with hay rake, cast iron, 1930s	50.00	75.00	100.00
Friction car, cast iron and wood, with figures	50.00	75.00	100.00
Friction toy with two riders, 1897	50.00	75.00	100.00
GMC "Greyhound Lines" cast iron bus, 7½" long, circa 1934	30.00	45.00	60.00
GIRARD Fire Chief siren coupe, 14" long	25.00	37.50	50.00
"Guided Missile Unit No. 10" truck, tin litho, circa 1960	5.00	7.50	10.00
Happy Sam driving wood truck, circa 1920s, 8" long	18.00	27.00	36.00
HOGE Fire chief car, 15" long	40.00	60.00	80.00
Hook and ladder, aluminum, with driver, 13" long	34.00	51.00	68.00
Hook and ladder truck, tin friction, 21" long	34.00	51.00	68.00
Hose Wagon, 1897, two riders, friction toy	54.00	81.00	108.00
"Huber" steam roller, cast iron, 7¼" long	90.00	135.00	180.00
Huber steam roller, cast iron, 7½" long	85.00	127.50	170.00
Huber steam roller, 8" long, cast iron, intricate, with chain	50.00	75.00	100.00

HUBLEY—The Hubley manufacturing company was founded at least as early as 1894 by John Hubley, and made iron toys from the start at its plant in Lancaster, Pennsylvania. All toys at the beginning were cast iron, and some early toys included coal ranges, circus wagons and mechanical banks. Hubley's cast iron toys were popular almost from the start, and have long been collector's items, as they were well-made and attractive. By 1940, however, the cast iron toy, due to the increased cost of freight and foreign competition, was slowly becoming a thing of the past. At this time, when Hubley was the largest producer of cast iron toys and cap pistols in the world, it began to introduce die cast zinc alloy toys. During the Second World War, Hubley was 98% engaged in war production, turing out over five million M-74 bomb fuses, which the Hubley engineers played a large part in developing. Since the war, Hubley manufactures die cast toys and plastic toys exclusively. In 1952, Hubley manufactured 9,763,610 toys and 11,184,878 cap pistols, about ten times the amount of toys and pistols they produced in 1930, but with a line of toys 80% smaller than in 1930. It is the combination of the relative scarcity (and multiplicity) of the older toys, plus the preference by collectors for cast iron over die cast zinc alloy and plastic toys that makes the pre-World War II toys the most attractive to collectors. Hubley was acquired by Gabriel Industries in late 1965, and puts out holster sets, cap pistols, vehicles, hobby kits, and a number of other toys.

	G	VG	M
HUBLEY Auto carrier, 10" long, with three cars and one pickup truck, circa 1939	100.00	150.00	200.00
HUBLEY Avery tractor, 4¾" long, very early	30.00	45.00	60.00
HUBLEY auto circa 1950s, black plastic wheels, die cast	1.00	1.50	2.00
HUBLEY Bell Telephone truck, 10" long, No. 41, 1936, with derrick and windlass, auger, trailer with 10" pole, three digging tools, and two loose ladders	80.00	120.00	160.00
HUBLEY "Borden's Milk Cream" No. 42.	150.00	225.00	300.00
HUBLEY Bulldozer, die-cast, front scoop, circa 1950, 10¼" long, rubber treads	10.00	15.00	20.00
HUBLEY bus, 8" long, 1930s	10.00	15.00	20.00
HUBLEY 2278 car and 2279 house trailer, circa 1939	70.00	105.00	140.00
HUBLEY Chemical Truck with ladders, 13" long	50.00	100.00	150.00
HUBLEY Chrysler Airflow racing car, circa 1938	26.00	39.00	52.00
HUBLEY Crash Car, three-wheel motor-cycle, chrome wheels	25.00	37.50	50.00
HUBLEY Crash Car, circa 1937, 4¾" long, white rubber tires	25.00	37.50	50.00
HUBLEY Dumpo Truck, circa 1938, 7½" long	30.00	45.00	60.00

	G	VG	M
HUBLEY Fire Engine pumper, early, No. 504	30.00	45.00	60.00
HUBLEY Fire Engine No. 526, 10½" long, circa 1936	34.00	51.00	68.00
HUBLEY Fire Engine, die cast, white rubber tires with wooden rims, circa 1941	5.00	7.50	10.00
HUBLEY Fire Truck with searchlight, white rubber tires with wooden rims	6.00	9.00	12.00
HUBLEY Jantzen Beach Patrol, 8" long, circa 1930s	1000.00	1500.00	2000.00
HUBLEY Log Truck with five chained logs, black rubber tires, die-cast, approx. 19" long	25.00	37.50	50.00
HUBLEY Motor Express tractor and trailer, black rubber tires, 500 series, approx. 19" long	30.00	45.00	60.00
HUBLEY race car, die-cast, black rubber tires	3.50	5.25	7.00
HUBLEY Huber road roller	74.00	111.00	148.00
HUBLEY Life Saver Truck, circa 1930, hole in rear is large enough to hold pack of Life Savers	50.00	75.00	100.00
HUBLEY Life Saver Truck, 1930, small hole in rear, can't hold Life Savers	150.00	225.00	300.00
HUBLEY Model A Ford, die-cast assembled kit, circa 1950	15.00	22.50	30.00
HUBLEY 2287 "Motor Express" truck and trailer, 8" long	32.50	48.75	65.00
HUBLEY Motorcycle and rider	15.00	22.50	30.00
HUBLEY Motorcycle, Harley Davidson, with policeman, white rubber wheels	75.00	112.50	150.00
HUBLEY Motorcycle, Harley Davidson, with side car and rider	40.00	60.00	80.00
HUBLEY Motorcycle No. 649 Hill Climber, 1936, 6¾" long	50.00	75.00	100.00
HUBLEY Motorcycle "Indian", with figure, 9¼" long	40.00	60.00	80.00
HUBLEY Mototcycle with side car, 8½" long, No. 46-F, two demountable policemen, 1936	40.00	60.00	80.00

	G	VG	M
HUBLEY Motorcycle, two-cylinder Indian, with side car, no riders.........	30.00	45.00	60.00
HUBLEY Motorcycle-"traffic car", four-cylinder Indian with stake sides on two-wheel cart.......................	140.00	210.00	280.00
HUBLEY Motorcycle, Parcel Post delivery, with two-wheel cart........	75.00	112.50	150.00
HUBLEY Motorcycle, four-cylinder P.D.Q. delivery....................	160.00	240.00	320.00
HUBLEY Motorcycle, three-wheel with stake sides, rider, chrome wheels......	20.00	30.00	40.00
HUBLEY Packard, 15 parts, 1929, 11" long	2500.00	3750.00	5000.00
HUBLEY Popeye Spinach Cycle, black rubber tires, three-wheel, 6" long.....	200.00	300.00	400.00
HUBLEY Race Car, 2241, 7½" long, 1930s	22.50	33.75	45.00
HUBLEY Racer 629, 1936 6¾" long.....	20.00	30.00	40.00
HUBLEY Service car, 5" cast iron, including wheels, 1930s.............	75.00	112.50	150.00
HUBLEY 726 Shovel Truck, 10" long, circa 1930.......................	44.00	66.00	88.00
HUBLEY No. 614 Stake Truck, circa 1930s	24.00	36.00	48.00
HUBLEY Stake Bed Truck, cast iron, 3½" long.......................	14.00	21.00	28.00
HUBLEY No. 452 stake-type truck, black rubber tires, circa post WW II........	7.50	11.25	15.00
HUBLEY Station Wagon, circa 1940s-1950s	5.00	7.50	10.00
HUBLEY Street Cleaner, 9" long, cast iron, with figures..................	600.00	900.00	1200.00
HUBLEY Tow Truck, 3¾" long, cast iron, circa 1930s..................	15.00	22.50	30.00
HUBLEY Tractor, steam boiler in front, 4¾" long, circa early 1920s..........	40.00	60.00	80.00
HUBLEY Transitional Fire Patrol, 12" cast iron, driver, firemen............	375.00	562.50	750.00
HUBLEY Wrecker, chrome wheels, Service Car.........................	20.00	30.00	40.00

	G	VG	M
HUSLER pull toy, three-wheeled cart with driver........................	6.00	9.00	12.00
"Ice" Stake Truck, circa 1940, streamlined fenders, pressed steel............	12.00	18.00	24.00
Ice Cream Truck, cast iron, 8" long.....	120.00	180.00	240.00
Indian cast iron motorcycle with side car, two figures, 9" long................	60.00	90.00	120.00
IVES horseless carriage runabout, 6½" long, 6" high to the top of jockey cap on driver........................	900.00	1350.00	1800.00
IVES steamer, cast iron, 19½" long, two drivers........................	200.00	300.00	400.00
Jaeger Cement Mixer, cast iron.........	30.00	45.00	60.00
Jeep, glass candy container, 4" long.....	2.00	3.00	4.00
"Jeepster", rubber tires, 14¼" long.....	2.00	3.00	4.00
KENTON Buckeye Ditching Machine...	205.00	302.50	410.00
KENTON Cement Mixer, rubber wheels, marked "Jaeger", 7" long, cast iron....	50.00	75.00	100.00
KENTON Cattle Truck, 8" long, cast iron, circa 1938...................	50.00	75.00	100.00
KENTON Cement Mixer..............	50.00	75.00	100.00
KENTON Fire pump truck, early, with driver..........................	10.00	15.00	20.00
KENTON Fire Truck, 15" long with pumper	90.00	135.00	180.00
KENTON Jaeger "Mixer", cast iron cement truck, 9" long...............	240.00	360.00	480.00
KENTON Patrol Wagon, marked "Patrol" on side, circa 1920s-1930s............	200.00	300.00	400.00
KENTON Pontiac, approx. 4" long......	50.00	75.00	100.00
KENTON "Coast-to-Coast" bus........	25.00	37.50	50.00
KENTON Emergency Truck, circa 1930s, black rubber tires, takes batteries for headlights and spotlight.............	40.00	60.00	80.00
KEYSTONE Fire Truck, wood steering wheel, two ladders, 22" long.........	55.00	82.50	110.00
KEYSTONE Mail Truck, grating sides, 26½" long, circa 1932..............	60.00	90.00	120.00

	G	VG	M
KEYSTONE Packard Army Truck, open cab, khaki paint, heavy canvas top marked "U.S. Army", 26" long, circa 1930	100.00	150.00	200.00
KEYSTONE Packard Dump Truck, front crank raises dump bed, 26" long, black with red trim	85.00	127.50	170.00
KEYSTONE Packard Mail Truck, 26½" long	120.00	180.00	240.00
KEYSTONE Steam Roller, red and black, air pressure whistle, brass bell, 20" long	65.00	92.50	130.00
KEYSTONE Steamshovel, 20¾" long, black with red trim	60.00	90.00	120.00
KEYSTONE U.S. Army Truck with canvas cover	34.00	51.00	68.00
KEYSTONE Water Pump and Tower Truck, 21" long, ladders, brass railing, aluminum running board, brass bell, klaxon horn	44.00	66.00	88.00
KEYSTONE Water Tower Fire Truck with pump, circa late 1920s, 30" long	37.50	56.25	75.00
KILGORE Stutz Roadster, 13 parts	350.00	525.00	700.00
KINGSBURY Aerial Ladder Truck, pressed steel wind-up circa 1941, 24" long, ladder rises automatically to height of 38 inches when the truck runs into any obstruction, fireman on ladder climbs up and down by turning crank at base of ladder	22.50	33.75	45.00
KINGSBURY Caterpillar, 8½" long, wind-up	100.00	150.00	200.00
KINGSBURY Fire Truck, 18" long	120.00	180.00	240.00
KINGSBURY ladder wagon fire truck, tin, rubber tires, 23½" long	12.50	18.75	25.00
KINGSBURY Roadster, 13" long, electric headlights, spring motor, luggage rack .	30.00	45.00	60.00

	G	VG	M
KINGSBURY Sunbeam Racer, sheet-metal, red with rubber tires on steel wheels, clockwork motor, 19" long....	75.00	112.50	150.00
KINGSBURY Tractor and cart, tin, with iron driver, white rubber wheels, circa 1930s	60.00	90.00	120.00
Ladder Truck, driver front and rear, cast iron, 5" long	18.00	27.00	36.00
LEHMANN Echo Motorcycle	150.00	225.00	300.00
LEHMANN No. 760 "Gallop" Racing car, circa 1927, 5¾" long	300.00	450.00	600.00
Log Truck (Beck), steers via horn on top of cab, late 1940s, large	7.50	11.25	15.00
M.I.C. TOYS, flat bed truck with removeable side racks	12.50	18.75	25.00
M.I.C. TOYS Tow Truck, heavy-duty, Auto-car Diesel	12.50	18.75	25.00
Mack Dump Truck, cast iron, 12" long...	90.00	135.00	180.00
Mack Stake Truck, 5" long, cast iron wheels, circa late 1920s	20.00	30.00	40.00
Mack Stake Truck, 5" long, white rubber wheels, circa 1930s	20.00	30.00	40.00
MANOIL Armored Car, circa 1940	6.00	9.00	12.00
MANOIL Cannon Truck No. 75, driver and man in rear	6.00	9.00	12.00
MANOIL "Gas" cart, circa 1940	5.00	7.50	10.00
MANOIL "Gasoline" cart, circa 1940....	5.00	7.50	10.00
MANOIL Kitchen Trailer, U.S. Army, circa 1940	6.00	9.00	12.00
MANOIL Pompom gun, five barrels, aimed skyward, wheeled, circa 1940...	5.00	7.50	10.00
MANOIL Shell Cart (single shell), circa 1940	5.00	7.50	10.00
MANOIL Tank, wooden wheels, circa 1940	4.00	6.00	8.00
MANOIL Torpedo Cart, circa 1940	5.00	7.50	10.00
MANOIL Tractor "USA", circa 1940....	5.00	7.50	10.00
MANOIL Water Trailer, circa 1940 "US 72"	4.00	6.00	8.00

	G	VG	M
MANOIL Siren Truck "75", white rubber tires, double-horned, two soldiers	10.00	15.00	20.00
MANOIL No. 700 sedan, futuristic	10.00	15.00	20.00
MANOIL No. 703 Wrecker, futuristic	12.00	18.00	24.00
MANOIL No. 704 Pat. No. 95791, lead alloy futuristic roadster, 1935	4.00	6.00	8.00
MANOIL No. 705 Pat. No. 95792, futuristic sedan, 1935	5.00	7.50	10.00
MANOIL No. 706 Pat. No. 95793, futuristic bus-type vehicle, 1935	5.00	7.50	10.00
MANOIL No. 708, streamlined MG roadster, black rubber tires	4.00	6.00	8.00
MARX Ambulance No. 8500, approx. 14" long, 1930s	27.00	40.50	54.00
MARX Ambulance No. 8600, approx. 14" long, 1930s	27.00	40.50	54.00
MARX "American Railroad Express Agency Inc.", early 1930s, open cab, 7"	30.00	45.00	60.00
MARX "Auto Transwalk" No. T-50447B, 1930s truck with three cars	40.00	60.00	80.00
MARX "Chief-Fire Dept. No. 1", "Friction Drive", circa 1948	3.00	4.50	6.00
MARX Coca Cola Truck, 10" long	8.00	12.00	16.00
MARX Dump Truck, two-color, No. T751, circa 1930s	15.00	22.50	30.00
MARX No. 1084 Dump Truck	10.00	15.00	20.00
MARX "Electrically Lighted Truck and Trailer Set" No. T-5715, circa 1930s 15" long	20.00	30.00	40.00
MARX Falcoln with plastic bubble top, black rubber tires	20.00	30.00	40.00
MARX G-Man Pursuit car, No. 7000, 15" long, 1930s	45.00	67.50	90.00
MARX Gang Buster Car No. 7200, approx. 14" long, 1930s	45.00	67.50	90.00
MARX "High-Boy Climbing Tractor" No. 950	7.50	11.25	15.00
MARX "Heavy Gauge Tractor" No. 926	7.50	11.25	15.00
MARX No. 1016 Machinery Moving Truck	10.00	15.00	20.00

MARX Machinery Moving Truck No. 1016.
Photo Courtesy PB84   (see page 36)

MARX Dump Truck No. 1084.
Photo Courtesy PB84   (see page 36)

MARX Stake Truck No. 1008
Photo Courtesy PB84   (see page 40)

MARX Power Grader, black wheels.
Photo Courtesy PB84   (see page 39)

MARX Rocker Dump.
Photo Courtesy PB84   (see page 39)

MARX Power Grader, white wheels
Photo Courtesy PB84   (see page 39)

	G	VG	M
MARX "Mammoth Truck Train" No. T-50-12345, circa 1930s, truck with five trailers	60.00	90.00	120.00
MARX Mystery Taxi, circa 1930s, press down to operate	30.00	45.00	60.00
MARX Panel Wagon	9.00	13.50	18.00

37

TOP: "Rocket Launcher" truck, "U.S.A.F." (see page 42)
Photo Courtesy PB84

MIDDLE: "Guided Missile Unit No. 10" Truck (see page 29)
Photo Courtesy PB84

BOTTOM: MARX "Rocket Fighter", circa 1950s (see page 127).
Photo Courtesy PB84

TOP: MARX Wrecker Truck No. T-16 (see page 40)
MIDDLE: MARX "Mammoth Truck Train" (see page 37)
BOTTOM: MARX "Auto Transwalk" (see page 36)
Photos Courtesy PB84

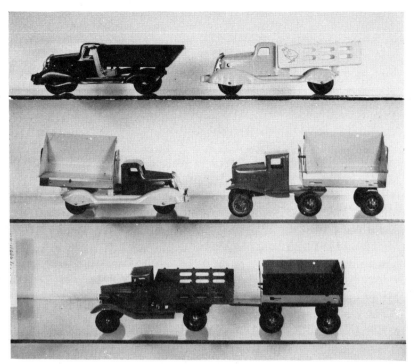

TOP, L TO R: MARX Dump Truck, two-color: (see page 36); MARX Stake-type truck, 3-color: (see this page);
MIDDLE, L TO R: MARX Side Dump Truck, four-color; (see this page); MARX Side Dump Truck and trailer: (see this page);
BOTTOM: MARX "Electrically Lighted Truck and Trailer Set". (see page 36)

	G	VG	M
MARX "Power Grader" No. 1759, black or white wheels, 17½" long..........	7.50	11.25	15.00
MARX Pure Milk Dairy Truck with glass bottles, pressed steel, tin wheels, circa 1940...........................	25.00	37.50	50.00
MARX Rocker Dump No. 1752, 17½" long	7.50	11.25	15.00
MARX Side Dump Truck, four-color No. T-475, circa 1940.............	15.00	22.50	30.00
MARX Side Dump Truck and Trailer, No. T-4045, circa 1930s............	15.00	22.50	30.00
MARX Siren Police Car No. 8300, 1930s, approx. 14" long.................	45.00	67.50	90.00
MARX Stake-type truck, 3-color, No. E-271, circa 1941...................	10.00	15.00	20.00

	G	VG	M
MARX No. 1008 Stake Truck	10.00	15.00	20.00
MARX "USA Army D-105", 7½" long, Mack Truck brown pressed steel, winds up	20.00	30.00	40.00
MARX Willys Jeep, steel, circa 1938, 12" long, hood opens, windshield folds down	10.00	15.00	20.00
MARX Willys Jeep and trailer, circa 1940s	15.00	22.50	30.00
MARX Wrecker Truck No. T-16, circa 1930s	25.00	37.50	50.00
METAL MASTERS Ambulance wind-up, circa 1940	15.00	22.50	30.00
METAL MASTERS bus, black plastic wheels, circa WW II, approx. 7" long	7.50	11.25	15.00
METAL MASTERS pickup truck with black plastic wheels, approx. 7" long . .	6.50	9.75	13.00
METAL MASTERS station wagon, like model 100, but not wind-up	17.50	26.25	35.00
METAL MASTERS station wagon, model 100, wind-up, circa 1940	20.00	30.00	40.00
METAL MASTERS Tow Truck No. 600, circa 1940, "Towing ABC Service"	17.50	26.25	35.00
METAL MASTERS Tow Truck with spring wind-up motor, like No. 600 otherwise	22.50	33.75	45.00
METALCRAFT Coca Cola Truck, 10 bottles, 10½" long, 1930s	40.00	60.00	80.00
METALCRAFT Coca Cola Truck, circa 1928, with bottles in racks	60.00	90.00	120.00
METALCRAFT "Goodrich Silvertone Tires" wrecker	50.00	75.00	100.00
METALCRAFT Hines Pickle Truck with tailgate, electric headlights	70.00	105.00	140.00
Model A Ford, coupe with spare tire on back, cast iron	24.00	36.00	48.00
Model A Tow Truck, cast iron, no maker imprinted, 7" long	45.00	67.50	90.00
Model T Ford, cast iron, 5" long	20.00	30.00	40.00
Model T Ford, cast iron, 8½" long	14.00	21.00	28.00

	G	VG	M
Model T Ford coupe, gray, with animated figures, cast iron, 1920s............	160.00	240.00	320.00
Model T Ford, tin...................	50.00	75.00	100.00
Model T Ford "C" Cab Truck, cast iron, circa early 1920s, 8½" long.....	44.00	66.00	88.00
MODEL TOYS MG TD Roadster, heavy die-cast body, 14" long, steel frame, leaf springs in rear, A-frames on front, pneumatic rubber tires.............	70.00	105.00	140.00
Motorcycle "Champion", cast iron, rubber wheels, policeman driver, 4¾" long	5.00	7.50	10.00
Motorcycle "Cop", 3¾" long, cast iron...........................	4.00	6.00	8.00
Motorcycle, Harley-Davidson, cast iron, 9" long.........................	56.00	84.00	112.00
OHLSSON & RICE, midget race car, aluminum body, rubber tires, circa 1940s	25.00	37.50	50.00
Oil and Gas Truck, cast iron, 8" long....	80.00	120.00	160.00
Open car, tin friction, red-painted, 9" long.........................	46.00	69.00	92.00
"Patrol" Motorcycle and rider, circa 1940, 6¼" long, cast iron............	20.00	30.00	40.00
Pedal Car, "American National Company Toledo Ohio, USA", sheet metal and wooden, dashboard with dials, rubber tread on wheels, 46" long...........	80.00	120.00	160.00
Pedal Car, circa 1905, chain drive, wooden spoke wheels..............	150.00	225.00	300.00
Pedal Car, Cadillac, circa 1915 TOLEDO METAL WHEEL CO., lithographed dashboard	120.00	180.00	240.00
Pedal Car, "Ford, 1896", Tubular frame with wire wheels, sheet metal seat with wooden back rest and steering lever, plate under seat has diagram of motor, 39" long........................	20.00	30.00	40.00
Pedal Car, green and yellow-painted, metal	24.00	36.00	48.00

	G	VG	M
Pickup Truck, cast iron, 3½" long, 1920s, white rubber tires on wooden wheels	20.00	30.00	40.00
Pickup Truck, cast iron, 4" long.	10.00	15.00	20.00
Pickup Truck, tin friction toy, 19" long, 1920s.	32.00	48.00	64.00
Plastic automobile, very early, futur- istic.	2.00	3.00	4.00
Racer "Parker Special", simple body of heavy steel with steel wheels, 11" long	15.00	22.50	30.00
PLAYBOY Dump Truck 22" long, tan. . .	55.00	82.50	110.00
PLAYBOY "Intercity Bus", 23½" long, cream color.	60.00	90.00	120.00
Race Car, friction, with driver, circa 1925	50.00	75.00	100.00
Race car, 8" long, circa 1918.	34.00	51.00	68.00
Racing Car, cast iron, 6½" long, with figure.	20.00	30.00	40.00
Racing Car, cast iron, with driver, full fugure, spiked wheels, early 1920s.	30.00	45.00	60.00
Racing Car, cast iron, 7¼".	20.00	30.00	40.00
"Radio Police" slush mold police car coupe, white rubber tires, circa 1940. .	5.00	7.50	10.00
"Railway Express" truck, cast iron, early, 1930s, 5" long.	40.00	60.00	80.00
RENWAL die-cast pickup truck, black rubber tires, approx. 7" long.	7.50	11.25	15.00
REPUBLIC Taxi Cab with driver, sheet- metal, friction motor, circa 1926.	55.00	82.50	110.00
Rex Mars Planet Patrol Space Tank.	30.00	45.00	60.00
Road Race Cars, 1/32, 1962-1965.	3.50	5.25	7.00
Roadster Tow Truck, cast iron, 5" long. .	40.00	60.00	80.00
"Rocket Launcher" truck, "U.S.A.F.", friction, pressed steel and plastic, circa 1960.	5.00	7.50	10.00
SCHUCO monkey driving racing car, 1928	100.00	150.00	200.00
Sedan, cast iron, four door, driver, 8" long.	125.00	187.50	250.00

	G	**VG**	**M**
Sedan motor car, cast iron.............	17.50	26.25	35.00
Sedan, die cast, black rubber tires,			
approx. 7" long, circa 1930s..........	7.50	11.25	15.00
Sedan, tin friction, four door, 9½"......	13.00	19.50	26.00
Sedan, tin friction, 17¾" long, 1920s....	50.00	75.00	100.00

"SMITTY TOYS"

by Ray Funk

A line of large cast metal and aluminum toy trucks hit the market in 1945, the Smith-Miller "Smitty Toys", "Famous Trucks in Miniature", produced in Santa Monica, California. These trucks were doomed from the beginning, as they were entering a highly competitive market, one that had toy producers of trucks dating back to the 30s and earlier, such as Buddy "L", Marx, Hubley, Tonka, and in the mid-1950s, Eldon plastics. However, despite the heavy competition, they fought to stay on the market for a full ten years, into 1955, outclassing virtually all toy trucks before and after, by far, although the last year they changed their profile from Mack Trucks to Auto-Car diesels, with opening doors and steering wheels that actually steered like the real thing. Their first trucks had two different classes, expensive replicas, and, still not cheap, though not actually true replicas, of a smaller type truck of no name that looked to be a half-breed Ford. I will list the cheaper line first.

No. 401 Tow Truck, 15" long, No. 402 Dump Truck 11½" long, No. 403 Scoop Dump, 14" long (same dump with scoop), all complete cast, cast wheels and rubber tires.

The larger scale models were cast and aluminum, such as No. 404 Lumber Truck (six wheels), 19" long, $10.75; No. 404T Lumber Trailer, 17" long, $6.95; No. 405 Silver Streak, 28" long (14 wheels) six wheel tractor and eight wheel bogey'd heavy duty grain trailer, $15.95; No. 406 Bekins Van, 29" long, six wheel tractor and four-wheel trailer (single axle); No. 407 Searchlight Truck, long (six wheel) based frame 18½" long with platform that has diesel motor (to hold batteries) and huge searchlight, at $16.95; No. 408 Blue Diamond ten wheel huge dump truck, last double set of duals bogey'd, 18½" long, $17.95; No. 409 Pacific Intermountain Express (P.I.E.) six wheel tractor semi with eight wheel bogey'd aluminum trailer, 29" long,

$19.75; No. 410 Aerial Ladder semi, six wheel tractor, and four wheel single axle trailer, 36" long, ladder extends to 48" high, $27.95. By 1950 some mid-West stores had the aerial ladder priced at $37.50, and various of the others higher-priced.

Later, various modifications were produced, one a straight Box bed truck, using the searchlight truck with metal box and rear double doors. Then yet another variation was the box truck employing the eight wheel bogey set-up, and the log trailer base with a same box to make a ten wheel straight truck and eight wheel trailer, as there were many on the California highways. Then the long base tractor (ten-wheeler) with bogey on rear eight wheels, hooked to Silver Streak and P.I.E. trailers, and yet other variations such as the P.I.E. eight wheel trailer minus top and raising rear door, as high-side grain hauler, and finally a long refrigerator trailer with small side door, all using ten-wheel tractors.

At the same time the company was putting the smaller wheels on the P.I.E. and Silver Streak trailers, and using the small six-wheeled cast "Half-Breeds" tractors, priced at lower competitive prices.

Their first Mack trucks were of the older 1940s types with running boards, old-type fenders and raised separate headlights, and all had fuel tanks, the later Mack trucks being 1954 macks with air horn on top.

The final year saw a complete change, Smith dropping out and Ironson coming in, changing the name to M.I.C. toys, Miller-Ironson Corporation, and to the best of my knowledge they produced only two different, all cast trucks, and thought no truck company name, definitely Auto-Car diesels. One was a heavy-duty tow truck, as tows large semis, and the other a flat bed with removable side racks, and turn-down, hydraulically lowering tailgate (up and down), door handles that worked to open doors, seat, steering wheel and front wheel which were steered like on the "model toy" fire trucks and other of the "model toy" line.

Honorable mention must be made, before closing, that one company in Minnesota, owned by Teamsters President Beck's son (in the late 1940s) put out a huge cast metal truck, mostly loggers and dumpers, which sterred via a horn on top of the cab, and two, Wyandotte put out in 1950, a very realistic cab over semi six wheel tractor of cast and eight wheel bogey'd long aluminum trailer, with beautifully realistic cast center replica wheels and rubber tires. The fifth wheel on the tractor was operational to couple and uncouple from the trailer, and though of no name, the cast tractor was finely detailed, fuel tanks and all. The Wyandotte sold at $10 while the aforementioned, name unknown, and very short-lived trucks, sold at $20 each, a much too high price for the 1940s. All are now gone, but live on in the minds of those who played with them. There were a few minor variations of the Smith-Miller which I did not mention, and no doubt possibly some on all items that I do not know about, nor have catalogs depicting. Any added information would be appreciated.

	G	VG	M
SMITTY (Smith-Miller) No., 401 Tow Truck, 15" long....................	7.50	11.25	15.00
SMITTY No. 402 Dump Truck, 11½" long............................	7.50	11.25	15.00
SMITTY No. 403 Scoop Dump, 14" long............................	7.50	11.25	15.00
SMITTY No. 404 Lumber Truck, 19" long............................	10.00	15.00	20.00
SMITTY No. 404T Lumber Trailer, 17" long............................	10.00	15.00	20.00
SMITTY No. 405 Silver Streak 6-wheel tractor, 28" long..................	12.50	18.75	25.00
SMITTY No. 406 Bekins Van, 29" long, six-wheel tractor and four-wheel trailer.....................	10.00	15.00	20.00
SMITTY No. 407 Searchlight Truck, 18½" long.......................	7.50	11.25	15.00
SMITTY No. 408 Blue Diamond 10-wheel dump truck, 18½" long.............	12.50	18.75	25.00
SMITTY No. 409 Pacific Intermountain Express (P.I.E.) six-wheel tractor semi with eight wheel aluminum trailer, 29" long........................	15.00	22.50	30.00
SMITTY No. 410 Aerial Ladder semi, six-wheel tractor, and four-wheel trailer, 36" long, "SMFD".................	15.00	22.50	30.00
SMITTY Box Truck with Box trailer, front truck ten-wheeler.............	20.00	30.00	40.00
SMITTY Box Truck with Box trailer, front truck six-wheeler..............	17.50	26.25	35.00
Steam Pumper, "Boston", with lamp, cast liron wheels, 15½" long.........	1400.00	2100.00	2800.00
Steam Pumper fire truck, cast iron, 5"...	4.00	6.00	8.00

	G	VG	M
Steam Pumper truck, cast iron, hard rubber wheels, driver, 12" long.......	60.00	90.00	120.00
Steam Pumper, tin and wooden chain and friction drive with driver, "National", 10"	75.00	112.50	150.00
Steam Pumper, tin and wooden friction drive 11" long....................	20.00	30.00	40.00
Steam Roller, steam-engine powered....	80.00	120.00	160.00
Steam Roller, cast iron, 4¾" long, circa early 1930s.......................	20.00	30.00	40.00
STEELCRAFT Coca Cola Truck, 12 bottles on side......................	105.00	152.50	210.00
STEELCRAFT "Heinz, Rice Flakes, Baked Beans, Bottle Vinegar" truck...	42.50	63.75	85.00
STEELCRAFT Shell Motor Oil truck with oil barrels...................	72.50	108.75	145.00
STEELCRAFT Tank truck, sheet metal, 25½" long.......................	25.00	37.50	50.00
STRUCTO Army truck, covered, metal, rubber tires....................	12.00	18.00	24.00
STRUCTO Coupe, convertible, circa 1920s	67.50	106.25	135.00
STRUCTO Caterpillar Tractor with Trailer, heavy spring clockwork motor, steel treads......................	88.00	124.00	176.00
STRUCTO Dump Truck, open cab, circa 1930, 18" long...............	25.00	37.50	50.00
STRUCTO Dump Truck, "Structo Excavating Co. No. 605 Phone 351" black rubber tires......................	20.00	30.00	40.00
STRUCTO Dump Wagon, cast iron, rubber tires......................	10.00	15.00	20.00

STRUCTO Caterpillar Whippet Tank
page 47

	G	VG	M
STRUCTO Guided Missile Launching Truck, truck metal, missiles, etc., plastic, rubber tires...............	15.00	22.50	30.00
STRUCTO Moving Van, 16" long, open cab, circa 1929..................	50.00	75.00	100.00
STRUCTO Renault Tank, clockwork, green with red turret...............	125.00	187.50	250.00
STRUCTO Searchlight Truck, truck metal, light and generator plastic, uses batteries, has rubber tires........	18.00	27.00	36.00
STRUCTO Tank, olive drab with orange turret, ten metal wheels, 12" long.....	55.00	82.50	110.00
STRUCTO Telephone Truck...........	14.00	21.00	28.00
STRUCTO Caterpillar Whippet Tank, 12" long, heavy spring clockwork motor enameled green, red and black, may read "Patented 1920"; on sale in 1929, No. 48.....................	90.00	130.00	180.00
STRUCTO Mail Truck 16" long........	55.00	82.50	110.00
STURDITOY Ambulance, 26" long, open cab, circa 1929..................	60.00	90.00	120.00
STURDITOY American Railway Express Truck, circa 1920s.................	50.00	75.00	100.00
STURDITOY Pumper, 26" long, circa 1930...........................	40.00	60.00	80.00
SUN RUBBER, auto, license No. S500R, 1930s	7.00	10.50	14.00
SUN RUBBER, Chrysler Airflow auto, white rubber tires.................	4.00	6.00	8.00
SUN RUBBER, Scout Car 7" long, four men firing machine guns, circa 1946...	8.00	12.00	16.00
Tin Auto with tin wheels, circa 1930s, looks like Chrysler Airflow (similar to Volkswagen)	3.00	4.50	6.00
TOLEDO METAL WHEEL CO. Fire Pumper Pedal car, red-painted, 59" long	220.00	330.00	440.00

TOOTSIE TOY (Compiled by C.B.C. LEE)

TOOTSIETOY 4528 Limousine circa 1910, in 1911-1928 catalogs..........	5.00	7.50	10.00

	G	**VG**	**M**
TOOTSIETOY 4570 Ford, Model T, open tourer, 1914, in catalog 1915-1926....	7.50	11.25	15.00
TOOTSIETOY 4610 Ford Model T pickup truck, 1914, in catalog 1919-1932..	7.50	11.25	15.00
TOOTSIETOY 4629 (Yellow Cab) sedan, 1921, in catalog 1923-1933..........	4.00	6.00	8.00
TOOTSIETOY 4630 (Federal) "Grocery" delivery van, 1921, in catalog 1924-1933............................	25.00	37.50	50.00
TOOTSIETOY 4631 (Federal) "Bakery" delivery van, 1921, in catalog 1924-1933............................	37.50	56.25	75.00
TOOTSIETOY 4632 (Federal) "Market" delivery van, 1921, in catalog 1924-1933............................	17.50	26.25	35.00
TOOTSIETOY 4633 (Federal) "Laundry" delivery van, 1921, in catalog 1924-1933............................	17.50	26.25	35.00
TOOTSIETOY 4634 (Federal) "Milk" delivery van, 1921, in catalog 1924-1933............................	5.00	7.50	10.00
TOOTSIETOY 4635 (Federal) "Florist" delivery van, 1921, in catalog 1924-1933............................	50.00	75.00	100.00

TOOTSIETOY vans in the 4630s made in special custom liveries for private department stores, including "Boggs & Buhl", "Watt & Shand", "Pomeroy's", Hochschild Kohn & Co.", "Bamberger's", "Alling Rubber Co.-Toys", "Jordan Marsh Co.", etc. Prices range on these from $75 to $250 in mint condition.

	G	**VG**	**M**
TOOTSIETOY 4636 coupe, 1921, in cataloge 1924-1933.....................	4.00	6.00	8.00
TOOTSIETOY 4638 Mack stake truck, 1922, in catalog 1925-1933...........	7.50	11.25	15.00
TOOTSIETOY 4639 Mack coal truck, 1922, in catalog 1925-1933...........	7.50	11.25	15.00
TOOTSIETOY 4640 Mack tank truck, 1922, in catalog 1925-1933...........	7.50	11.25	15.00
TOOTSIETOY 4641 closed tourer, 1924, in catalog 1925-1933...............	5.00	7.50	10.00

	G	VG	M
TOOTSIETOY 4642 cannon, in catalog 1931-1941	2.50	3.75	5.00
TOOTSIETOY 4643 Mack AA Gun truck, 1922, in catalog 1931-1941...........	5.00	7.50	10.00
TOOTSIETOY 4644 mack searchlight truck, 1922, in catalog 1931-1941.....	5.00	7.50	10.00
TOOTSIETOY 4645 Mack "US Mail-Airmail Service", 1922, in catalog 1931-1933	12.50	18.75	25.00
TOOTSIETOY 4646 Caterpillar tractor, in catalog 1931-1939..............	7.50	11.25	15.00
TOOTSIETOY 4647 (Renault) tank, 1915, in catalog 1931-1941...........	10.00	15.00	20.00
TOOTSIETOY 4648 steamroller, in catalog 1931-1934....................	17.50	26.25	35.00
TOOTSIETOY 4651 (Fageol) safety coach circa 1927, in catalog 1927-1933.	5.00	7.50	10.00
TOOTSIETOY 4652 fire engine-hook and ladder, in catalog 1927-1933........	15.00	22.50	30.00
TOOTSIETOY 4653 fire engine-water tower, in catalog 1927-1933..........	15.00	22.50	30.00
TOOTSIETOY 4654 farm tractor, in catalog 1927-1932.................	12.50	18.75	25.00
TOOTSIETOY 4655 Ford, Model a, coupe, 1928, in catalog 1928-1933.....	7.50	11.25	15.00

The earlier Tootsietoys enjoyed a wide market and lasted a long time, so are not in short supply. They bring from about $10 to $25.
Caption and Photo by C.B.C. Lee

	G	VG	M
TOOTSIETOY 4656 (Buick) coupe in tinplate garage, 1930, in catalog 1931-1932	20.00	30.00	40.00
TOOTSIETOY 4657 (Buick) sedan in tinplate garage, 1930, in catalog 1931-1932	20.00	30.00	40.00
TOOTSIETOY 4658 Mack insurance patrol in garage, in catalog 1931-1932	20.00	30.00	40.00
TOOTSIETOY 4666 Bluebird I Daytona record car, 1927, in catalog 1932-1941	7.50	11.25	15.00
TOOTSIETOY 4670 Mack tractor and two semi-trailers, 1927, "A&P", "American Express", in catalot 1929-1932	37.50	56.25	75.00
TOOTSIETOY 4670 Mack tractor and two semi-trailers, 1927, "Overland Bus Lines", in catalog 1929-1933	22.50	33.75	45.00
TOOTSIETOY 23 racer with driver, in catalog 1927-1933	7.50	11.25	15.00
TOOTSIETOY 190 Mack auto transport (3 Buicks), 1922, in catalog 1931-1933	35.00	52.50	70.00
TOOTSIETOY 190 Mack auto transport (4 Buicks), 1922, in catalog 1933-1936	62.50	93.75	125.00
TOOTSIETOY 5101 Funnies Set, "Andy Gump" roadster, in catalog 1932-1933, standard version	50.00	75.00	100.00
TOOTSIETOY 5102 Funnies Set, "Uncle Walt" roadster, in catalog 1932-1933, standard version	65.00	97.50	130.00
TOOTSIETOY 5103 Funnies Set, "Smitty" motorcycle with sidecar, in catalog 1932-1933, standard version	42.50	63.75	85.00
TOOTSIETOY 5104 Funnies Set, "Moon Mullins" police wagon, in catalog 1932-1933, standard v	42.50	63.75	85.00

The 1932 Funnies series was manufactured only in that year and sold poorly. They are much sought by both toy and comic art collectors. Though made in equal numbers, they vary in rarity today. Those in front (Uncle Walt, Andy Gump, K.O. Ice Truck, shown here in the simple 10 ' version) are scarcer than those behind (Uncle Willie and Mamie, Smitty and Herbie, and Moon Mullins and cop, shown here in the deluxe versions). Values range from about $75 for the boat up to about $200 for Uncle Walt, the deluxe versions fetching about 15% more than the standard ones.
Caption and Photo by C.B.C. Lee

	G	VG	M
TOOTSIETOY 5105 Funnies Set, "Kayo" ice wagon, in catalog 1932-1933, standard v.	45.00	67.50	90.00
TOOTSIETOY 5106 Funnies Set, "Uncle Willie" rowboat, in catalog 1932-1933, standard v.	37.50	56.25	75.00
TOOTSIETOY 6001 Buick Roadster, 1926, in catalog 1927-1933.	12.50	18.75	25.00
TOOTSIETOY 6002 Buick coupe, 1926, in catalog 1927-1933.	12.50	18.75	25.00
TOOTSIETOY 6003 Buick Brougham, 1926, in catalog 1927-1933.	12.50	18.75	25.00
TOOTSIETOY 6004 Buick sedan, 1926, in catalog 1927-1933.	12.50	18.75	25.00
TOOTSIETOY 6005 Buick closed touring car, 1926, in catalog 1927-1933.	20.00	30.00	40.00
TOOTSIETOY 6006 Buick screenside panel delivery, 1926, in catalog 1927-1933.	12.50	18.75	25.00
TOOTSIETOY 6101 Cadillac roadster, 1926, in catalog 1927-1933.	17.50	26.25	35.00
TOOTSIETOY 6102 Cadillac coupe, 1926, in catalog 1927-1933.	17.50	26.25	35.00

	G	VG	M
TOOTSIETOY 6103 Cadillac brougham, 1926, in catalog 1927-1933..........	17.50	26.25	35.00
TOOTSIETOY 6104 Cadillac sedan, 1926, in catalog 1927-1933..........	17.50	26.25	35.00
TOOTSIETOY 6105 Cadillac closed touring car, 1926, in catalog 1927-1933....	25.00	37.50	50.00
TOOTSIETOY 6106 Cadillac panel delivery van, 1926, in catalog 1927-1933............................	17.50	26.25	35.00
TOOTSIETOY 6201 Chevrolet roadster, 1926, in catalog 1927-1933..........	15.00	22.50	30.00
TOOTSIETOY 6202 Chevrolet coupe, 1926, in catalog 1927-1933..........	15.00	22.50	30.00
TOOTSIETOY 6203 brougham, 1926, in catalog 1927-1933.................	15.00	22.50	30.00
TOOTSIETOY 6204 Chevrolet sedan, 1926, in catalog 1927-1933..........	15.00	22.50	30.00
TOOTSIETOY 6205 Chevrolet closed touring car, 1926, in catalog 1927-1933............................	22.50	33.75	45.00
TOOTSIETOY 6206 Chevrolet panel delivery van, 1926, in catalog 1927-1933............................	15.00	22.50	30.00
TOOTSIETOY 6301 Oldsmobile roadster. 1926, in catalog 1927-1933......	15.00	22.50	30.00
TOOTSIETOY 6302 Oldsmobile coupe, 1926, in catalog 1927-1933..........	15.00	22.50	30.00
TOOTSIETOY 6303 Oldsmobile broughham, 1926, in catalog 1927-1933......	15.00	22.50	30.00
TOOTSIETOY 6304 Oldsmobile sedan, 1926, in catalog 1927-1933..........	15.00	22.50	30.00
TOOTSIETOY 6305 Oldsmobile closed touring car, 1926, in catalog 1927-1933............................	22.50	33.75	45.00
TOOTSIETOY 6306 Oldsmobiel panel delivery van, 1926, in catalog 1927-1933............................	15.00	22.50	30.00
TOOTSIETOY 6-01 roadster, 1926, in catalog 1933 only.................	25.00	37.50	50.00

	G	VG	M
TOOTSIETOY 6-02 coupe, 1926, in catalog 1933 only..................	25.00	37.50	50.00
TOOTSIETOY 6-03 brougham, 1926, in catalog 1933 only..................	25.00	37.50	50.00
TOOTSIETOY 6-04 sedan, 1926, in catalog 1933 only..................	25.00	37.50	50.00
TOOTSIETOY 6-05 closed touring car, 1926, in catalog 1933 only...........	32.50	48.75	65.00
TOOTSIETOY 6-06 panel delivery van, 1926, in catalog 1933 only...........	25.00	37.50	50.00
TOOTSIETOY, unnumbered, Ford Model A van marked "U.S. Mail", sold only in sets...................	15.00	22.50	30.00
TOOTSIETOY 4654 farm tractor made in special version for Army Field battery set No. 5071, with cannons....	20.00	30.00	40.00
TOOTSIETOY Box trailer and road-scraper raker, sold only in boxed set Farm Tractor No. 7003..............	50.00	75.00	100.00
TOOTSIETOY 6665 Ford Model A sedan, 1928, in catalog 1929-1933...........	10.00	15.00	20.00
TOOTSIETOY 101 Buick coupe (see no. 4656), 1930, in catalog 1932-1934.....	5.00	7.50	10.00
TOOTSIETOY 102 Buick roadster, 1930, in catalog 1932-1934................	5.00	7.50	10.00
TOOTSIETOY 103 Buick sedan (see no. 4657) 1930, in catalog 1932-1934......	5.00	7.50	10.00
TOOTSIETOY 104 Mack insurance patrol (see 4658), in catalog 1932-1934.........................	5.00	7.50	10.00
TOOTSIETOY 105 Mack tank truck, in catalog 1932-1934.................	5.00	7.50	10.00
TOOTSIETOY 108 Caterpillar tractor, in catalog 1932-1934...............	5.00	7.50	10.00
TOOTSIETOY 109 Ford? stake pick-up truck, in catalog 1932-1934........	5.00	7.50	10.00
TOOTSIETOY 110 Bluebird I Daytona record car, 1927, in catalog 1932-1934.	5.00	7.50	10.00

In the 1933 catalog, rubber tires were introduced, and many earlier models became available with optional rubber tires. Their catalog number was then preceded by the digit "0", so that the "Yellow Cab" with rubber tires, for example was designated as 04629. New models with rubber tires only were also shown with a prefix of "0", so that the 1932 Macks, Grahams, etc., are thus listed below. However, all "0" prefixes were dropped in the 1937 and later catalogs. Also in the 1933 catalog, use of the new alloy (Zamac) was announced. Earlier models had been of lead and lead alloys. Some lead contamination in later castings resulted in the deterioration of the zamac. Lead-free zamac endures well.

C.B.C. LEE

These trucks with store names on the side (cast in, by decal, and by a separate tin plate attached by tabs) are very choice and sell for $75 to $250 depending on rarity. A cache of six or so of a particular version can plummet the price by 50%. Thirteen different versions of the older "Federal" type and six versions of the 1936 Ford "camelback" are known to this writer, but others are sure to turn up. The same trucks with generic trades on the side are worth only about 30% of the above range, the one marked FLORIST being the rarest.

Caption and Photo by C.B.C. Lee

	G	VG	M
TOOTSIETOY 0191 Mack dumper train, 3 carts, 1932 in catalog 1933-1941	37.50	56.25	75.00
TOOTSIETOY 0192 Mack "Tootsietoy Dairy" train semi-trailer plus two full trailers, 1932, in catalog 1933-1941	37.50	56.25	75.00
TOOTSIETOY 0198 Mack car transport (three fords), 1932, in catalog 1935-1941	30.00	45.00	60.00
TOOTSIETOY 0801 Mack "Express" stake semi-trailer, 1932, in catalog 1933-1941	12.50	18.75	25.00

TOOTSIETOY 0802 Mack "Domaco"

	G	VG	M
tank semi-trailer, 1932, in catalog 1933-1939	15.00	22.50	30.00
TOOTSIETOY 0803 Mack "Long Distance Hauling", cargo van, semi-trailer, 1932, in catalog 1933-1936	20.00	30.00	40.00
TOOTSIETOY 0804 Mack "City Fuel Co." ten-wheel truck, 1932, in catalog 1933-1935	22.50	33.75	45.00
TOOTSIETOY 0804 "City Fuel", four wheels only, in catalog 1936-1938	20.00	30.00	40.00
TOOTSIETOY 0805 Mack "Tootsietoy Dairy" semi-trailer truck, 1932, in catalog 1933-1939	15.00	22.50	30.00
TOOTSIETOY 0806 Graham wrecker, 1932, in catalog 1933-1939	10.00	15.00	20.00
TOOTSIETOY 0807 delivery motorcycle (adapted from 5103), in catalog 1933-34	25.00	37.50	50.00
TOOTSIETOY 0808 Graham "Tootsietoy Dairy" van, 1932, in catalog 1933-1938	20.00	30.00	40.00
TOOTSIETOY Graham "Commercial Tire & Supply Co." delivery van was sold only in sets. 05300 set is shown in 1935 catalog	25.00	37.50	50.00
TOOTSIETOY 0809 Graham ambulance, 1932, in catalog 1935-1941	20.00	30.00	40.00
TOOTSIETOY 0810 Mack "Railway Express Co." van (with Wrigley's ad), 1932, in catalog 1935-1939	22.50	33.75	45.00

The larger 1932 Macks were first issued in two-piece castings and dual wheels. In 1936 they were issued as one-piece castings with single rear wheels, worth about $10 less in mint. The tractor for the dumper train was never cast in the later one-piece (set 0191), and the car transport (0198) was never issued in the earlier two-piece casting. TOOTSIETOY Graham Series: There were several minor changes in chassis castings. Initially, there were none without spare tire on either the sides or the rear. The "convertible" coupes and sedans listed below are castings identical to the non-convertible coupe and sedan, but painted two-toned with tan top. The same applies to the later 1934 Fords and 1935 LaSalles.   **C. B. C. LEE**

	G	VG	M
TOOTSIETOY 0511 Graham roadster, five-wheel, 1932, in catalog 1933-1935	22.50	33.75	45.00
TOOTSIETOY 0512 Graham coupe, five-wheel, 1932, in catalog 1933-1935	12.50	18.75	25.00
TOOTSIETOY 0513 Graham sedan, five-wheel, 1932, in catalog 1933-1935	12.50	18.75	25.00
TOOTSIETOY 0514 Graham convertible coupe, five-wheel, 1932, in catalog 1933-1935	12.50	18.75	25.00
TOOTSIETOY 0515 Graham convertible sedan, five-wheel, 1932, in catalog 1933-1935	12.50	18.75	25.00
TOOTSIETOY 0516 Graham town car, five-wheel, 1932, in catalog 1933-1935	20.00	30.00	40.00
TOOTSIETOY 0611 Graham roadster, six-wheel, 1932, in catalog 1933-1935	22.50	33.75	45.00
TOOTSIETOY 0612 Graham coupe, six-wheel, 1932, in catalog 1933-1935	12.50	18.75	25.00
TOOTSIETOY 0613 Graham sedan, six-wheel, 1932, in catalog 1933-1935	12.50	18.75	25.00
TOTTSIETOY 0614 Graham convertible coupe, six-wheel, 1932, in catalog 1933-1935	12.50	18.75	25.00
TOOTSIETOY 0615 Graham convertible sedan, six-wheel, 1932, in catalog 1933-1935	12.50	18.75	25.00
TOOTSIETOY 0616 Graham town car, six-wheel, 1932, in catalog 1933-1935	20.00	30.00	40.00
TOOTSIETOY (number not known) Graham roadster, four-wheel, 1932	25.00	37.50	50.00
TOOTSIETOY (number not known) Graham coupe, four-wheel, 1932, in catalog 1935?-1939 (Build-A-Car)	12.50	18.75	25.00
TOOTSIETOY (number not known) Graham sedan, four-wheel, 1932, in catalog 1935?-1939 (Build-A-Car)	12.50	18.75	25.00

These are among the more desirable kinds of standard issue Tootsie toys, the LaSalles (front, left, made in a sedan also) go for around $75. The Grahams (2nd, front, made in 15 versions) sell for about $25 and up to $45 for roadsters, town cars and tour vans. The G.M. series (front, right) vary from $25 to $75 depending on the body and which G.M. chassis (Buick, Chevrolet, Oldsmobile, Cadillac, and "no-name"). The Lincoln and trailer, left rear, is rare, and has sold for as much as $250. Not to be confused with the somewhat nicer but commoner "Doodlebug", right rear, which is about equal in value to the Grahams. Tootsietoys have dropped in value over the last decade as supply has caught up with demand. The real rarities have held their value.
Caption and Photo by C.B.C. Lee

	G	VG	M
TOOTSIETOY 0712 LaSalle coupe, 1935, in catalog 1936-1938..............	37.50	56.25	75.00
TOOTSIETOY 0713 LaSalle sedan, 1935, in catalog 1936-1938..............	37.50	56.25	75.00
TOOTSIETOY 0714 LaSalle convertible coupe, 1935, in catalog 1936 only.....	37.50	56.25	75.00
TOOTSIETOY 0715 LaSalle convertible sedan, 1935, in catalog 1936 only.....	37.50	56.25	75.00

.Beware of copies, fakes and reproductions! None of these is a Tootsietoy! Many are now being made in both U.S. and Great Britain. Some collectors have an interest in old contemporary counterfeits, which were also made in many foreign countries, and I confess that I am one such.
Caption and Photo by C.B.C. Lee

	G	VG	M
TOOTSIETOY 0716 (Briggs Lincoln) prototype "Doodlebug", 1933, in catalog 1936-1937	15.00	22.50	30.00
TOOTSIETOY 6015 Lincoln (only the grille is accurate, the rest of the body being the same as the Briggs prototype, which was never publicaly sold) Zephyr, 1936, in catalog 1937-1939	40.00	60.00	80.00
TOOTSIETOY 6016 Lincoln wrecker, 1936, in catalog 1937-1938	60.00	90.00	120.00

TOOTSIETOY Ford series: The coupe and sedan in single color and convertible versions and the wrecker were issued in 1935 as 1934 Fords, having a separate grille-piece like the Grahams, and rubber tires mounted on metal hubs. The following year they were recast in one piece as 1935 Fords with slight changes also to the hood louvres and fender skirts and fitted with solid rubber wheels. The roadster, pick-up truck, etc., were not in the 1934 series.

C.B.C. LEE

	G	VG	M
TOOTSIETOY 0111 Ford V-8 sedan, 1934, in catalog 1935 only	12.50	18.75	25.00
TOOTSIETOY 0111 Ford V-8 sedan, 1935, in catalog 1936-1939	5.00	7.50	10.00
TOOTSIETOY 0112 Ford V-8 coupe, 1934, in catalog 1935 only	12.50	18.75	25.00
TOOTSIETOY 0112 Ford V-8 coupe, 1935, in catalog 1936-1939	5.00	7.50	10.00
TOOTSIETOY 0113 Ford V-8 wrecker, 1934, in catalog 1935 only	15.00	22.50	30.00
TOOTSIETOY 0113 Ford V-8 wrecker, 1935, in catalog 1936-1941	5.00	7.50	10.00
TOOTSIETOY 0114 Ford V-8 convertible coupe, 1934, in catalog 1935 only	7.50	11.25	15.00
TOOTSIETOY 0115 Ford V-8 convertible sedan, 1934, in catalog 1935 only	7.50	11.25	15.00
TOOTSIETOY 0116 Ford V-8 roadster, 1935, in catalog 1936-1939	7.50	11.25	15.00
TOOTSIETOY 0117 Zephyr railcar, in catalog 1935-1936	5.00	7.50	10.00
TOOTSIETOY 0118 DeSoto Airflow sedan, 1935, in catalog 1935-1939	10.00	15.00	20.00

	G	VG	M
TOOTSIETOY 0120 Oil Tank Truck, in catalog 1936-1939	5.00	7.50	10.00
TOOTSIETOY 0121 Ford pick-up truck, 1935, in catalog 1936-1939	5.00	7.50	10.00
TOOTSIETOY 0123 Ford "Special Delivery" van, 1936, in catalog 1937-1939	5.00	7.50	10.00

This "camelback" van was also issued in several custom liveries by use of a tin-plate insert on the side panels. Price on these in mint condition is $75 and up.-C.B.C. LEE

	G	VG	M
TOOTSIETOY 180 set, Lincoln Zephyr and Roamer house-trailer issued in 1938 with clockwork motor, in 1939 without motor, 1936, in catalog 1938-1939	75.00	112.50	150.00
TOOTSIETOY 187 Mack car transport (up-tilted), 1932, in catalog 1941	37.50	56.25	75.00
TOOTSIETOY 4634 Army supply truck (adapted from 1042), in catalog 1939-1941	10.00	15.00	20.00
TOOTSIETOY 4635 Armored Car, in catalog from 1938 to at least 1941	10.00	15.00	20.00
TOOTSIETOY 1006 "Standard" oil truck, in catalog from 1939 to at least 1941	7.50	11.25	15.00

Trucks are valued in the same range as their contemporary cars, from $25 to $75 depending on the version and its scarcity.
Caption and Photo by C.B.C. Lee

	G	VG	M
TOOTSIETOY 1007 "Sinclair" oil truck, in catalog from 1939 to at least 1941	7.50	11.25	15.00
TOOTSIETOY 1008 "Texaco" oil truck, in catalog from 1939 to at least 1941	7.50	11.25	15.00
TOOTSIETOY 1009 "Shell" oil truck, in catalog from 1939 to at least 1941	7.50	11.25	15.00
TOOTSIETOY 1010 "Wrigley" box van, in catalog from 1940 to at least 1941	17.50	26.25	35.00
TOOTSIETOY 1011 Farm tractor, in catalog 1941	15.00	22.50	30.00
TOOTSIETOY 1016 (Auburn) roadster "torpedo", 1934, in catalog 1936 to at least 1941	2.50	3.75	5.00
TOOTSIETOY 1017 torpedo coupe, in catalog from 1936 to at least 1941	2.50	3.75	5.00
TOOTSIETOY 1018 torpedo sedan, in catalog from 1936 to at least 1941	2.50	3.75	5.00
TOOTSIETOY 1019 pick-up truck, in catalog from 1936 to at least 1941	2.50	3.75	5.00
TOOTSIETOY Greyhound bus (see 1045), in catalog 1941	7.50	11.25	15.00
TOOTSIETOY (no number known) Transamerica bus, in set only, in 1941 catalog	25.00	37.50	50.00
TOOTSIETOY 1027 wrecker, in catalog 1938-1941	2.50	3.75	5.00
TOOTSIETOY 1040 hook & ladder, in catalog 1937-1941	10.00	15.00	20.00
TOOTSIETOY 1041 hose car, in catalog 1937-1941	10.00	15.00	20.00
TOOTSIETOY 1042 Insurance patrol with open rear, in catalog 1937-1938	10.00	15.00	20.00
TOOTSIETOY 1042 Insurance patrol with single rear ladder and rear fireman in catalog 1939-1941	10.00	15.00	20.00

Other die-cast toy vehicles from the 1920s and 1930s include **TIP-TOP TOYS, ERIES,** MANOILS, and BARCLAYS, shown here these are comparable in value in Tootsietoys of similar age and rarity.

Caption and Photo by C.B.C. Lee

	G	VG	M
TOOTSIETOY 1043 Ford and small house trailer, 11935, in catalog 1937-1941	10.00	15.00	20.00
TOOTSIETOY 1044 Roamer house-trailer (see 180 set), in catalog 1937 only	25.00	37.50	50.00
TOOTSIETOY 1045 Greyhound deluxe bus, 1935, in catalog 1937 to at least 1941	7.50	11.25	15.00
TOOTSIETOY 1046 station wagon, circa 1939, in catalog 1940 to at least 1941	7.50	11.25	15.00
TOOTSIETOY 230 (LaSalle) sedan, circa 1939, in catalog 1940 to at least 1941	4.50	6.75	9.00
TOOTSIETOY 231 coupe, circa 1939, in catalog 1940 to at least 1941	4.50	6.75	9.00
TOOTSIETOY 232 open touring car, circa 1939, in catalog from 1940 to at least 1941	4.50	6.75	9.00
TOOTSIETOY 233 boat-tail roadster, circa 1939, in catalog from 1940 to at least 1941	4.50	6.75	9.00
TOOTSIETOY 234 box van, in catalog from 1940 to at least 1941	4.50	6.75	9.00
TOOTSIETOY 235 oil tank truck, in catalog from 1940 to at least 1941	4.50	6.75	9.00

	G	VG	M
TOOTSIETOY 236 fire engine, hook & ladder, in catalog from 1940 to at least 1941	4.50	6.75	9.00
TOOTSIETOY 237 fire engine, insurance patrol, in catalog from 1940 to at least 1941	4.50	6.75	9.00
TOOTSIETOY 238 fire engine, hose wagon, in catalog from 1940 to at least 1941	4.50	6.75	9.00
TOOTSIETOY 239 station wagon, circa 1939, in catalog from 1940 to at least 1941	4.50	6.75	9.00

TOOTSIETOY 260 Paramount Air-N-Lite taxi "Yellow", 261 Paramount Air-N-Lite taxi "Checker", 262 fire engine and 263 hook & ladder were a "Giant Series", shown in 1941 catalog but never released.   End of List by C.B.C. LEE

	G	VG	M
TOOTSIETOY Chev. Cameo car, black plastic wheels	1.50	2.35	3.00
TOOTSIETOY Ford automobile circa 1950s, black plastic tires	.50	1.00	1.50
TOOTSIETOY Ford, black rubber tires, 1950s sedan	1.50	2.25	3.00
TOOTSIETOY Ford Thunderbird, black rubber tires	1.25	1.88	2.50
TOOTSIETOY Greyhound Bus No. 747, black rubber tires	3.00	4.50	6.00
TOOTSIETOY Jaguar auto, black rubber tires	1.50	2.25	3.00
TOOTSIETOY Jaguar XK140 black plastic tires	3.00	4.50	6.00
TOOTSIETOY Jeep, metal, black wooden wheels, circa 1945-1946	2.00	3.00	4.00
TOOTSIETOY Lark Auto, black plastic tires	.60	.90	1.20
TOOTSIETOY Oldsmobile circa 1950, black plastic tires, has trailer hitch	2.00	3.00	4.00
TOOTSIETOY Packard, circa 1950s, has trailer hitch, black plastic tires	2.00	3.00	4.00

	G	VG	M
TOOTSIETOY Panel truck with black rubber tires............................	1.00	1.50	2.00
TOOTSIETOY Pick-up truck with plastic tires..............................	.50	.75	1.00
TOOTSIETOY racer, black plastic wheels, No. 01044, driver...........	2.00	3.00	4.00
TOOTSIETOY Road Builder Set, has roadgrader with black rubber tires, bulldozer, dumptruck with plastic wheels, semi-truck with plastic wheels that carries bulldozer, trailer has rubber tires, six diecast road signs. Circa 1947........................	12.50	18.75	25.00
TOOTSIETOY Station wagon circa 1950s, black rubber tires...........	1.50	2.25	3.00
TOOTSIETOY Tank Truck No. 13 oil tanker, black wooden wheels, 1950s?..	1.50	2.25	3.00
"TOOTSIETOY TRUCK LINE SET", five pieces, black rubber tires, circa 1950s..............................	11.25	16.48	22.50

Only a few exceptionally accurate and well cast slush mold toys are worth more than $5. Some exceptions are shown here, which would sell for $20 to $80 on an open market at a collector's meet. Slush molding is easy, and some are being recast today from old molds.
Caption and Photo by C.B.C. Lee

	G	VG	M
Touring car, tin, friction, 6"...........	10.00	15.00	20.00
Touring car, tin and wooden friction drive, with cast iron driver and two cast iron women, 10½" long.........	100.00	150.00	200.00
Tow truck, cast iron, 5¾" long.........	15.00	22.50	30.00

	G	**VG**	**M**
Tow truck, cast iron, 7½", rubber wheels	26.00	39.00	52.00
Tractor with front loader and driver, cast iron, rubber wheels, 9½" long. . . .	200.00	300.00	400.00
Trailer truck, wooden, plastic wheels, "Coast to Coast Fast Freight", approx. 8¼" long.	3.00	4.50	6.00
Truck, cast iron, flat back, 1920s, approx. 4¼" long, looks like Model A Ford semi-tractor.	17.00	25.50	34.00
Truck cab with interchangeable flat bed and tank, sheet metal with wooden wheels, 10¾".	7.00	10.50	14.00
TURNER Bulldog mac closed cab dump truck, red and green steel, 23" long. . . .	55.00	82.50	110.00
TURNER Fire Engine Pumper, 15" long.	34.00	51.00	68.00
TURNER Hook and ladder, 15" long, circa 1930s.	34.00	51.00	68.00
Two-door sedan, slung-back cab, 1930s, slush-mold die cast, white rubber tires.	5.00	7.50	10.00
"U.S. Army Shooting Tank", 6" wood, pre WWII, 6" long, metal action.	4.00	6.00	8.00
U.S. Army truck, boat, and cement carrier, three pieces.	3.00	4.50	6.00
U.S. Motor Unit truck, slush mold.	5.00	7.50	10.00
U.S.A.W. No. 60118 half-track, black wooden wheels, die-cast, approx. 4¾".	3.50	5.25	7.00
VINDEX hay loader.	42.50	63.75	85.00
VINDEX "P&H" power shovel, cast iron, 12" (17" extended), wheels in caterpillar base, handle revolves rig.	450.00	675.00	900.00
WILKENS fire engine, circa 1900, with driver, steam boiler.	50.00	75.00	100.00
Willys Knight, cast iron, 8" long, 1920s, with driver.	50.00	75.00	100.00
WYANDOTTE Ambulance, 11¼" long, swinging rear door.	24.00	36.00	48.00
WYANDOTTE Army Truck, 10" long, steel with wood wheels.	10.00	15.00	20.00

	G	VG	M
WYANDOTTE boattail racer, 8½" long, steel, red with white rubber tires, electric headlamps................	20.00	30.00	40.00
WYANDOTTE Coupe, circa 1935, red with white rubber tires, electric headlights, 8½" long..................	20.00	30.00	40.00
WYANDOTTE Dump Truck, pressed steel, approx. 6½" long, circa 1940....	6.00	9.00	12.00
WYANDOTTE Dump Truck, circa mid-1930s, 15" long, white rubber tires....	16.00	24.00	32.00
WYANDOTTE "Express" trailer truck, tin wheels.......................	30.00	45.00	60.00
WYANDOTTE Ice Truck, marked "ICE" on sides, circa 1940................	25.00	37.50	50.00
WYANDOTTE LaSalle car with trailer, 25½" long, 1930s.................	44.00	66.00	88.00
WYANDOTTE Trailer truck, 1950......	4.50	6.75	9.00
WYANDOTTE Truck with stake sides, 12" long, circa 1930s...............	12.50	18.75	25.00
WYANDOTTE "Wyandottey", pressed steel two-door sedan, sweeping long fenders, circa WWII, black plastic wheels	5.00	7.50	10.00
Yellow Cab, 1930s, 7½" long, white rubber tires, rear suitcase rack........	290.00	345.00	580.00
Yellow Cab, cast iron, with driver, 7¾" long........................	150.00	225.00	300.00

ANIMAL-DRAWN

In this category, the toys generally commanding the highest prices are the horse-drawn cast iron pieces. One reason for the eye-opening prices is that horse-drawn cast iron toys have considerable value apart from their lure as toys. There is an air of genuine Americana about them, and they are likely to attract the interest of many who otherwise pay no attention to toys (decorators figure largely in this area). As an example of the popularity of these toys, the highest price in this book for a toy was paid for the HUBLEY four-seat brake, at $5750 in good to very good condition.

Since prices are often so high, reproductions, whether honest or dishonest, can be a problem. Things to look for when a reproduction is suspected include a rougher surface than an old toy would have (recastings are invariably rougher), uneven fit of pieces, a blurring of details, and "aging" that doesn't have the patina of age. Since at least one company, John Wright (formerly Grey Iron), is still manufacturing turn-of-the-century horse-drawn vehicles, some of them from the original molds, it is wise to become familiar with the field before investing heavily.

CONDITION OF A TOY
AND ITS RELATION TO PRICE

The price of a toy depends not only on its desirability, but on its condition. A toy in mint condition is generally worth twice what that same toy would bring in good condition, with "very good" falling about equally in between good and mint.

"Mint" means just that; the condition in which it was originally issued-perfect, regardless of age, not the slightest blemish. Needless to say this is a fairly rare state of affairs, but enough toys exist in mint condition to make it an employable term. Many people hoping to dispose of items are tempted to call a toy "mint" when it is really "near mint", "very good", or sometimes even just "good". Inevitably this can result in unhappiness all around, and not infrequently, a cancelled sale.

"Very Good" indicates a toy which has obviously seen use, with signs of wear and aging, but in general having a freshness to its appearance that makes it attractive and collectible to all but the most discriminating.

"Good" signals a toy which has seen considerable wear, shows its age, but is basically sound. A collector will collect it, but will often not be wholly satisfied with it as an example of his collection, and thus prices are often drastically below that which the same item in mint can command.

Condition below good results in another drastic drop in price, and toys with missing parts, although otherwise in excellent condition, will usually fall into this lower-priced category. Rust, even small spots of it, can seriously lower the price of a toy. "Near-Mint", "Fine", "Very Fine" and similar terms often found in sellers' descriptions denote conditions between Mint and Very Good, and are priced accordingly.

The key to grading is to avoid wishful thinking. Grading can sometimes be a problem for the uninitiated, but common sense will usually prevail, and when possible, a consultation with an expert in the field can often clear up lingering doubts. A toy in its original box is worth up to 10 to 20% more if the box is in mint condition, with the price dropping as condition lessens.

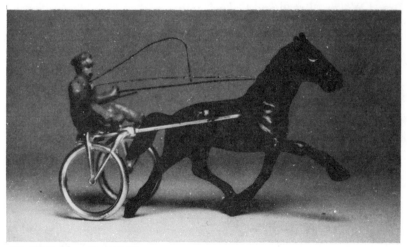

ALL-NU Trottler   (see page 68)
Photo by Bill Kaufman
Courtesy Al Rizzolo, THE RED PONY

ANIMAL-DRAWN

	G	VG	M
"ALDERNEY DAIRY" milk truck, two-horse, wood and lithographed paper...	140.00	210.00	280.00
ALL-NU trotter, lead alloy, 1941.......	6.00	9.00	12.00
ARCADE "Contractors Dump Wagon", 13¼", two-horse, driver, 1930s (note: all ARCADE toys are cast iron).......	80.00	120.00	160.00
ARCADE Farm Wagon, two-horse, driver	60.00	90.00	120.00
ARCADE McCormick Deering Farm Wagon, two-horse................	44.00	66.00	88.00
ARCADE McCormick Deering manure spreader, with team of horses........	50.00	75.00	100.00
ARCADE McCormick Spreader with team of horses....................	190.00	285.00	380.00
ARCADE Sulky plow, one horse, 10½"..	70.00	105.00	140.00
Bakery Wagon, one horse, 13" long, cast iron.........................	33.00	49.50	66.00
Bell Toy with horse, 8" long............	20.00	30.00	40.00
"Borden's Farm Products", wood, horse-drawn wagon pull-toy with articulated legs..............................	46.00	69.00	92.00
Bread Wagon "Bread and Cakes" with driver, tin horse, 12½"..............	350.00	525.00	700.00
Brewery Wagon, cast iron and pressed steel, two horse with driver, 20½"....	250.00	375.00	500.00
Buckboard, cast iron, 14" long, one horse and driver..................	100.00	150.00	200.00
Buggy, pressed steel, cast iron wheels and horse.........................	20.00	30.00	40.00
Buggy with driver, cast iron, 6½" long..	33.00	49.50	66.00
CARPENTER two-horse dump cart.....	150.00	225.00	300.00
"Carpenter" fire patrol, cast iron, two horses, driver and three figures.......	200.00	300.00	400.00
CARPENTER hook and ladder, cast iron, two horse with driver and rear man, ladders. Circa 1883-1890, 26½" long..	150.00	225.00	300.00
CARPENTER ox cart, two oxen, cast iron, circa 1880-1903, 11" long.......	66.00	99.00	132.00

CARPENTER Ox Cart, two oxen, cast iron, circa 1880-1903. 11" long. (see page 68)
Photo Courtesy PB84

	G	VG	M
Carriage, cast iron, one-horse, 7½" long.	60.00	90.00	120.00
Carriage, one horse, cloth and wicker, 56" long	20.00	30.00	40.00
Carriage, metal and wood, one horse, malleable iron horse with articulated legs and tail, carriage made of wood	220.00	330.00	440.00
Cart, cast iron lion, two wheels, 8" long	30.00	45.00	60.00
Cart, one horse, cast iron, 9" long	25.00	37.50	50.00
Cart with driver and buffalo, 7½" long, cast iron	350.00	525.00	700.00
Cart with cast iron woman and prancing horse, 10¼" long	70.00	105.00	140.00
Cart with elephant, cast iron, 7" long	25.00	37.50	50.00
Cart, stake sides, one horse, 7" long, early cast iron	20.00	30.00	40.00
Chariot, cast iron, with driver, 7½" long	33.00	49.50	66.00
Chariot drawn by tin horse, highly decorated, 13½" long	40.00	60.00	80.00
Chief's Wagon, cast iron "Chief", one horse, circa 1915-1920, 12" long	50.00	75.00	100.00
"Chief" fire chief wagon, cast iron, one-horse, 15½" long	86.00	129.00	172.00
Circus Wagon, iron and tin, two horses, lion cage, 9" long	100.00	150.00	200.00
Circus Wagon, cast iron and wood, containing carved wood bear, 13" long	110.00	165.00	220.00

	G	**VG**	**M**
Coal Wagon, cast iron, small...........	50.00	75.00	100.00
"Coal" Wagon, cast iron, with driver and coal shovel, 9¼" long...........	66.00	99.00	132.00
Conestoga Wagon, cast iron, with cloth cover and two horses, 12½"...........	7.50	11.25	15.00
"Contractor's Dump Wagon", cast iron, three horse, driver, 13" long.........	46.00	69.00	92.00
Courtland Circus Parade, tin...........	12.50	18.76	25.00
Covered Wagon, tin, driver and horse, Indian head lithographed on side.....	12.00	18.00	24.00
DENT buckboard, rider, one horse, very early, primitive-looking.........	33.00	49.50	66.00
DENT Contractors Dump Wagon, two horse, 15" long....................	30.00	45.00	60.00
DENT Coupe, one horse, driver, 9¾"...	46.00	69.00	92.00
DENT Fire Engine Pumper, silver with white horses, two horse, 21" long.....	100.00	150.00	200.00
DENT Fire Engine steam pumper, three horses, 21" long....................	70.00	105.00	140.00
DENT No. 57 Hansom cab, two-wheeled, one horse........................	64.00	96.00	128.00
DENT Hook and ladder, three-horse, extra large......................	180.00	270.00	360.00
DENT Hook and ladder, cast iron, with figures, ladders....................	175.00	262.50	350.00
DENT Hose-reel, three horse, 24", 10" horse, figures.....................	200.00	300.00	400.00
DENT Hose-reel, large, three-horse, figures and hose...................	175.00	262.50	350.00
DENT horse and cart, cart is tin........	20.00	30.00	40.00
DENT horse and cart, low sides, all cast iron.........................	20.00	30.00	40.00
DENT "Ice" wagon, two horse, 12".....	30.00	45.00	60.00
DENT "Ice" wagon, one horse, 14" long	80.00	120.00	160.00
DENT Ice Wagon, cast iron, black horse pulling yellow and orange ice wagon, with driver, circa 1910, 15½" long....	120.00	180.00	240.00
DENT one horse coupe................	70.00	105.00	140.00

	G	VG	M
DENT ox cart, stake sides, one ox	10.00	15.00	20.00
DENT police patrol, three horses, driver and four patrolmen, 21" long	155.00	232.50	310.00
DENT pony cart with driver, stake sides, horse	30.00	45.00	60.00
DENT pony cart No. 20 has driver, team of horses, stake sides on cart	70.00	105.00	140.00
DENT small truck wagon, stake sides	56.00	84.00	112.00
DENT one horse truck wagon, stake sides, with driver, 16" long	60.00	90.00	120.00
DENT sulky with jockey	30.00	45.00	60.00
DENT surrey, horse has wheel attached to one leg	44.00	66.00	88.00
Dog cart (baby carriage), black cloth top, 5½" long, tin	10.00	15.00	20.00
Donkey and cart, cast iron, with driver	40.00	60.00	80.00
Dray, cast iron, one horse, black horse pulling yellow dray	90.00	130.00	180.00
Dray Wagon, cast iron, driver and two horses, 15" long	16.00	24.00	32.00
"Dry Goods" cloth and wood two-horse drawn wagon pull-toy, circa 1860, 26" long	80.00	120.00	160.00

"Dry Goods", cloth and wood two-horse drawn wagon pull-toy circa 1860 26" long (see this page).
Photo Courtesy PB84

71

	G	VG	M
"Dump Cart", horse pulling cart pull toy, 7¾" long	32.00	48.00	64.00
Dump Truck, cast iron and tin, one horse	33.00	49.50	66.00
Farm Wagon and donkey, cast iron, 10½" long	33.00	49.50	66.00
Farm Wagon, cast iron, two horse, 10"	15.00	22.50	30.00
Farm Wagon, cast iron, 14" long, two unusual horses, with driver	40.00	60.00	80.00
Farm Wagon, cast iron, large heavy horses, body wood, 25½" long	83.00	124.50	166.00
Farm Wagon, tin, with horse, 10½" long	10.00	15.00	20.00
"Fine Groceries", tin wagon, two horses, 14" long	60.00	90.00	120.00
Fire Patrol Wagon, no horses, early	46.00	69.00	92.00
"Fire Patrol" cast iron three horse wagon contains two firemen and driver, 17" long	160.00	240.00	320.00
"Fire Patrol" three-horse, 18¾" long, driver, riders	150.00	225.00	300.00
"Fire Patrol" cast iron, two horse, three firemen and driver, circa 1910, 19" long	260.00	390.00	520.00
Fire Pumper cast iron, three horse, 11¼"	26.00	39.00	52.00
Fire Pumper, cast iron, two horse with driver, 13" long	46.00	69.00	92.00
Fire Pumper, cast iron, three horse, 14½" long	33.00	49.50	66.00
Fire Pumper, cast iron, two horse, 17" long	60.00	90.00	120.00
Fire Pumper, circa 1910, cast iron, three horse, 17½" long	200.00	300.00	400.00
Fire Pumper, cast iron, three horse with driver, fireman, circa 1910, 18¼" long	140.00	210.00	280.00
Gig, cast iron, one horse, figure	45.00	67.50	90.00

	G	VG	M
GIRARD wagon, two tin horses, stake sides	30.00	45.00	60.00
Goat Cart, 7½" long, iron goat and wheels, tin cart	30.00	45.00	60.00
Gong Bell Pull Toy, two cast iron horses	34.00	51.00	68.00
Grass Cutter, two horse, driver, two-wheeled cart, cast iron	500.00	750.00	1000.00
Hansom Cab, cast iron, no horse or figures	700.00	1050.00	1400.00
Hansom Cab with driver, cast iron, 9½" long	35.00	52.50	70.00
Hansom Cab, cast iron, with driver, 9¾"	24.00	36.00	48.00
Hansom Cab with driver, cast iron, 9¾"	50.00	100.00	150.00
Hansom Cab, one horse, driver, 10" long, cast iron	70.00	105.00	140.00
"Hood's Milk", RICH TOYS, wood and tin, horse-drawn wagon pull-toy	46.00	69.00	92.00
Hook and Ladder, cast iron, tin and wood, two-horse with driver and three ladders, 16½" long	26.00	39.00	52.00
Hook and Ladder, cast iron and tin, three horse, two firemen, ladders, 21" long	33.00	49.50	66.00
Hook and Ladder, cast iron, two-horse, 22¾" long	50.00	75.00	100.00
Hook and Ladder, cast iron, three-horse, with driver, 25" long	60.00	90.00	120.00
Hook and Ladder truck, cast iron, three-horse, 25½" long	60.00	90.00	120.00
Hook and Ladder truck, cast iron, three-horse, two drivers, four ladders, circa 1910-1914, 31¼" long	266.00	399.00	532.00
Hook and Ladder, pressed steel and iron, figures, ladders, unusual hanging horses	94.00	141.00	188.00

Hansom Cab, cast-iron, no horse or figures. (see page 73)

L TO R: "Transfer Wagon", 3 horses and driver, cast iron, wagon bolted to team, 19" long (see page 87).

	G	VG	M
Hook and Ladder, three horses, 27½" long, driver	140.00	210.00	280.00
Hook and Ladder, wood ladder with figurines, three-horse, 29½" long	200.00	300.00	400.00
Horse and Cart, lithograph paper on wooden horse, tin cart	14.00	21.00	28.00
Horse pulling two wheel buggy, tin pull toy, 8" long	30.00	45.00	60.00
Horse with open carriage and driver in top hat, tin, 5½" long	64.00	96.00	128.00
Hose Reel, cast iron, one horse with driver, 11" long	80.00	120.00	160.00

	G	VG	M
Hose Reel, cast iron, one horse with driver, 12" long...................	90.00	135.00	180.00
Hose Reel Wagon, cast iron with driver and cord fire hose, one horse, 12½" long..........................	110.00	165.00	220.00
Hose Reel, early, two-horse with driver, cast iron, 14¼"...................	60.00	90.00	120.00
Hose Reel, early, two-horse, cast iron, 14½" long, with figure.............	80.00	120.00	160.00
Hose Reel, Wagon, cast iron, driver, two horses, man standing on rear bumper, 21" long........................	24.00	36.00	48.00
Hose Reel, cast iron, circa 1910-1914, three horse with driver and fireman, 21" long........................	200.00	300.00	400.00
Hose Wagon, cast iron, two firemen, three horses and bell, 21½" long......	130.00	195.00	260.00
Hose Reel, early, cast iron, unusual horse............................	175.00	262.50	350.00
HUBLEY cart and horse...............	20.00	30.00	40.00
HUBLEY chariot, cast iron, 8¾".......	110.00	165.00	220.00
HUBLEY fire pumper, cast iron, two horses with driver, circa 1910, 14" long	66.00	99.00	132.00

HUBLEY Ice Wagon, cast iron, two-horse, black horses pulling green wagon, with driver. Circa 1906. 15½" long. (see page 78)
Photo Courtesy PB84

HUBLEY Hook and Ladder. Three horse, two firemen, two wooden ladders circa 1906-1910.
Lenght 27¾". (see page 77)
Photo Courtesy PB84

HUBLEY Hose Reel, cast iron three-horse with driver. Circa 1906. 19" long.
Photo Courtesy PB84 (see page 78)

IVES Hose Reel, cast iron, one-horse, driver, "Phoenix", circa 1880-1910. 15" long.
Photo Courtesy PB84 (see page 80)

Hook and Ladder Truck, cast iron, three-horse, two drivers, four ladders, circa 1910-1914. 31¼"
long. (see page 73)
Photo Courtesy PB84

	G	VG	M
HUBLEY fire pumper, cast iron, two horse, white-painted, circa 1906-1910, 19" long	80.00	120.00	160.00
HUBLEY fire pumper, two horse, cast iron, with driver and two firemen, 20" long	48.00	72.00	96.00

HUBLEY cast-iron four-seat Brake, carriage drawn by four horses and containing eight articulated passengers. 28" long. (see this page)

Photo Courtesy PB84

* Note: Hubley four-seat Brake is **most valuable** toy in book.

	G	VG	M
HUBLEY fire pumper, three-horse with driver, circa 1906-1910, 20½" long...	130.00	195.00	260.00
HUBLEY fire pumper, two horses, cast iron with American Eagle, circa 1905-1910, 21" long....................	110.00	165.00	220.00
HUBLEY Four Seat BRAKE, carriage drawn by four horses and containing eight articulated passengers, 28" long Sold in Good-Very Good Condition for $5750			
HUBLEY Hook and ladder, three-horse, two firemen, two wooden ladders, circa 1906-1910, 27¾" long.........	120.00	180.00	240.00

Hubley Fire Pumper, three-horse with driver, circa 1906-1910. 20½" long.   (see page 77)

L TO R: KENTON Dray, cast iron, two-horse, two dark horses pulling a green cart, with driver. 14¾" long; (see page 81); KENTON laundau, cast iron, white horse pulling green carriage, with driver. Circa 1910. Length 15"; (see page 81)

L TO R: DENT Ice Wagon, cast iron, black horse pulling yellow and orange ice wagon, with driver. Circa 1910. 15½" long; (see page 70). "Fire Patrol" cast iron 3-horse wagon contains two firemen and driver. 17" long; (see page 72).

	G	VG	M
HUBLEY hook and ladder wagon, three-horse, 33" long with eagle and shield on side...........................	150.00	225.00	300.00
HUBLEY Hose reel, cast iron, three-horse with driver, circa 1906, 19" long	170.00	255.00	340.00
HUBLEY ice wagon, cast iron, two horse, black horses pulling green wagon, with driver, circa 1906, 15½" long....	100.00	150.00	200.00
HUBLEY log wagon, two oxen, driver, circa 1905, 15" long...............	110.00	165.00	220.00
HUBLEY lady in sleigh, circa 1900, 15" long.........................	250.00	375.00	500.00

	G	VG	M
HUBLEY "Royal Circus" two horse, driver, bear in cage, 12" long.........	150.00	225.00	300.00
HUBLEY Santa Claus with two reindeer and sleigh, 14¾".................	175.00	262.50	350.00
HUBLEY surrey, clockwork, 1894, cast iron, brass works, 9" long, five colors, first of Hubley's toys...............	225.00	337.50	450.00
Ice Cart, tin, horse-drawn............	66.00	99.00	132.00

IVES Fire Patrol, cast iron, two-horse, driver and six firemen, circa 1880-1910. 20½" long. (see page 80)   Photo Courtesy PB84

"Fire Patrol". Cast iron, two-horse, three firemen and driver. Circa 1910. 19" long. (see page 72)
Photo Courtesy PB84

CARPENTER Hook and ladder, cast iron, two-horse with driver and rear man, ladders. Circa 1883-1890. 26½" long. (see page 68)   Photo Courtesy PB84

WILKINS Dray, cast-iron and tin barrel drawn by two horse, driver in derby hat. Circa 1910. 20½" long. (see page 88)   Photo Courtesy PB84

	G	VG	M
"Ice" wagon, one horse, 12", cast iron	26.00	39.00	52.00
Ice Wagon, cast iron, two-horse, 12" long	60.00	90.00	120.00
IVES Doctor's cart, two wheels, 10¼"...	250.00	375.00	500.00
IVES dog pulling stake cart	100.00	150.00	200.00
IVES "Fire Patrol" cast iron with driver, running horse	100.00	150.00	200.00
IVES Fire Patrol, cast iron, two horse, driver and six firemen, circa 1880-1910, 20½" long	180.00	270.00	360.00
IVES Hose reel, cast iron, one horse, driver, "Phoenix", circa 1880-1910, 15" long	150.00	225.00	300.00
IVES Steam pumper, two-horse, 20½"..	160.00	240.00	320.00
IVES Walking Horse, pull toy, late 19th century, horse which walks by means of wheel mechanism under it, pulling a two-wheeled cart	425.00	637.50	850.00

KENTON—Kenton Lock Manufacturing Co. was incorporated in May, 1890, in Kenton, Ohio. In November of 1894, it became the Kenton Hardware Manufacturing Company, and around this period, began producing toys. It ceased production of horse-drawn toys in the early 1920s (except for a 1930s beer wagon), but in 1939 introduced a completely new line of horse-drawn pieces, running through 1954.

	G	VG	M
KENTON Bakery wagon, marked "Bakery", 1941	120.00	180.00	240.00
KENTON Band Wagon, musicians, driver, rider on horse	120.00	180.00	240.00
KENTON Circus Cage Wagon, two horses, two riders, driver, animal in cage	90.00	135.00	180.00
KENTON covered wagon, cast iron, two-horse	20.00	30.00	40.00
KENTON dray, 13¼" long	37.50	56.25	75.00
KENTON dray, cast iron, two horse, black and white horses pulling green dray, with driver, 13½" long	50.00	75.00	100.00

	G	VG	M
KENTON dray wagon with horse and driver, cast iron, 14¾"..............	30.00	45.00	60.00
KENTON dray, cast iron, two-horse, two dark horses pulling a green cart, with driver, 14¾" long.............	74.00	111.00	148.00
KENTON dump wagon, two-horse, lever releases bottom of wagon..................	20.00	30.00	40.00
KENTON farm wagon, two-horse cast iron, 14½" with figure.............	30.00	45.00	60.00
KENTON farm wagon, two-horse, 15" with driver......................	20.00	30.00	40.00
KENTON fire ladder wagon, front driver only, 12" long....................	25.00	37.50	50.00
KENTON fire ladder wagon, horse-drawn, 17" long, drivers front and rear.............................	15.00	22.50	30.00
KENTON fire pumper, cast iron, 26½" long, horses 11" long...............	220.00	330.00	440.00
KENTON goat cart, 7", figure with large ears.............................	75.00	112.50	150.00
KENTON Hansom cab, 15½" long, figures, horse.....................	60.00	90.00	120.00
KENTON hook and ladder, wagon, three horses, 17" long...................	30.00	45.00	60.00
KENTON hook and ladder, cast iron, three-horse, circa 1910, 19" long......	50.00	75.00	100.00
KENTON landau, cast iron, white horse pulling green carriage with driver, circa 1910, 15" long...............	250.00	375.00	500.00
KENTON log wagon, one horse with driver, 14½" long.................	60.00	90.00	120.00
KENTON "Milk" wagon, with horse and driver......................	50.00	75.00	100.00
KENTON "Overland Circus" two-horse, cast iron with driver, cage containing bear, circa 1940s-1950s, 13¾" long...	100.00	150.00	200.00
KENTON "Overland Circus" cast iron, two-horse with driver, cage containing cloth bear, 14" long...............	66.00	99.00	132.00

KENTON Bakery Wagon marked "Bakery", 1941 (see page 80)

	G	VG	M
KENTON "Overland Circus" cast iron, two-horse with driver, cage containing cast iron bear, 14" long, 1940s	66.00	99.00	132.00
KENTON Rabbit, 5" long, pulling cart with two wheels and seat, cast iron	40.00	60.00	80.00
KENTON Victoria cab and horse, cast iron, with driver and woman, 15½" long	60.00	90.00	120.00
KENTON No. 3, one-horse wagon, with driver, 15" long	60.00	90.00	120.00
KENTON No. 5 wagon, one horse, 15" long	20.00	30.00	40.00
KENTON wagon with driver, two-horse, 10¼" long	28.00	42.00	56.00
KENTON stake wagon, two-horse	20.00	30.00	40.00
KENTON surrey, two-horse cast iron with driver and passenger, 12½"	20.00	30.00	40.00
KENTON surrey, with fringe top, driver and passenger, two-horse (circa 1943?)	30.00	45.00	60.00
KENTON sulky and driver, cast iron, 7" long	30.00	45.00	60.00
KENTON team of horses with log and black driver	250.00	375.00	500.00
KENTON two horse stake wagon, 15" long, driver with reins	100.00	150.00	200.00
"The Klondike Ice Co., New York" tin ice wagon, two-horse, 17½" long	120.00	180.00	240.00
Ladder Wagon, cast iron, two ladders and three galloping horses, 13½" long	10.00	15.00	20.00
Ladder Wagon, cast iron, with two horses, three sections of ladder, bell, 25½" long	110.00	165.00	220.00

	G	VG	M
Ladder Wagon, cast iron with two drivers, four sections of ladder and three horses, Dart type, 30½" long....	44.00	66.00	88.00
LANCASTER hook and ladder, two-horse cast iron, 25" long.................	60.00	90.00	120.00
LANCASTER hook and ladder, cast iron, 28" long, two horses, two drivers......	50.00	75.00	100.00
LANCASTER hook and ladder, 28" long, iron, three horses, two drivers........	57.00	85.50	114.00
LANCASTER HUBLEY No. 58 Surrey, no driver........................	30.00	45.00	60.00
LANCASTER HUBLEY No. 174, surrey with one seat, driver, horse..........	60.00	90.00	120.00
Landau, four-horse, 24" with driver.....	150.00	225.00	300.00
LEHMANN "Africa" tin friction toy, ostrich pulling cart.................	90.00	120.00	180.00
LEHMANN tin friction Rooster pulling egg cart with a rabbit perched on top..	130.00	195.00	260.00
Log Wagon, cast iron with driver and two oxen, 15¼" long...............	170.00	255.00	340.00
Mail Cart, tin, horse-drawn...........	20.00	30.00	40.00
McCormick Deering farm wagon, two-horse, 12½" long, cast iron..........	22.50	33.75	45.00
Mess Cart, WW I-type, tin, two-horse drawn, painted....................	26.00	39.00	52.00
"Milk" wagon with driver, 12½" long...	12.00	18.00	24.00
"Milk" wagon, driver and one horse, 12¾" long.......................	34.00	51.00	68.00
Mower, two horses and driver, cast iron, 10" long........................	66.00	99.00	132.00
"National Express" wagon, tin litho, horse 15" long....................	90.00	120.00	180.00
Omnibus, "People's", tin, with two horses, driver, circa 1880s-1890s......	2600.00	3900.00	5200.00
"Overland Circus" band wagon with driver, two riders, four musicians, two horses, cast iron, 15½"..........	90.00	135.00	180.00
"Overland Circus" band wagon with driver, four musicians, two horses, cast iron, 15½" long...............	96.00	138.00	192.00

	G	VG	M
"Overland Circus" cage van, 13" with driver	35.00	56.25	70.00
"Overland Circus" calliope wagon with driver, calliope player and two riders, 14" long, cast iron	100.00	150.00	200.00
Ox Cart, cast iron, 5" long, with ox	28.00	42.00	56.00
Ox Cart, cast iron, 11½" long	35.00	56.25	70.00
Phaeton, one-horse with driver, 16" long	200.00	300.00	400.00
Plow, one horse, cast iron, 10¾"	60.00	90.00	120.00
Police Patrol Wagon, cast iron, 11½" long, figures and driver, one horse	40.00	60.00	80.00
"Police Patrol", cast iron, one-horse, 12"	60.00	90.00	120.00
"Police Patrol" wagon, cast iron, with driver and five policemen and two horses, 15"	150.00	225.00	300.00
PRATT & LETCHWORTH Gig, cast iron and pressed steel, 10½" long, seven colors, one horse, one rider	175.00	262.50	350.00
PRATT & LETCHWORTH hose reel, one horse, 14¼"	425.00	637.50	850.00
Pull Toy, tin, horse and cart, iron wheels, 11" long	100.00	150.00	200.00
Pull Toy, horse and covered delivery wagon, tin, 5¼" long	25.00	37.50	50.00
Pull Toy, horse and wagon, two wheels, tin 9¼" long	40.00	60.00	80.00
Pull Toy horse pulling water wagon, tin, iron wheels, 6¾" long	162.50	243.75	325.00
Pull Toy, horse-drawn carriage, tin, 12" long	60.00	90.00	120.00
Pull Toy, horse pulling water wagon, tin, iron wheels, 7¼" long	40.00	60.00	80.00
Pull Toy, tin horse and wheels, wooden platform and animated figure with composition head and tin arms, playing tin drum and cymbal, 13½" long	100.00	150.00	200.00
Pull Toy, wood, horse-drawn, RICH TOYS, 27" long	26.00	39.00	52.00

	G	VG	M
Pumper, cast iron, with driver and two horses	8.00	12.00	16.00
Pumper, cast iron, three horses with figure, 13" long	30.00	45.00	60.00
Royal Circus Wagon, two horses with driver and animal in cage	174.00	261.00	348.00
"Sand and Gravel", wagon with driver, cast iron, 9½" long	16.00	24.00	32.00
Sand and Gravel Wagon, cast iron, 10" long, two horses	15.00	22.50	30.00
"Sand and Gravel" wagon, cast iron, driver, two-horse, 14¾" long	20.00	30.00	40.00
"Sand and Gravel" wagon, with driver and two horses, cast iron, 15"	30.00	45.00	60.00
Santa Claus reindeer pulling sled, two reindeer pulling white sled containing black-painted Santa Claus	46.00	69.00	92.00
Sheep, cast iron, pulling two-wheeled tin wagon, 8" long	25.00	37.50	50.00
"Sheffield Farms Company", wood horse-drawn milk wagon, horse has articulated legs, 21" long	110.00	165.00	220.00
Spring Wagon, cast iron with driver, horse, 11"	10.00	15.00	20.00
Spring Wagon, cast iron, driver, one horse, 14½" long	12.00	18.00	24.00
Spring Wagon, driver and two horses, cast iron, 14½" long	17.00	24.50	34.00
Spring Wagon, driver and two horses, minature pick, shovel, sledgehammer, 14¼" long, cast iron	75.00	112.50	150.00
Spring Wagon, cast iron, two horses, 15"	10.00	15.00	20.00
Stagecoach with cowboy driver and two horses, 11" long, cast iron	30.00	45.00	60.00
Stake Bed Wagon, cast iron, one horse, 14¾"	70.00	105.00	140.00
"Stanley" surrey with driver, lady passenger, two-horse, 14¾" long	10.00	15.00	20.00

	G	VG	M
Steam Pumper with stationary driver, two horses, cast iron, 9¼" long......	15.00	22.50	30.00
Steam Pumper, cast iron, stationary driver, three horses, 10½" long......	15.00	22.50	30.00
Steam Pumper, cast iron, 15" long with stationary driver and two horses......	120.00	180.00	240.00

Fire Pumper, cast iron, three-horse with driver, fireman. Circa 1910. 18¼" long. (see page 72)
Photo Courtesy PB84

L TO R: Sulky, cast iron, with driver, circa 1890s, 8½" long; (see page 87); Chief's Wagon, cast iron "Chief" one horse, circa 1915-1920, length 12". (see page 69)
Photo Courtesy PB84

Fire Pumper, cast iron three-horse drawn circa 1910, 17½" long.   (see page 72)
Photo Courtesy PB84

Hose Reel, three-horse, cast iron with driver and fireman, circa 1910-1914, 21" long. (see page 75)
Photo Courtesy PB84

	G	VG	M
Steam Pumper, cast iron, two horses, stationary driver, 15¼" long	100.00	150.00	200.00
Steam Pumper, cast iron, driver, three horses, bell, 17½" long	70.00	105.00	140.00
Steam Pumper, two-horse, cast iron with driver, 18" long	116.00	174.00	232.00
Steam Pumper, cast iron, driver and two horses, 20½" long	180.00	270.00	360.00
Steam Pumper, cast iron, three horses and bell, 21¼" high	150.00	225.00	300.00
Steamer with driver, two horses, 17"	183.00	274.50	366.00
Sulky, cast iron, with driver, 7¼" long	12.50	18.75	25.00
Sulky, cast iron, with driver, circa 1890s, 8½" long	60.00	90.00	120.00
Sulky, cast iron, with rider, 8¾"	20.00	30.00	40.00
Sulky Rig, horse and driver pull toy, comic style, 10" long, 8" high, 1¼" thick	14.00	21.00	28.00
Surrey, cast iron, two-horse, 13" long	10.00	15.00	20.00
Transfer Wagon, cast iron, two-horse, driver	95.00	142.50	190.00
"Transfer Wagon", three horses and driver, cast iron, wagon bolted to team, 19" long	120.00	180.00	240.00
"Transfer" Wagon, cast iron, driver and two horses, 19½" long	17.00	25.50	34.00
U.S. Mail wagon, tin, two-horse, 17" long	110.00	165.00	220.00
Wagon, two-wheeled, with driver, cast iron, 7¼"	10.00	15.00	20.00
Wagon, cast iron, mule, driver, two-wheeled wagon, 9½" long	50.00	75.00	100.00
Wagon, two-seater, cast iron, one horse	80.00	120.00	160.00
Walking horse and sulky cart, horse of wood, moving legs and cart of tin, wheels cast iron, 7" long	35.00	52.50	70.00
Water Tower with three horses, cast iron and pressed steel, 43" long, horse 11" long	200.00	300.00	400.00

	G	VG	M
WILKINS "City Truck", cast iron, two-horse with driver	300.00	450.00	600.00
WILKINS Donkey cart, 13¼" long	175.00	262.50	350.00
WILKINS Dray, cast iron and tin barrel, drawn by two horses, driver in derby hat, circa 1910, 20½"	90.00	120.00	180.00
WILKINS Fire Chief buggy, one horse with rider	45.00	67.50	90.00
WILKINS Fire Chief Engine pumper, two horses, 19" long	60.00	90.00	120.00
WILKINS Fire Patrol wagon, four firemen in wagon, 12" long	30.00	45.00	60.00
WILKINS hook and ladder, two-horse, horses sit on pegs, has ladders, figures	240.00	360.00	480.00
WILKINS Ice Wagon, horse, tin and cast iron, 10" long	34.00	51.00	68.00
WILKINS steam engine, two-horse, with driver, 17" long	140.00	210.00	280.00

PAPER TOYS
(see also Premiums, Comic Characters)

American Paper Toys
by Barbara and Jonathan Newman

The subject of paper toys has been only superficially treated even in books limited to just that medium. Even though, some brief introduction should be attempted. They have been called cut-outs, punch outs and press outs. By whatever name, forts, planes, trains, ships and much much more have been produced in paper. What adult does not have some memories (usually fond, often frustrating) of crisp booklets, shiny boxes, or just complicated sheets of paper and cardboard toys?

Throughout the period from the end of the last century to the period after World War II, paper was, if not king, certainly close to the throne. It was in many ways, the plastic of its day. Every subject matter found in toys can also be found in its own version in paper or cardboard.

Certainly for a start, no collector of military toys or toy soldiers can be unfamiliar with the whole world of paper soldiers, even though they were never quite as popular as in Europe where paper soldiers were born almost a century before. American companies by the turn of the century were turning out paper troops by the thousands. The most popular was easily the McLoughlin Bros. Company which started out with paper toys in 1857 in N.Y.C. and moved to Springfield, Massachusetts in 1920. Their range included beautifully lithographed covered boxed sets of cardboard figures on wooden stands, or, for the young boy with less resources, over a hundred different sheets of American and foreign armies to be cut out and mounted on stands by the purchaser.

During this same general time period, centered around the 10 years from 1895 to 1905, almost every major newspaper in the country (at least those Big City ones with large Sunday Editions) had Sunday "Art Supplements" which varied their "give away" fare from Armies or Navies of the world to historical panoramas illustrating our history, from political figures and personalities of the day to cut-out dolls of celebrities with vast wardrobes of clothes. Even the "Globe Quadruple Perfecting Press" itself was offered as a cut out to construct a complete diorama as the Boston Sunday Globe's offering of August 6th, 1896.

Paper houses and villages, a great favorite with little girls of the day, were sold by a wide variety of companies. The earlier ones included the ubiquitous McLoughlin Bros. and Milton Bradley (yes, they're still around) and more recent ones were the World War II era giants in the field, Built-Rite and Megow.

In fact, while there was no shortage in the 20's and 30's, it's W.W.II that was really the Golden Age of paper toys in this country. The reason is obvious and the lack of any alternative material to paper even caused the King of toy train companies, Lionel, to produce as its only offering in the war, a complete train set in die-cut cardboard. Who would have thought such a poor substitute in 1943 would be a sought after and valuable rarity today? If you have one in mint condition you've got a real gem in both the world of toy trains and paper toys.

During these war years every conceivable type of toy, usually given a wartime, patriotic theme, was available. Punchout cardboard sets of "Rap-A-Jap", "Sink The Axis", "Camouflage Defense Force", books of punch out Naval Craft by Rigby, etc. were the birthday, Christmas or other presents of the forties. A whole range of Built-Rite forts, trenches, troops and doll houses are among our own fond memories.

The list and illustrations could go on and on and someday soon perhaps a reasonably definitive book will be written. For the meantime, just settle for a brief taste in words and pictures to either jog your own memory or kindle an interest in a lifetime passion for paper toys.

Left
see page 92

Right
see page 95

Photos courtesy Barbara and Jonathan Newman

BARBARA and JONATHAN NEWMAN own and operate The Paper Soldier in Clifton Park, NY which specializes in antique and new paper toys from around the world. As collectors and dealers they are recognized leading experts on all toys made of paper and cardboard.

CONDITION OF A PAPER TOY
AND ITS RELATION TO PRICE

The price of a paper toy depends not only on its desirability, but on its condition. A paper toy in mint condition is generally worth twice what that item would bring in good condition, with "very good" falling about equally in between good and mint.

"Mint" means just that; the condition in which it was originally issued—perfect, regardless of age, any white sections being near white to white, no printing or cutting defects, still retains its original printing lustre, no damage, no matter how slight, to any part. Happily, for paper toy collectors, this is not as unusual a state at it is for many other toys. Nevertheless, it is still fairly rare compared to these items in lesser condition, and therefore, mint items command a premium price.

"Very Good" indicates a paper toy that has obviously seen some wear, and perhaps use, but in general having a crispness to its appearance that makes it attractive and collectible to all but the most discriminating.

"Good" signals a paper toy that has seen considerable wear, shows its age, but is basically sound. A collector will collect it, but will often not be wholly satisfied with it as an example of his collection, and thus prices are often drastically below that which the same toy in mint can command.

Condition below good results in another drastic drop in price, and paper toys with parts cut out or missing, although otherwise in excellent condition, will usually fall into this lower-priced category, as will anything brittle, no matter how "mint" it may appear otherwise.

"Near-Mint", "Fine", "Very Fine" and similar terms often found in sellers' descriptions denote conditions between Mint and Very Good, and are priced accordingly.

The key to grading is to avoid wishful thinking. Grading can sometimes be a problem to the uninitiated, but common sense will usually prevail, and when possible, a consultation with an expert in the field can often clear up lingering doubts.

PAPER TOYS
(see also Premiums)

(Note: Where not specifically noted, paper toys listed are paper dolls)

	G	VG	M
AMERICAN BEAUTIES PAPER DOLLS, circa 1942, REUBEN LILJA & CO. No. 917	4.00	6.00	8.00
AMOS & ANDY—Cut-out cardboard of just Andy, 8½" high, stand-up	2.50	3.75	5.00
ARMY AIRFORCES AIRCRAFT IDENTIFICATION SILHOUETTE MODEL—Feb. 1943, 1/72 scale of Japanese fighter Najajima T-97, A.N.F. 7X11" envelope	5.00	7.50	10.00
BABY PAT 1963 WHITMAN No. 2072	.50	.75	1.00
BARBARA BRITTON Paper Dolls with Magic Stay-On Costumes, 1954, SAALFIELD 5190. Boxed Set	5.00	7.50	10.00
BARBIE AND KEN 1962 WHITMAN No. 4797, 7X12" boxed set	2.50	3.75	5.00
BARBIE AND SKIPPER 1964 WHITMAN No. 1957, Yachting outfits	1.00	1.50	2.00
BARBIE BOUTIQUE 1973 WHITMAN No. 1954	1.00	1.50	2.00
BETSY MCCALL AROUND THE WORLD PAPER DOLLS, circa 1962	5.00	7.50	10.00
BETSY MCCALL DRESS'N PLAY PAPER DOLLS, 1963, STANDARD/TOYKRAFT/MCCALL No. 802 12x18" boxed set	5.00	7.50	10.00
BETSY ROSS AND HER FRIENDS-1963, PLATT AND MUNK No. 224B, 7x11" boxed set	2.00	3.00	4.00
BETTY AND JOAN, 1941, 1945, WHITMAN No. 1015, Joan also appears in Mary and Joan, Lois & Joan	3.00	4.50	6.00
BETTY SUE—A CUT OUT DOLL—circa 1940 No. 1010	4.50	6.75	9.00

	G	VG	M
THE BEVERLY HILLBILLIES—Jed, Jethro, Granny and Elly May WHITMAN No. 1955, 1964	2.50	3.75	5.00
BIG INVASION PUNCH-OUT BOOK, 1964, WHITMAN No. 1936, Punchout of beach landing	1.50	2.25	3.00
BOBBY SOCKS CUT OUT DOLLS designed by Doris Lane Butler, 1945, WHITMAN No. 988	4.00	6.00	8.00
BRENDA LEE, 1964, No. 4360 DE JOURNETTE, 6½x10" boxed set, includes toy phonograph and records	4.00	6.00	8.00
BROTHER AND SISTER STATUETTE DOLLS, 1950, WHITMAN 1182-15, two heavy cardboard 7½" dolls	2.00	3.00	4.00
BUFFY paper Dolls ("Family Affair") 1968, WHITMAN No. 1955	1.00	1.50	2.00
BUFFY AND JODY, 1970 ("Family Affair"), WHITMAN 4764, Two magic dolls with Stay-On wardrobes	1.00	1.50	2.00
Built Rite Doll House Set 10, 1940s	12.50	18.75	25.00
Built Rite Doll House Set 36, 1940s	17.50	26.25	35.00
Built Rite Doll House No. 415, circa 1943, 13x20" boxed set with 19" house and garage, 27 pieces of furniture, sedan, baby buggy, shrubbery, etc	5.00	7.50	10.00
Built Rite Fort No. 25A, 1930s-40s	17.50	26.26	35.00
Built Rite Village, Drug Store and Church, price per building	2.50	3.75	5.00

Built Rite Doll House Set No. 10 (see this page)
Photo by Jonathan A. Newman
Courtesy Barbara and Jonathan Newman

Built Rite Fort No. 25A (see this page)
Photo by Jonathan A. Newman
Courtesy Barbara and Jonathan Newman

Built Rite Doll House Set No. 36 (see page 93)
Photo by Jonathan A. Newman

Courtesy Barbara and Jonathan Newman

	G	VG	M
Built Rite Village, School and Station, price per building	2.50	3.75	5.00
CAMOUFLAGE DEFENSE FORCE— Airplane, soldiers, anti-aircraft guns all hidden within farm buildings. Heavy cardboard. JAY LINE MANU-FACTURING CO., 431, boxed. Circa 1943	5.00	7.50	10.00
CAREER GIRLS WITH CLOTH-LIKE CLOTHES, 1944, WHITMAN No. 973 by Doris Lane Butler	3.00	4.50	6.00
CHEERLEADER—TEEN AGE DOLL, 1950s? STEPHENS PUBLISHING CO. No. 182, Mary and Elaine and four pages of clothes	1.00	1.50	2.00
CHILDREN FROM OTHER LANDS, 1961, WHITMAN No. 2089, 8 cut-out dolls and native costumes	1.50	2.25	3.00
CIRCUS DAY—1946 by Art Tanchon, STEPHENS PRINTING No. 135, Animals, clown, circus cages and wagons	.75	1.13	1.50
CLOTH-LIKE CLOTHES FOR 3 CUTE GIRLS, 1949, WHITMAN No. 1178:15, Flocked clothes	3.50	4.75	7.00
COLORGRAPHICS STATUE-ETTES, 1943, 3-Dimensional stand-up paper dolls of Marine, Soldier, Sailor, Nurse, WAAC, WAVE, boxed	2.50	3.75	5.00

	G	VG	M

CONNIE FRANCIS, 1963, WHITMAN
No. 1956........................ 4.00 6.00 8.00

CORONATION PAPER DOLLS AND
COLORING BOOK, 1953, SAAL-
FIELD No. 4450, 10½x15" book.
Queen Elizabeth, Prince Philip, young
Prince Charles and Princess Ann...... 6.00 9.00 12.00

THE CRADLE CROWD, 1948, Four doll
babies with cloth-like clothes, WHIT-
MAN No. 1173.................... 3.50 4.75 7.00

CUT-OUT DOLLS WITH PAINTS AND
CLOTHES TO COLOR, by Avis Mac,
WHITMAN No. 983, Circa 1930s
11x18" book with four 17" children
and 16 pages of clothing and sheet
of paints........................ 10.00 15.00 20.00

DAVY CROCKETT PUNCH OUT
BOOK, 1955 No. 1943............. 5.00 7.50 10.00

DEBS AND SUB DEBS Paper Doll
Book, 1941, No. 2361 SAALFIELD,
20 Punchouts.................... 20.00 30.00 40.00

DECALCO-LITHO CO. Paper Dolls
Sheets. Circa 1920s, 8x10½" sheets,
1. Woman and girl and 9 outfits.
2. Woman and girl and 10 outfits.
3. Two women and 7 outfits. Price
per sheet........................ 1.50 2.25 3.00

DIANE AND DAPHNE THE ROUND
ABOUT DOLLS BOOK, 1937, No. 545
McLOUGHLIN BROS. Large cut-outs
by Campbell..................... 12.50 18.75 25.00

DICK THE SAILOR, circ 1942,
SAMUEL LOWE No. L1074......... 5.00 7.50 10.00

DISNEYLAND PARK PUNCH OUT,
1960, No. 175.................... 1.00 1.50 2.00

DODIE FROM MY THREE SONS TV
series, 1971, ARTCRAFT No. 5115,
Dodie and dolly.................. 1.00 1.50 2.00

DOLLS THAT WALK—"They Walk—
They Dance—They Play,", designed

	G	VG	M
by Emily Sprague Wurl, WHITMAN No. 977, 1939, two identical girls and two identical boys..............	9.00	13.50	18.00
DONNA REED PAPER DOLLS, 1960, SAALFIELD/ARTCRAFT No. 5197, 9x12" boxed set....................	4.00	6.00	8.00
DR. KILDARE AND NURSE SUSAN, early 1960s, LOWE No. 2740........	2.00	3.00	4.00
DOROTHY PROVINE, 1962, WHIT-MAN No. 1964....................	3.00	4.50	6.00
DOUBLE DATE CUT-OUT DOLLS by Eileen Fon Vaughan, 1949, WHIT-MAN No. 962.....................	3.00	4.50	6.00
DRESS UP FOR THE NEW YORK WORLD'S FAIR, 1963, SPERTUS....	3.00	4.50	6.00
ESKIMO CUT OUTS by Milo Winter, 1939, WHITMAN 1054.............	3.00	4.50	6.00
EVELYN RUDY—Little Star of Screen and Television, 1958, SAALFIELD No. 1745.........................	1.25	1.88	2.50
FABULOUS HIGH FASHION MODELS, 1958, BONNIE BROOKS/CHILD CRAFT No. 2776.................	1.75	2.63	3.50
FAIRY PRINCESS PAPER DOLLS, 1958, MERRILL No. 1548...............	2.50	3.75	5.00
FARM CUT-OUTS by Milo Winter, 1938, WHITMAN No. 1054, 6½x10½", six pages of heavy paper cut-outs........	3.00	4.50	6.00
THE FASHION BOOK OF THE ROUND ABOUT DOLLS, 1936, McLOUGH-LIN BROS. Over an inch thick, eight thick stand-up dolls, plus scissors and pack of paper dolls clothes in package. By Betty Campbell................	20.00	30.00	40.00
FAWCETT PAPER DOLLS, 1942, Ibis, Commando Yank, Golden Arrow, Mr. Scarlet, Spy Smasher, Bulletgirl, Pinky, perhaps others....................	7.50	11.25	15.00
FIFTEEN ABC BLOCKS TO PLAY AND LEARN, 1933, WHITMAN No. 976,			

	G	VG	M
book containing 15 die-cut blocks to put together. Illustrations of nursery rhymes, alphabet letters, animals and numbers on each block..............	6.00	9.00	12.00
FIRE HOUSE P-18 by MEGOW, 1945, Brick firehouse. Boxed set............	4.00	6.00	8.00
THE FLYING NUN, 1968, 1969, ART-CRAFT No. 4417.................	2.00	3.00	4.00
FOURTEEN DOGS TO CUT OUT AND STAND UP, Copyright 1930, WHIT-MAN No. 935, 12 pages of dogs, cardboard punchouts..............	10.00	15.00	20.00
FRENCH INFANTRY—Milton Bradley? circa 1915, approx. 6" high. Single figure...........................	1.00	1.50	2.00
FUN FARM, Reed and Associates.......	1.25	1.88	2.50
GENE AUTRY MELODY RANCH CUT-OUT DOLLS, 1950, WHITMAN No. 990-10	7.00	10.50	14.00
GENE AUTRY RANCH cut-out book, 1953...........................	10.00	15.00	20.00
GIRL FRIEND-BOY FRIEND PAPER DOLLS, 1955, SAALFIELD No. 1605.	1.75	2.63	3.50
GIRL FRIENDS paper dolls, 1944, WHITMAN No. 974...............	3.00	4.50	6.00
GIRLS IN UNIFORM PAPER DOLLS BOOK, circa 1942, No. L1048........	8.00	12.00	16.00
GLAMOUR PARADE CUT-OUT DOLLS, STEPHENS PUBLISHING CO., No. 184, 1950s? Four models and four pages of clothes....................	1.00	1.50	2.00
GRACE KELLY, 1956, WHITMAN No. 2069...........................	7.50	11.25	15.00
GULLIVER'S TRAVELS cut-outs, 1939.	25.00	37.50	50.00
HARRY THE SOLDIER, 1941, SAMUEL LOWE No. L1074.................	5.00	7.50	10.00
HAYLEY MILLS, "THE MOON-SPINNERS", 1964, WHITMAN No. 1960	3.00	4.50	6.00

	G	VG	M
HEAVY CRUISER "This Is The Navy", circa 1943 SKYLINE MFG. CO.	2.50	3.75	5.00
HEE HAW, 1971, ARTCRAFT No. 5139.	1.50	2.25	3.00
HISTORICAL DOLLS TO CUT OUT AND DRESS, 1962, PLATT & MUNK No. 226B, 7x11" boxed set. Mother, father, and two children of heavy cardboard, plus outfits.	2.50	3.75	5.00
HOLIDAY PAPER DOLLS, 1950s, SAALFIELD No. 1742.	.75	1.13	1.50
HOUSE THAT JACK BUILT, circa 1895, BLISS, R.I., paper litho, house and story's characters with stands.	200.00	300.00	400.00
HOWDY DOODY Puppet Show Punch-out Book Copyright 1952, WHITMAN No. 211129, Punchout cardboard puppets may be controlled by strings. Includes Howdy, Bluster, Inspector, Dilly Dally, Clarabell, and Flubadub.	17.50	26.25	35.00
HOWDY DOODY STICKER FUN, copyright 1951, WHITMAN No. 219525.	7.50	11.25	15.00
HOWDY DOODY STICKER FUN, copyright 1953, WHITMAN No. 215825.	7.50	11.25	15.00
HOWDY DOODY STICKER FUN CIRCUS, Copyright 1955, WHITMAN No. 2165.	7.50	11.25	15.00
JACK AND JILL, 1962, MERRILL No. 1561, 6 dolls and clothes from storyland.	1.50	2.25	3.00
JANE RUSSELL, 1955, SAALFIELD No. 2611.	2.50	3.75	5.00
JANET LEIGH, 1958, ABBOTT No. 1805.	3.00	4.50	6.00
"JULIA"—DIAHANN CARROLL, Julia, Corey, Marie and Earl J. Waggedorn, 1968, ARTCRAFT No. 5140.	1.50	2.25	3.00
JUNIOR BOMBARDIER, 1943, EINSON & FREEMAN CO. No. 202.	10.00	15.00	20.00
KIDDIELAND VILLAGE, circa 1935, WHITMAN No. 2004, 11½x15" boxed			

	G	VG	M
set, nine buildings and 65 cut-out figures	9.00	13.50	18.00
LENNON SISTERS, 1961, WHITMAN No. 1983	3.50	5.25	7.00
LIBERTY BELLES PAPER DOLL BOOK, 1943, No. 3477, MERRILL	10.00	15.00	20.00
LITTLE BALLET DANCERS, 1950s? SAALFIELD No. 1743	.75	1.13	1.50
LITTLE BROTHERS AND SISTERS, 1953, WHITMAN No. 971:10, Tim, Kay, Ann and Pete	1.50	2.25	3.00
LITTLE FRIENDS PAPER DOLLS, 1950s, SAALFIELD No. 1746	1.00	1.50	2.00
LITTLE LULU "Shape Book", 1971, WHITMAN No. 1970	.25	.38	.50
LITTLE MISS AMERICA Paper Doll Book, 1941, SAALFIELD No. 2358, 15 punchouts by Campbell	10.00	15.00	20.00
LITTLE NURSE CUT-OUT BOOK, early 1940s, REUBEN H. LILJA AND CO., INC. No. 909	2.00	3.00	4.00
LITTLE ORPHAN ANNIE JUNIOR COMMANDOS, 1943, SAALFIELD No. 299	7.50	11.25	15.00
LOIS AND JOAN CUT-OUT DOLLS, 1941, 1945, WHITMAN No. 1015 (Jean also appears in Betty & Joan and Lois & Joan)	3.00	4.50	6.00
THE LONE RANGER RIDES AGAIN punch-out set, DEJOURNETTE MFG. CO., makes fences, figures of LR and Tonto, horses, campfire	7.50	11.25	15.00
LOOK-ALIKE CUT-OUT DOLLS, 1952, WHITMAN No. 97210, two mother and daughter pairs of dolls	2.00	3.00	4.00
LOOK WHO I AM! 1952, HART PUBLISHING CO., by Doris Stelberg, 18" doll with 15 costumes, Spiral bound	2.50	3.75	5.00

	G	VG	M
LORI MARTIN IN NATIONAL VELVET 1962, WHITMAN No. 4612, 6x11½" boxed set, paper dolls........	3.00	4.50	6.00
LOST HORIZON, 1973, ARTCRAFT No. 5112.........................	1.50	2.25	3.00
MAGIC MARY, 1955, MILTON BRADLEY No. 4010-1, 10½x10½" boxed set, complete with magnetic doll and strips to put on clothes.............	3.50	5.25	7.00
MARY AND JOAN, 1941, 1945, WHITMAN No. 1015 (Joan also appears in Lois & Joan and Betty & Joan)........	3.00	4.50	6.00
MARY JANE—A CUT OUT DOLL, by Florence Winship, 1939, 1941, WHITMAN No. 1010 with suitcase for accessories....................	4.50	6.75	9.00
MARY LEE—A CUT OUT DOLL WHITMAN No. 1010, circa 1939.....	4.50	6.75	9.00
MARY OF THE WACS—A Young American, by Hilda Miloche and Wilma Kane, WHITMAN No. 1012, 1943....	4.00	6.00	8.00
MARY POPPINS, 1973, WHITMAN No. 1977............................	1.25	1.88	2.50

McLOUGHLIN BROS. OF BROOKLYN, NEW YORK

McLoughlin Brothers was the largest American producer of paper soldiers, and one of the earliest in the paper-doll field. The firm, which traced its founding to 1828, began producing paper dolls at least as early as 1857. Among the other paper toys it sold were dollhouse furniture, toy theatres with actors and scenery, and blocks.

	G	VG	M
McLOUGHLIN BROS., Circa 1884, Mounted U.S. Cavalry, Hussar type,			

MCLOUGHLIN BROS. Zouaves c. 1884 (see page 101)

Photo by Jonathan A. Newman
Courtesy Barbara and Jonathan Newman

MCLOUGHLIN BROS. 100 Soldiers On Parade, c. 1898. (see page 102)
Photo. by Jonathan A. Newman   Courtesy Barbara and Jonathan Newman

	G	VG	M
charging, several different poses. Price per figure	1.00	1.50	2.00
McLOUGHLIN BROS. Infantry Soldiers printed 1857, price per each $5, complete set $150-175.			
McLOUGHLIN BROS. Infantry circa 1875, price per each	1.50	2.25	3.00
McLOUGHLIN BROS. Zouaves, 1884, price per each	.75	1.13	1.50
McLOUGHLIN Bros. Brass Band, 1890, price per each	.75	1.13	1.50
McLOUGHLIN BROS. Grenadiers, 1890, price per each	.75	1.13	1.50
McLOUGHLIN BROS. Zouaves 0203, 1905, price per each	.50	.75	1.00
McLOUGHLIN BROS. Brass Band, 1890, price per each	.75	1.13	1.50
McLOUGHLIN BROS. Grenadiers, 1890, price per each	.75	1.13	1.50
McLOUGHLIN BROS. Zouaves 0203, 1905, price per each	.50	.75	1.00
McLOUGHLIN BROS. French soldiers 4026, 1917, per sheet	5.00	7.50	10.00
McLOUGHLIN BROS. Paper Dolls 1860-1890, price per cut set, $15-25, uncut			

	G	VG	M
$30-60, depending on title, date, etc.			
McLOUGHLIN BROS. 100 Soldiers on Parade circa 1898..................	100.00	150.00	200.00
McLOUGHLIN BROS. 100 Soldiers on Parade, second set, circa 1898........	100.00	150.00	200.00
McLOUGHLIN BROS. 260 series, circa 1880-1895, i. Bandsmen—verious instruments. Per figure...................	.75	1.13	1.50
McLOUGHLIN BROS. 260 series, circa 1880-1895, j. Navy-U.S.S. Boston; k. Grenadier Guards. Per figure........	.63	.93	1.25
McLOUGHLIN BROS. 260 series, circa 1880-1895, l. Annapolis Cadets. Per figure...........................	.50	.75	1.00
McLOUGHLIN BROS. 260 series circa 1885-1890, Grenadier Guards. Price per figure....................,......	1.00	1.50	2.00
McLOUGHLIN BROS. Grenadiers 4½" high, with red tunics and black fur busbys, circa 1890. Officer and men. Price per figure..................	1.00	1.50	2.00
McLOUGHLIN BROS. Printed 1898, sailor 5¼" high, landing party for USS Texas......................	1.00	1.50	2.00
McLOUGHLIN BROS. U.S. Infantry from Spanish-American War circa 1898. Approx. 6" high on wooden blocks. Price per figure.............	1.00	1.50	2.00
McLOUGHLIN BROS. Circa 1898, small glossy series, 4½" high, West Point Cadets. Price per figure............	1.00	1.50	2.00
McLOUGHLIN BROS. circa 1898,			

	G	VG	M
British Infantry red coats, spiked helmets, 6" high on small wooden blocks. Price per figure....................	1.00	1.50	2.00
McLOUGHLIN BROS. circa 1898, U.S. Zouaves, Civil War era, blue coats, red baggy trousers, 6" high on small wooden blocks.....................	1.00	1.50	2.00
McLOUGHLIN BROS. "02" series, circa 1905-1910 a. British Highlanders b. U.S. Zouaves c. U.S. Continentals d. U.S. Navy e. U.S. Infantry in Campaign Uniforms (Spanish American War) h. American Indians, kneeling and standing. Price per figure.....	.50	.75	1.00
McLOUGHLIN BROS. Same as above. g. West Point Cadets (round base), circa 1915.........................	.38	.57	.75
McLOUGHLIN BROS. No. 0103 Dutch Paper Doll, boy of the Village of Vollendam. Circa 1910. 10½x10½" sheet............................	6.00	9.00	12.00
McLOUGHLIN BROS. No. 0201, Circa 1905-1910, British Highlanders. Single figure............................	.88	1.31	1.75
McLOUGHLIN BROS. Series 0202, circa 1910, American Indian, kneeling and standing types. Price per figure.......	.88	1.31	1.75
McLOUGHLIN BROS. Series 0205, circa 1915, round base, U.S. Navy. Price per figure........................	.50	.75	1.00
McLOUGHLIN BROS. Series 0205, circa 1915, West Point Cadets, single figure.	.75	1.13	1.50
McLOUGHLIN BROS. Circa 1915. Boy Scouts holding rifles across chests.....	.88	1.31	1.75
McLOUGHLIN BROS. Series No. 4026 10½x10½" Paper soldiers on sheet, Seven soldiers plus officer (5½" high) in field uniform. Circa 1916. 1. Belgium. 2. France. 3. Italy. 4. Britain. Price per sheet....................	4.00	6.00	8.00

	G	VG	M
ME AND MIMI, 1957, A Bonnie Story Book Doll, 6x8" in the style of the Little Golden Books. A doll and her Dolly Story Book, plus dolls and their dresses	5.00	7.50	10.00
MEXICAN CUT OUTS by Milo Winter, 1938, WHITMAN 1054, six pages of people, animals, houses, etc.	3.00	4.50	6.00
MICKEY AND MINNIE MOUSE PAPER DOLLS, 1930s, 2 10" figures with clothes	7.50	11.25	15.00
MODEL BATTLESHIP by Reed, circa 1945, 7x10"	1.25	1.87	2.50
MODEL FLAT-TOP by Reed, circa 1945	1.25	1.87	2.50
MOLLY BEE, 1962, WHITMAN No. 2091	2.50	3.75	5.00
MOMMY AND ME, 1954, WHITMAN No. 977:10	2.00	3.00	4.00
MOUSEKETEER CUT OUTS, 1957, WHITMAN No. 1974	4.00	6.00	8.00
MOVIE STARLETS PAPER DOLLS, circa 1949, STEPHENS PUBLISHING CO., No. 178. Four dolls—Miss Premiere, Miss Stardust, Miss Hollywood, Miss Preview, and four pages of costumes	1.00	1.50	2.00
MRS. BEASLY Paper Doll Book, 1970 ("Family Affair" TV show) WHITMAN No. 1973	.25	.37	.50
MY FAIR LADY, 1965, OTTENHEIMER PUBLISHERS No. 2960-2, by Evon Hartmann	3.00	4.50	6.00
MY VERY FIRST PAPER DOLL BOOK, 1957, A Bonnie Book No. 4732 SAMUEL LOWE	1.50	2.25	3.00
NANNY AND THE PROFESSOR, 1971, ARTCRAFT No. 5114	1.00	1.50	2.00
NAVY SCOUTS PAPER DOLL BOOK, 1942, MERRILL No. 3428	7.50	11.25	15.00

	G	VG	M
NEW YORK WORLD'S FAIR MAKE A MODEL, 1963, by Ottenheimer. SPERTUS No. 600-50. Includes Unisphere, Swiss Ride, N.Y. Port Authority Heliport, etc...................	5.00	7.50	10.00
NIGHT BEFORE CHRISTMAS WITH CUTOUTS Whitman No. 948........	7.50	11.25	15.00
19 FARMYARD ANIMALS TO CUT OUT AND STAND UP—Copyright 1930, WHITMAN No. 935, 12 pages...	10.00	15.00	20.00
ONE HUNDRED SOLDIERS PUNCH-OUT BOOK, 1943, WHITMAN 999...	7.50	11.25	15.00
OUR NURSE NANCY—A Young American, by Hilda Miloche and Wilma Kane, 1943, cutouts, WHITMAN No. 1012............................	4.00	6.00	8.00
OUR SAILOR BOB, 10" doll with uniforms, WHITMAN. circa 1943.......	5.00	7.50	10.00
OUR SOLDIER JIM, 1943, WHITMAN No. 3980, Designed by Hilda Miloche and Wilma Kane, 10½" standup doll with uniforms....................	5.00	7.50	10.00
OUR WAVE JOAN—A Young American, by Hilda Miloche and Wilma Kane, 1943, WHITMAN No. 1012..........	4.00	6.00	8.00
OUTDOOR PAPER DOLLS, 1941, SAALFIELD No. 1958, fourteen dolls and four pages of clothes...........	1.25	1.87	2.50
PAPER DOLLS FROM MOTHER GOOSE, 1957, SAALFIELD No. 2758 Mary, Bo-Peep, Boy Blue, Bobbie Shaftoe, Miss Muffet, Jack Horner....	1.50	2.25	3.00
PAPER DOLLS PETER AND PEGGY, 1935, WHITMAN No. 965, 64 pages by Dixon. Very large punchouts on front and back....................	12.50	18.75	25.00
PATSY A WOODEN DOLL WITH DRESSES (actually a 10" standup cardboard doll with wood backing) Circa 1938, WHITMAN 3037........	6.00	9.00	12.00

	G	VG	M
PETER AND PEGGY, 1950, WHITMAN No. 99210	1.50	2.25	3.00
PHOTO FASHIONS, 1953, WHITMAN No. 973	1.50	2.25	3.00
PILOT AND STEWARDESS PAPER DOLL BOOK No. 3423, 1941, MERRILL	7.50	11.25	15.00
PIPER LAURIE, 1953, MERRILL No. 2551	7.50	11.25	15.00
PLAYHOUSE DOLLS, 1949, STEPHENS PUBLISHING CO. No. 165, Four dolls and four pages of clothes	1.13	1.72	2.25
PLAYMATES, 1952, WHITMAN No. 99510	2.00	3.00	4.00
PLAYTHINGS TO CUT OUT AND STAND UP, circa 1935, WHITMAN No. 934. Contains ventriloquist's dummy, floating ships, general's hat, lantern, animals, other moving toys	5.00	7.50	10.00
PLAY TIME, 1952, WHITMAN 210525	2.25	3.37	4.50
PRETTY VILLAGE, 1897 School House Set, McLOUGHLIN	40.00	60.00	80.00
PORTRAIT GIRLS WITH CLOTH-LIKE CLOTHES, 1947, designed by Hilda Miloche and Wilma Kane, WHITMAN No. 1170	4.00	6.00	8.00
POWER MODELS CUT OUT DOLLS BOOK, 1942, WHITMAN No. 981, Six dolls	10.00	15.00	20.00
PROM TIME, 1962, WHITMAN No. 2084, 2 dolls and party clothes	1.00	1.50	2.00
QUEEN HOLDEN! QUEEN HOLDEN! BETTY AND BOB, 1952, 12½" high children, WHITMAN 99110	6.00	9.00	12.00
QUEEN HOLDEN! QUEEN HOLDEN! HAIR-DO DOLLS, 1948, 3 dolls, clothes and 31 different hair-dos, WHITMAN No. 991	7.50	11.25	15.00
"RAP-A-JAP", circa 1943 WOODBURN MFG. No. C1	2.50	3.75	5.00

	G	VG	M
READY CUT VILLAGE, 1930s, no mfr. listed	15.00	22.50	30.00
RICKY NELSON paper dolls, 1959	2.50	3.75	5.00
RIGBY'S EASY TO BUILD MODELS OF FIGHTING PLANES	15.00	22.50	30,00
RIGBY'S EASIER TO BUILD MODELS OF NAVAL CRAFT, 24 models of warships, 27 pages, 11½x14", designed by Wallace Rigby, 1944, includes Battleship North Carolina, aircraft carrier, cruiser, destroyer, etc.	9.00	13.50	18.00
RIGBY FLYING MODELS OF JET AND ROCKET PLANES, ten planes, 1949, GARDEN CITY BOOKS	5.00	7.50	10.00

Rigby's Flying Models of Jet and Rocket Planes (see this page)
Photo by Jonathan A. Newman
Courtesy Barbara and Jonathan Newman

	G	VG	M
RIGBY'S MODEL BOOK OF FLYING CLIPPERS, 11x14" book designed by Wallace Rigby, two scale models of Douglas DC-Jet Clipper and Douglas DC-7C, 1957	4.00	6.00	8.00
RIGBY'S MODEL SPORTS CARS OF THE WORLD, 1954, includes 18" "sports-racer", Chevette, Jaguar, Mercedes-Benz, etc	5.00	7.50	10.00
RIGBY'S NAVAL CRAFT, 1944, GARDEN CITY PUBL. CO.	7.50	11.25	15.00
ROBIN HOOD AND MAID MARIAN, 1950s, SAALFIELD, No. 1761, paper dolls	1.50	2.25	3.00
ROCK HUDSON paper dolls, 1957, WHITMAN No. 2087	4.50	6.75	9.00

	G	VG	M
ROWAN & MARTIN'S LAUGH-IN PUNCH OUT PAPER DOLL BOOK, 1969, SAALFIELD No. 1325, Rowan, Martin, Jo Ann Worley, Arte Johnson, Judy Carne and Goldie Hawn.........	2.00	3.00	4.00
ROY ROGERS STICKER FUN BOOK, 1953, No. 2161....................	5.00	7.50	10.00
RUTH NEWTON'S CUT OUT DOLLS AND ANIMALS "with over 80 pieces to cut out and play with", 1934, 11x17"	10.00	15.00	20.00
SALLY ANN A CUT OUT DOLL, circa 1940, WHITMAN No. 1010.....	4.50	6.75	9.00
SANDRA AND SUE STATUETTE DOLLS AND THEIR CLOTHES, by Lee Lunzer, 1948, WHITMAN No. 1180	3.50	5.25	7.00
SANDRA DEE, 1959, Boxed, two dolls and 34 costume pieces, SAALFIELD No. 5511.........................	2.00	3.00	4.00
SANDY AND SUE, 1963, WHITMAN No. 1956.........................	1.75	2.63	3.50
SCISSORS BIRD PAPER DOLLS, 1946, STEPHENS No. 137...............	1.00	1.50	2.00
6 GOOD LITTLE DOLLS, no date, STEPHENS PUBLISHING CO. No. 183	.88	1.31	1.75
SKATING PARTY PAPER DOLL BOOK, 1941, No. 2328, SAALFIELD, 17 Punchouts	12.50	18.75	25.00
SMASH THE AXIS, 1943, ELECTRIC CORP. OF AMERICA..............	5.00	7.50	10.00
SNOW WHITE AND THE SEVEN DWARFS PAPER DOLLS, 1938, 12x17", WHITMAN No. 970.........	35.00	52.50	70.00
SOLDIER SET by J. PRESSMAN AND CO. INC., NEW YORK, No. 1551, circa 1940, contains five cardboard soldiers, 4½" high, and marbles......	.75	1.13	1.50

	G	VG	M
SOLDIERS, Cardboard, approx. 6" high on wooden blocks, Navy, both officer and sailors circa 1920. Price per single figure	1.00	1.50	2.00
SOLDIERS, Cardboard, approx. 6" high on wooden blocks. Sailor, U.S.	1.00	1.50	2.00
SOLDIERS, Cardboard, approx. 6" high on wooden blocks. U.S. Infantry in campaign hats, mounted. Price per single figure	.88	1.31	1.75
SOLDIERS, Cardboard, approx. 6" high on wooden blocks. U.S. Infantry circa 1910, khaki uniforms with red trim. Officers, enlisted men. Price per single figure	1.00	1.50	2.00
SOLDIERS, Cardboard, approx. 6" high on wooden blocks. West Point Cadets	1.00	1.50	2.00
SOLDIERS, heavy cardboard, 5" high with folding stands, circa 1942. No. 101 Soldier with flat helmet, marching	.63	.93	1.25
Circa 1942 No. 112 General MacArthur	1.25	1.87	2.50
Circa 1942 No. 113 Nurse	.80	1.20	1.60
Circa 1942 No. 119 Skitrooper	.80	1.20	1.60
Circa 1942 No. 116 Soldier on wireless radio	.75	1.13	1.50
Circa 1942 No. 152 Two soldiers and AA Gun	.88	1.31	1.75
Circa 1942 No. 154 Ambulance	1.00	1.50	2.00
SOLDIERS ON PARADE, early, Milton Bradley No. 4518, set of 10	12.50	18.75	25.00
SPARKLE PLENTY Paperdoll Set, 1948, SAALFIELD No. 5160	7.50	11.25	15.00
SPORTS TIME, 1952, WHITMAN No. 210525	2.25	3.38	4.50
STATUETTE DOLLS, 1943, WHITMAN No. 992, Two women	2.50	3.75	5.00
STATUETTE DOLLS AND THEIR CLOTHES, 1942, WHITMAN No. 998	6.00	9.00	12.00
STATUETTE DOLLS AND THEIR CLOTHES, 1946, WHITMAN No.			

	G	VG	M
986, Two girls and a boy...........	2.50	3.75	5.00
STENCILS LARGE AND SMALL by Roy Best, circa 1935, No. 954 (Whitman?) folder of 30 animals to punch out and use as stencils. Comes with tiny box of crayons........................	5.00	7.50	10.00
STOCK FARM SET, circa 1944, CONCERN No. 123, boxed, 100 die-cut pieces, including house, barn, silo, chicken house, tractor, etc.......	3.00	4.50	6.00
THE STORY OF CINDERELLA, A Fold A-Way Toy book designed by Will Pente. Circa 1925, REILLY & BRITTON CO.....................	3.50	5.25	7.00
SUNBONNET SUE, 1951, WHITMAN No. 2062-29......................	2.50	3.75	5.00
SUSAN DEY AS LAURIE ("Partridge Family" TV show), 1972, ARTCRAFT, Fashions by Kate Greenaway.........	1.50	2.25	3.00
SWEETIE PIE TWINS, 1949, STEPHENS PUBLISHING CO. No. 166, Jane and Jean................	1.13	1.72	2.25
SWING-A-PLANE by J.L. Schilling Co., Model of a Flying Tiger, 1944, flies on string...........................	3.00	4.50	6.00
TAMMY, 1963, A LITTLE GOLDEN STORY BOOK with paper dolls to cut out and dress. Illustrated by Ada Salvi...........................	1.00	1.50	2.00
THAT GIRL—MARLO THOMAS, 1967, SAALFIELD No. 1351..............	1.50	2.25	3.00
THAT GIRL—MARLO THOMAS, 1967, SAALFIELD No. 1379..............	1.50	2.25	3.00
THEY STAND UP, by Avis Mac, 1939, WHITMAN No. 932, 13x18" with five children........................	17.50	26.25	35.00
30 TOY SOLDIERS, circa 1943, WHIT-MAN No. 2950....................	7.50	11.25	15.00
THREE BEARS CUT OUT BOOK, Copy-			

	G	VG	M
right 1939, WHITMAN No. 1020, Goldilocks and 3 Bears.............	11.25	16.88	22.50
THREE FLYING MODELS of Famous Allied Fighting Planes by Judd Reed, 9x12", contains Hell Cat, Spitfire, and Stormovik planes. Included is "American Ace Spotter", with turning dial of 48 3-view silhouettes of 16 planes in little windows, 1944........	3.00	4.50	6.00
THREE LITTLE GIRLS WHO GREW AND GREW AND THIS IS HOW THEY GREW, 1945, WHITMAN No. 99410..........................	3.00	4.50	6.00
THREE LITTLE GIRLS WHO GREW AND GREW AND GREW AND THIS IS HOW THEY GREW, with cloth-like clothes, flocked 1945, WHITMAN No. 1176........................	3.50	5.25	7.00
THREE LITTLE PIGS CUT OUT BOOK, Copyright 1939, WHITMAN No. 1020, Pigs and Big Bad Wolf......	11.25	16.88	22.50
THREE SWEET BABY DOLLS TO CUT OUT AND DRESS, 1954, WHITMAN No. 975...........................	1.50	2.25	3.00
TINY CHATTY TWINS PAPER DOLLS, 1963, WHITMAN No. 1985..........	1.00	1.50	2.00
TOBY TYLER CIRCUS PLAYBOOK PUNCH OUT, 1959, No. 1936........	2.50	3.75	5.00
TOM CORBETT SPACE CADET Punch Out Book, 1952, SAALFIELD No. 4304, 14" long, 10½" wide..........	6.00	9.00	12.00
TOM THE AVIATOR, circa 1942, SAMUEL LOWE No. L1074.........	5.00	7.50	10.00
TOY TOWN, 1916, series of 50 different buildings by AMERICAN COLOR-TYPE CO., 1916..................	2.50	3.75	5.00
TRANSFER PICTURES, Copyright 1939, WHITMAN No. 1085, 100 decalcomanias	7.50	11.25	15.00

	G	VG	M
TREASURE HOUR PUPPET BOOK No. 4, 1968, MURRAY SALES AND SERVICE, The Rustlers of Rocky Ranch, a play of cowboys and Indians in five scenes. Cut-out section makes model theatre.....................	2.00	3.00	4.00
TRICIA PAPER DOLLS, 1970, SAALFIELD No. 1248, White House tour game, White House stand-up doll of Tricia Nixon and costumes...........	2.00	3.00	4.00
TUESDAY WELD Paper Dolls, 1960, SAALFIELD No. 5112, boxed two dolls and 58 costume pieces..............	2.00	3.00	4.00
TV STAR TIME PAPER DOLLS, circa 1950s, ABBOTT No. 1367...........	1.25	1.87	2.50
22 ANIMALS TO CUT OUT AND STAND UP, copyright 1930, WHITMAN No. 935, rabbits, bears, owls, squirrels, etc......................	10.00	15.00	20.00
TWIGGY Paper Doll, 1967, WHITMAN No. 1999, with "plastilon" Twiggy dress for small girls.................	2.50	3.75	5.00
UMBRELLA GIRLS, 1956, MERRILL No. 2562, wrap-around dresses.......	2.50	3.75	5.00
UNITED STATES SOLDIERS, 1942, SAMUEL LOWE No. L1063.........	7.50	11.25	15.00
U.S. INFANTRY—Spanish American War, approx 6" high soldier on small wooden block.....................	1.00	1.50	2.00
WALKING PAPER DOLL FAMILY No. 1074, SAALFIELD 1934.........	15.00	22.50	30.00
WALT DISNEY'S LET'S BUILD DISNEYLAND, 1957, WHITMAN No. 1986, forms sets for Adventureland, Frontierland, Tomorrowland and Fantasyland......................	5.00	7.50	10.00
WALT DISNEY MATCH AND PATCH STICKER FUN, 1953, WHITMAN, Mickey Mouse, Donald Duck, Pluto, Goofy, etc........................	5.00	7.50	10.00

	G	VG	M
WALT DISNEY STICKER FUN BOOK, 1951, WHITMAN...................	5.00	7.50	10.00
WALT DISNEY STICKER FUN WITH PETER PAN, 1952, WHITMAN......	5.00	7.50	10.00
WHITE HOUSE PARTY DRESSES, 1961, MERRILL No. 1550............	3.50	5.25	7.00
WHITMAN No. 1146, little 3½" x 7½" paper doll books, copyright 1939. A. Nancy and Tommy B. Ann and Arthur C. Kitty and Billy D. Muriel and David E. Cynthia and Bobby F. Judy and Dick....................	3.00	4.50	6.00
WHITMAN PAPER DOLL BOOK, 1933, No. 3059, four dolls, ten sheets of clothes in folder...................	12.50	18.75	25.00
YOUNG PATRIOT INVASION SET, circa 1944, COLORGRAPHIC No. 500, contains destroyer, amphibian tractor, tank, jeep, anti-tank gun, bomber and dive bomber, 10½ x 13" boxed set.........................	7.50	11.25	15.00
YOUNG PATRIOT—LEARN TO KNOW YOUR ARMY, 1943, COLOR-GRAPHIC No. 350, tank, howitzer, jeep, antitank gun, bomber, fighter and soldiers. Guns shoot, bombs drop, etc.	10.00	15.00	20.00
YOUNG PATRIOT—LEARN TO KNOW YOUR NAVY, 1943, COLOR-GRAPHIC construction set No. 360, 10 x 14" boxed set includes battle-ship, destroyer, aircraft carrier, mosquito boat, submarine, planes, depth charges, etc., with moveable parts...........................	10.00	15.00	20.00
ZOO CUT OUTS by Milo Winter, 1938, WHITMAN No. 1054, six pages of heavy cut-out animals..............	3.00	4.50	6.00

TIN WIND-UP
(see also Movie, Comic Character)

Tin Wind-up toys, always popular, have become even more so as the result of a number of recent well-publicized auctions, particularly those held by PB84 (Sotheby Parke Bernet) in New York, Los Angeles, and London, when a large part of the LOUIS MARX collection was auctioned off. Unlike most of the toys in this book, tin wind-ups do not "feel" particularly good in the hand, and depend more on the lure of motion and colorful lithography. Esthetically the most appealing, perhaps, are those of Lehmann, a German company which also patented a number of its toys in the United States, and which holds a strong attraction for a large number of collectors.

CONDITION OF A TOY
AND ITS RELATION TO PRICE

The price of a tin wind-up toy depends not only on its desirability, but on its condition. A wind-up in mint condition is generally worth twice what that same toy would bring in good condition, with "very good" falling about equally in between good and mint.

"Mint" means just that; the condition in which it was originally issued—perfect, regardless of age, not the slightest blemish. Needless to say, this is a fairly rare state of affairs, but enough toys exist in mint condition to make it an employable term. Many people hoping to dispose of toys are tempted to call an item "mint" when it is really "near mint", "very good", or sometimes even just "good". Inevitably this can result in unhappiness all around, and not infrequently, a cancelled sale.

"Very Good" indicates a toy which has obviously seen use, with signs of wear and aging, but in general having a freshness to its appearance that makes it attractive and collectible to all but the most discriminating.

"Good" signals a toy that has seen considerable wear, shows its age, but is basically sound. A collector will collect it, but will often not be wholly satisfied with it as an example of his collection, and thus prices are often drastically below that which the same item in mint can command.

Condition below good results in another drastic drop in price, though this does not apply to the wind-up mechanism itself, as it can generally be replaced easily, and collectors seem not to worry much about whether the mechanism is original. Toys with missing parts, although otherwise in excellent condition, will usually fall into this lower-priced category, and rust, even small spots of it, can seriously lower the price of a toy. "Near-Mint", "Fine", "Very Fine" and similar terms often found in sellers' descriptions denote conditions between Mint and Very Good, and are priced accordingly.

The key to grading is to avoid wishful thinking. Grading can sometimes be a problem for the unitiated, but common sense will usually prevail, and when possible, a consultation with an expert in the field can often clear up lingering doubts. A toy in its original box is worth up to 10 to 20% more if the box is in mint condition, with the price dropping as condition lessens.

TIN WIND-UP

	G	VG	M
"Acrobatic Marvel", monkey on pole, with rocking base, circa 1937	20.00	30.00	40.00
Aircraft Carrier, circa post WW II, tin litho, approx 15" long	22.50	33.75	45.00
"Aircraft Carrier X53", with five jet planes, tin litho, circa 1950s	10.00	15.00	20.00
Band, two monkeys and a clown, cloth suits, 4½" high	20.00	30.00	40.00
Banjo Player, early	26.00	39.00	52.00
Barber—animal, perhaps cat, with animal customer in chair, circa 1940s	7.50	11.25	15.00
Barnacle Bill, looks like Popeye, circa 1930s	42.50	63.75	85.00
Battleship, "U.S.S. Washington"	12.50	18.75	25.00
Biplane, very early, Wright Bros.-like, paper propeller blades, 6" long	300.00	450.00	600.00
Bird in Cage, 3½" high	25.00	37.50	50.00
Bird with flapping wings, 6½" long	9.00	13.50	18.00
Black boy eating watermelon, with dog biting his backside, 6½" high	110.00	165.00	220.00
Boy on St. Bernard on rocker, 6¾" long . .	110.00	165.00	220.00
Boy on Tricycle, 9½" high	20.00	30.00	40.00
Buffalo Bill, hand-painted, hand-soldered	100.00	150.00	200.00
"The Cackling Hen of Paradise", 8" long, turn side handle and hen cackles; Patented	7.50	11.25	15.00
"Cakewalk Dancers", short black man dancing with tall, heavy black woman .	350.00	525.00	700.00
Camel, 5¼" high	28.00	42.00	56.00
"Candy" cart driven by monkey in cap, also marked "candy", circa 1950s	3.50	5.25	7.00
Car with electric headlights, hard rubber wheels, 9" long	22.00	33.00	44.00
Carousel with four biplanes and pilots, paper vanes, flag finial, 17" high	900.00	1200.00	1800.00

	G	VG	M
Carousel with four double horse and riders that alternate with four women in cars, velvet top with ball fringe, flag finial, 17" high..................	950.00	1275.00	1900.00
Carousel with four men in canoes, propellors with paper vanes, 11" high....	300.00	450.00	600.00
CARTER "Pan-Gee The Funny Dancer", 1921...........................	150.00	225.00	300.00
Cat pushing cage with two mice, 8¼" long............................	200.00	300.00	400.00
CHEIN bear with hat, pants, shirt, bowtie, circa 1938....................	5.00	7.50	10.00
CHEIN boy skiing, 8" long, 1940s.......	10.00	15.00	20.00
CHEIN chick, brightly colored clothes and polka dot bowtie, 4" high........	7.00	10.50	14.00
CHEIN clown, 4¾" high..............	5.00	7.50	10.00
CHEIN "Drummer Boy" 9" high, with shako, circa 1930s.................	6.00	9.00	12.00
CHEIN duck, long-beaked, in orange sailor suit, not Donald Duck, but similar. Waddles, 6" high..............	20.00	30.00	40.00
CHEIN "Mechanical Aquaplane", boatlike pontoons, 1932................	30.00	45.00	60.00
CHEIN Penguin in tuxedo type jacket, circa 1940........................	4.00	6.00	8.00
CHEIN Rabbit in shirt and pants, circa 1938.............................	3.00	4.50	6.00
CHEIN "Roller Coaster", circa 1938....	30.00	45.00	60.00
Chicken............................	7.00	10.50	14.00
Circus-Type Trainer, baton in hand, revolves, with rooster on each side, 3½" long, musical......................	22.00	33.00	44.00
Clown Dancer, 8" high...............	12.00	18.00	24.00
Clown in Donkey Cart, 7½" long.......	60.00	90.00	120.00
Clown in Hoop, 6½" high.............	60.00	90.00	120.00
Clown Musicians, four, on a pedestal, musical, 8" high..................	200.00	300.00	400.00
Clown pulled by goat................	16.00	24.00	32.00
CORTLAND Ice Cream Car, "Ice Cream 5¢", man driving, bell on cart, circa			

	G	VG	M
1940	12.50	18.75	25.00
Dachshund, 7" long.	25.00	37.50	50.00
Dancing dogs, two, and boy with whip. .	100.00	150.00	200.00
Dancing horse, two small bells on top of bridle, 7½" high.	60.00	90.00	120.00
Dodgem-type car, man and woman riders, circa 1938.	22.50	33.75	45.00
Dog, monkey on back, 9" high.	8.00	12.00	16.00

Ferris Wheel carrying eight gondolas, the gondolas containing a total of 16 small bisque dolls. Height 33½". (see page 119) . Photo Courtesy PB84.

	G	VG	M
Duck	7.00	10.50	14.00
Duckling	2.50	3.75	5.00
Ferris Wheel carrying eight gondolas, the gondolas containing a total of 16 small bisque dolls, 33½" high	666.00	999.00	1332.00
Ferris Wheel, carved with figures and music box, 17"	230.00	345.00	460.00
Fish, speckled trout, 5½" long, litho	7.50	11.25	15.00
Freight cart pulled by man in cap, with luggage on cart, circa 1940	5.00	7.50	10.00
"George the Drummer Boy" in shako, circa 1940	6.00	9.00	12.00
GIRARD bus with driver, 12½" long	25.00	37.50	50.00
GIRARD Man pushing wheelbarrow, 5½"	5.00	7.50	10.00
Hansom Cab, horse moves backward and forward, as wheels rotate, driver atop cab, 5¾" long	80.00	120.00	160.00
Hopping Rabbit, 4½" long	10.00	15.00	20.00
HY LINE car, ultra-streamlined two-door coupe type, circa 1938	16.00	24.00	32.00
HY-LO, BUFFALO TOYS Ferris Wheel, 14½" high	60.00	90.00	120.00
Indian, like cigar store Indian, circa 1937	7.50	11.25	15.00
KI CO. Boy On Motorcycle, 8 3/8" long	160.00	240.00	320.00
KINGSBURY Convertible with rumble seat, electric headlamps, hard rubber wheels, 12½" long	30.00	45.00	60.00
KINGSBURY fireman's ladder truck, hard rubber wheels, driver, 23½" long	12.50	18.75	25.00
KINGSBURY Roadster, electric headlamps, 12½" long	150.00	225.00	300.00
LEHMANN "Alabama Coon Jigger", "Lehmann, Oh-My", 10" high	90.00	120.00	180.00
LEHMANN "Bucking Broncho, Wild West", 6½" long	100.00	150.00	200.00

	G	VG	M

LEHMANN Clown in donkey cart, 7½"
long 37.50   56.25   75.00

TOP, Left to Right: LEHMANN walking sailor, 7½" high (see page 121); LEHMANN "Tut-Tut"
man in motorcar with horn, length 7" (see page 121)   Photos Courtesy PB84.

WOLVERINE "Zilotone" with six
interchangeable records; 1930s (see page 132)

Photo Courtesy PB84.

BOTTOM, Left to Right: Ice, Cart, tin horse-drawn (see page 79)
Banjo Player, early (see page 116)
Photo Courtesy PB84.

	G	VG	M
LEHMANN Early car with two excited woman passengers, driver in top hat and dog with turning head, 5½" long	175.00	262.50	350.00
LEHMANN "Express", porter pulling cart, circa 1927 6" long	125.00	187.50	250.00
LEHMANN "Jennie The Balking Mule"	50.00	75.00	100.00
LEHMANN Man driving horse cart, wheels marked with elf, 6" long	100.00	150.00	200.00
LEHMANN "Masuyama", coolie pulling rickshaw	100.00	150.00	200.00
LEHMANN "Nunu" No. 733, rickshaw with puller and rider, circa 1913, 4½" long	137.50	196.25	275.00
LEHMANN People and Dog, pat. 1903	160.00	240.00	320.00
LEHMANN "Quack-Quack", mother duck pulling cart with three small ducks	85.00	127.50	170.00
LEHMANN "Rad-Cycle", 5" long, circa 1927	187.50	281.25	375.00
LEHMANN "Tom" climbing monkey, 8" long	25.00	37.50	50.00
LEHMANN "Tut-Tut", man in car with horn, 6¾" long	140.00	210.00	280.00
LEHMANN Walking Couple	150.00	225.00	300.00
LEHMANN Walking Sailor, 7½" high	250.00	375.00	500.00
LINDSTROM "Lindstrom's Ferry Boat", approx 8¼", litho	15.00	22.50	30.00
LINDSTROM "Miss America" speedboat, litho	10.00	15.00	20.00
LUPOR METAL PRODUCTS N.Y. Racer No. 8, 1930s	8.00	12.00	16.00

L TO R: LINDSTROM "Miss America" (see this page); LINDSTROM "Lindstrom's Ferry Boat" (see this page); Speedboat, "G.E. 200" (see page 130).

	G	VG	M
Man And Woman Dancing, both white, 8" high	215.00	322.50	430.00
Man Pushing Wheelbarrow	26.00	39.00	52.00
Marine, hand on belt, smiling, circa 1940	4.00	6.00	8.00

LOUIS MARX—By the 1950s, LOUIS MARX was the largest manufacturer of toys in the world; six large factories in the U.S., and ownership or interest in factories in seven other countries. Marx, born in Brooklyn in 1896, was working for "Toy King" Ferdinand Strauss when he was in his teens, and by the age of twenty his energy and enterprise had made him a director of that company. A falling out with Strauss persuaded him to go into business for himself, and in 1921 he and his brother began making their own toys, including some adaptations of items by the now-defunct Strauss. Marx's watchword seems to have been quality at the lowest possible price, and he was such a favorite with toy buyers that he had virtually no need for salesmen or advertising. Although Marx made virtually every type of toy with the exception of dolls, his tin wind-up toys are probably the most favored by toy collectors.

	G	VG	M
MARX Airplane No. 90, light fuselage	15.00	22.50	30.00
MARX Airplane No. 90, medium fuselage	15.00	22.50	30.00
MARX "Army Dive Bomber" No. 482	25.00	37.50	50.00
MARX "Beat!! The Komikal Kop", 1930s	32.00	48.00	64.00
MARX "Big Parade", moving vehicles, soldiers, etc., 1929	112.50	168.75	225.00
MARX Bomber, two engine, 18" wingspan	12.50	18.75	25.00
MARX Boy on Trapeze	17.00	25.50	34.00
MARX Brutus Dippy Dipper, celluloid figure, circa 1930, eccentric car	150.00	225.00	300.00
MARX Bumper Auto, streamlined, circa 1939, large bumpers front and rear	20.00	30.00	40.00
MARX "Busy Bridge", vehicles on bridge, 1935	60.00	90.00	120.00

MARX Rookie Pilot (see page 127).
Photo Courtesy PB84.

	G	VG	M
MARX "The Butter and Egg Man" walker	57.50	86.25	115.00
MARX cat with ball in front, two wheels in back, circa 1938	3.50	5.25	7.00
MARX "Champion Skater" ballet dancer, pull spinning rod out of motor, place skater in upright position and he spins	15.00	22.50	30.00
MARX "Charleston Trio", one adult, two child dancers, 1921	100.00	150.00	200.00
MARX Chicken Snatcher, black holding chicken, dog biting at the seat of his pants, circa 1927	100.00	150.00	200.00
MARX "Coast Defense", circular, with three cannon, revolving airplane, 1929	100.00	150.00	200.00
MARX Cowboy on horse, circa 1941, cowboy with lariat on dapple horse	15.00	22.50	30.00
MARX "Dapper Dan Coon Jigger", 1910	125.00	187.50	250.00

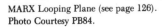

MARX Looping Plane (see page 126).
Photo Courtesy PB84.

MARX Army Dive Bomber (see page 122).
Photo Courtesy PB84.

MARX "Busy Bridge"

(see page 122)
Photo Courtesy PB84

	G	VG	M
MARX "Dippy Dumper", early.........	65.00	97.50	130.00
MARX Donkey pulling cart, with rider...	30.00	45.00	60.00
MARX Drummer, 9" high, in shako.....	6.00	9.00	12.00
MARX Fireman on Ladder, 24" high....	34.00	51.00	68.00
MARX "Flipo the Jumping Dog, See Me Jump", on hind legs, circa 1940, 3½x4"..........................	10.00	15.00	20.00
MARX Golden Pecking Goose, 9½" long, dated July 8, 1924, hops along, pecking at ground.................	9.00	13.50	18.00

MARX "Looping Plane" (see page 126).
Photo Courtesy PB84.

MARX Roll-Over Plane (see page 127).
Photo Courtesy PB84.

MARX Airplane, No. 90 (see page 122).
Photo Courtesy PB84.

MARX Airplane, No. 90 (see page 122).
Photo Courtesy PB84.

Charleston Trio

Some steppers! Very snappy action. When strong spring is wound up Charleston Charlie dances while the small negro fiddles and the animal nods his approval. Made of metal, lithographed in attractive colors. L'gth, 4⅜ inches; height, 9 in. Shipping wt., 1 pound.

49K5727
45c

MARX Charleston Trio (see page 123).

HeeHaw—TheBalkyMule 42c

Real Action

He Balks
He Kicks

Bigger and better hit each year. A comical toy. Uncanny how it operates. This mule has real pep and is some kicker. He backs up when he should go forward and rears up on his hind legs so that the poor driver doesn't know what to do. Metal, and finished in attractive natural colors. Assorted designs. Strong spring. Average length, about 9 inches; 5¾ inches high. Shipping weight, 1 pound.

49K5747 .... **42c**

MARX Hee Haw (see page 126).

Real Clever

Brand New
87c

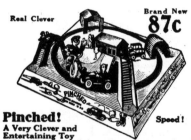

Pinched!
A Very Clever and Entertaining Toy

Speed!

See this speedy little roadster shoot round and round, through the bridges and tunnels, and all of a sudden, the motorcycle cop shoots out from behind the station, stops him and "pinches" him. When cop is pushed back behind station again, the auto starts away automatically, only to be "pinched" over and over again. Made of metal, lithographed in bright natural colors. Size, over all, 10 inches square, 3½ inches high. Shpg. wt., 1¼ lbs. **87c**

49K5738 .... **87c**

MARX Pinched! (see page 127).

Chicken Snatcher

45c

One of our most novel toys. When the strong spring motor is wound up the scared looking negro shuffles along with a chicken dangling in his hand and a dog hanging on the seat of his pants. Very funny action toy which will delight the kiddies. Nicely lithographed metal. Height, 8½ in. Shpg. wt., ¾ lb.

49K5728
45c

MARX Chicken Snatcher (see page 123).

Main Street
24 In. Long

The Newest Sensation—A Whole Town In Itself

Standard
$1.50 Toy

$1.00

One of the biggest mechanical toy sensations this year. A little town in itself. Just wind the strong spring motor, then release the brake, and see street cars, autos and trucks, hurry back and forth, some one way and some the other. Lithographed in attractive colors. Real enjoyment for the kiddies. Made of metal and measures 24x3¾x2¾ inches. Shipping weight, 2 pounds. **$1.00**

49K5732 .... **$1.00**

MARX Main Street (see page 126).

125

	G	VG	M
MARX "Hee-Haw" balky mule, 1929, 10¾" long, six-color litho, goes backward, forward, and rears, farmer and his dog on seat and five milk cans in cart	25.00	37.50	50.00
MARX "Honeymoon Express", old-fashioned train on circular track, 1927	75.00	112.50	150.00
MARX "Honeymoon Express", circa 1940 circling train and plane	30.00	45.00	60.00
MARX "Honeymoon Express", streamlined train on circular track, 1947	25.00	37.50	50.00
MARX Jalopy Pickup Truck, 7"	17.00	25.50	34.00
MARX "Joy-Rider", 1929, 8" long, College Boy driver with bag, wording on car "goes backward, forward, circles and rears" head moves	40.00	60.00	80.00
MARX Jumpin' Jeep, circa WWII, 6"	15.00	22.50	30.00
MARX "Looping Plane", No. 182	25.00	37.50	50.00
MARX "Looping Plane" No. 382	25.00	37.50	50.00
MARX "Main Street", moving vehicles, traffic cop, etc., 1929	80.00	120.00	160.00
MARX Mammy's Boy, eyes move, litho	80.00	120.00	160.00
MARX Merrymakers, four mice, three in band, one a dancer, 1929	150.00	225.00	300.00
MARX Minstrel figure, 11" high	60.00	90.00	120.00
MARX "Motorcyle Trooper", 1935	50.00	75.00	100.00
MARX "New York," circular, with train, 1929	80.00	120.00	160.00
MARX Nodding Goose	20.00	30.00	40.00

MARX Honeymoon Express
1927   (see this page)

49c

Famous Honeymoon Express, 49c

Every kiddie loves choo-choo trains

One of the most popular mechanical toys ever brought out. Sells like hot cakes. After spring motor is wound up a miniature train travels round and round swiftly through three tunnels, while the flagman signals with his flag. Beautifully lithographed in snappy colors on metal. Lots of action and attractive in appearance. Diam., 9½ inches. Height, 2¼ inches. Shipping weight, 1 lb. **49c**

	G	VG	M
MARX "Old Jalopy", 1920s, many sayings on car, "Use No Hooks", "Hop Inn", etc.	18.00	27.00	36.00
MARX "Pinched" roadster, motorcycle cop in circular track, circa 1927	80.00	120.00	160.00
MARX "Police Patrol", motorcycle with sidecar, 1935	40.00	60.00	80.00
MARX Racing car, 12", litho, circa 1940, two-man team	25.00	37.50	50.00
MARX Racing car, "27", litho, plastic driver circa 1950	10.00	15.00	20.00
MARX Reversing Road Roller	25.00	37.50	50.00
MARX "Roadside Rest Service Station", four pumps, car, garage, 1930	125.00	187.50	250.00
MARX "Rocket Fighter", circa 1950s	15.00	22.50	30.00
MARX "Rodeo Joe", 1933	100.00	150.00	200.00
MARX "Roll Over Plane", circa 1920s	22.50	33.75	45.00
MARX Rookie Pilot, 7" long, No. 77, circa 1940	20.00	30.00	40.00
MARX "Sand and Gravel Truck— Builders Supply Co.", 1920	25.00	37.50	50.00
MARX "Service Station Pumps" (3?), 1920	25.00	37.50	50.00
MARX Soldier, prone, firing rifle, WW I helmet	15.00	22.50	30.00
MARX "Sparkling Climbing Tank", 1939	37.50	56.25	75.00
MARX "Sparkling Tractor," tractor with plow blade, 1939	25.00	37.50	50.00
MARX Sparkling Warship, 14" long	30.00	45.00	60.00
MARX "Spic and Span, the Hams What Am", drummer and dancer, 1924	200.00	300.00	400.00
MARX "Spic Coon Drummer", 1924, 8½" high	200.00	300.00	400.00
MARX "Sunnyside Service Station", four pumps, car and garage, 1939	100.00	150.00	200.00
MARX Tank, raked, soldier pops out of back with rifle, weapons on top and jutting out of sides	24.00	36.00	48.00
MARX Tank, soldier pops out of back with rifle, very small circles on "treads"	24.00	36.00	48.00

TOP: Racing Car "711" (see page 129)
MIDDLE: MARX racing car "27" (see page 127);
BOTTOM: MARX racing car "12" (see page 127).

MARX Drummer, in shako (see page 124).

	G	VG	M
MARX Tank, soldier pops out of back with rifle, wheels represented on side, circa 1930s......................	24.00	36.00	48.00
MARX "Tidy Tim", Streetcleaner pushing wagon, 1933......................	50.00	75.00	100.00
MARX tractor, early 1940s.............	10.00	15.00	20.00
MARX trolley, lithographed, headlight, bell, 9" long......................	48.00	72.00	96.00
MARX "Uncle Wiggily, He Goes A' Ridin'", 1935......................	75.00	112.50	150.00
MARX Whoopee Car, laughing cows on wheels, driver looks like cowboy, 1929.	80.00	120.00	160.00
MARX Zeppelin, 27" long.............	60.00	90.00	120.00
Milk Wagon, "Milk & Cream, Toyland Farm Products", 9½" long...........	14.00	21.00	28.00
Monkey on Tricycle, tin and cloth.......	50.00	75.00	100.00
Motorcycle with Rider................	70.00	105.00	140.00

MARX "Dippy Dumper"
(see page 124).

MARX "Charlie McCarthy in His Benzine Buggy" (see page 222).

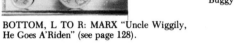

BOTTOM, L TO R: MARX "Uncle Wiggily, He Goes A'Riden" (see page 128).

Photo Courtesy PB84.

	G	VG	M
Native, small, on giant turtle, circa 1935	15.00	22.50	30.00
Newsboy, "Extra", with cap and bell, circa 1940s	10.00	15.00	20.00
Open Touring Car, "Number 50", Carette, 8" long	450.00	675.00	900.00
Parrot, rocks on perch and lifts wing, 11½" high	100.00	150.00	200.00
Patrol Car No. 7, no mfr. listed, circa 1948	5.00	7.50	10.00
Pecking Birds (pair) with plush cloth covering, 4½" long	22.50	33.75	45.00
Pecking Chicken, 5½" high	20.00	30.00	40.00
"PT 10", tin litho PT boat, circa 1941	10.00	15.00	20.00
Pump Cart with figure, 4¾" long	50.00	75.00	100.00
Racing Car "711" litho, driver in fedora-type hat, 13½" long	30.00	45.00	60.00
Roadster, orange and green	20.00	30.00	40.00

	G	VG	M
Santa Claus in red cloth suit and holding Christmas tree, 5½" high............	50.00	75.00	100.00
Santa Claus with green sleigh, Christmas tree, presents and white celluloid reindeer, bell, sleigh on three wheels, 8½" long...............................	6.00	9.00	12.00
Speedboat, "G.E. 200", tin litho, circa 1930...........................	15.00	22.50	30.00
Spinning Globe, tin litho, two tin planes circling it, circa 1930..............	66.00	99.00	132.00
Stagecoach, 8¾" long, with horses......	50.00	75.00	100.00
Steam Roller, circa 1925..............	28.00	42.00	56.00
Steam Shovel, large size, rubber wheels, early...........................	10.00	15.00	20.00
STRAUSS "Alabama Coon Jigger", 1910, 9¾"..........................	100.00	150.00	200.00
STRAUSS "Big Trixo", climbing monkey, 10" long........................	16.00	24.00	32.00
STRAUSS Circus Wagon, containing lion and tamer......................	60.00	90.00	120.00
STRAUSS "Ham and Sam The Minstrel Team", piano player and banjoist, 1921, 6½" long..................	150.00	225.00	300.00
STRAUSS "Jackee The Horn Pipe Dancer", 8½" long...............	160.00	240.00	320.00

L TO R: Submarine, tin litho, rear deck gun, stepped conning tower (see page 131); Submarine, tin litho, has keel, no deck gun (see page 131); Submarine, tin litho, American flag decorates conning tower (see page 131).

BOTTOM, L to R: "Aircraft Carrier X53", with five jet planes, tin litho, circa 1950s (see page 116); Aircraft Carrier, circa post WW II, tin litho, approx. 15" long (see page 116).
Photo Courtesy PB84.

	G	VG	M
STRAUSS "Jazzbo Jim The Dancer on the Roof", 1910, 10" high...............	75.00	112.50	150.00
STRAUSS "Jenny the Balky Mule", 10" long, six-color litho, goes backward, forward and rears, farmer holding extended tin grain pail from his seat in front of mule's face to keep him moving, vegetables in cart...............	27.00	40.50	54.00
STRAUSS "Red-Cap Porter", porter pushing a large trunk...................	70.00	105.00	140.00
STRAUSS Rollo Chair, black man pushing boardwalk chair, "Stock, DRGM, December 6, 1921".................	40.00	60.00	80.00

Battleship, "U.S.S. Washington" (see page 116).
Photo Courtesy PB84.

	G	VG	M
STRAUSS "Trikauto".................	80.00	120.00	160.00
STRUCTO red and black painted tin wind-up automobile, 15" long........	35.00	52.50	70.00
STRUCTO racer, early 1920s..........	26.00	39.00	52.00
Submarine, tin litho, American flag decorates conning tower, has forward deck gun..........................	15.00	22.50	30.00
Submarine, tin litho, has keel, no deck gun, approx. 13" long...............	12.50	18.75	25.00
Submarine, tin litho, rear deck gun, stepped conning tower.............	12.50	18.75	25.00
"Super Rocket Racer", tin litho, 1940s?..	30.00	45.00	60.00
Sweeping Mammy...................	30.00	45.00	60.00

"Super Rocket Racer" (see page 131).
Photo Courtesy PB84.

	G	VG	M
Tom Turkey, "B&S", 6" long, turkey struts, tail spreads, then moves up and down	20.00	30.00	40.00
Trolley, horse-drawn	50.00	75.00	100.00
Two rotating blimps and two cars, with passengers, that spin and rotate, 11¼" high	300.00	450.00	600.00
UNIQUE "Dandy Jim" dancer, 1921	125.00	187.50	250.00
UNIQUE "G.I. Joe and His Jouncing Jeep", post WW II, 7"	15.00	22.50	30.00
UNIQUE "G.I. Joe and the K-9 Pups", circa 1941, 9" high	15.00	22.50	30.00
UNIQUE Goose, smiling, circa 1938	7.50	11.25	15.00
UNIQUE "Jazzbo Jim" dancer, 1921	75.00	112.50	150.00
UNIQUE Kiddy cyclist, rings a bell	35.00	52.50	70.00
UNIQUE "Lincoln Tunnel", moving vehicles, cop, 1935	37.50	56.25	75.00
UNIQUE nodding goose	14.00	21.00	28.00
UNIQUE "Rollover Motorcyle Cop", 1935	60.00	90.00	120.00
UNIQUE "Skyrangers" plane and zeppelin revolving from tower, 1933	50.00	75.00	100.00
WOLVERINE "Drummer Boy", 14" high	25.00	37.50	50.00
WOLVERINE "Sandy Andy Circus", dancing toy	34.00	51.00	68.00
WOLVERINE "Zilotone" with six interchangeable records, 1930s	150.00	225.00	300.00
"The Wonder Cyclist", boy on tricycle, circa 1930, 8¾" high	90.00	135.00	180.00
WOODHAVEN Tractor, 1916	25.00	37.50	50.00

	G	VG	M
World on base, wind-up plane circles it..	36.00	54.00	72.00
WYANDOTTE Duck pulling tin Easter cart, 15" long, litho, wooden wheels...	4.50	6.75	9.00
WYANDOTTE "Red Ranger Ride 'Em Cowboy", circa 1930s..............	17.50	26.25	35.00
WYANDOTTE "Ride 'Em Cowboy"....	20.00	30.00	40.00

TOY SOLDIERS

Until recently, toy soldier collectors ignored American-made figures, concentrating instead on the imported kind. Now, however, there is considerable interest in the approximately 3¼" high lead alloy, cast iron and rubber "soldiers" (which includes civilian figures, cowboys and Indians, etc.) made in the United States prior to World War II. Since toy soldiers were produced in the millions every year from the mid-1930s till the end of 1941, prices are considerably lower than for most toys in this book.

CONDITION OF A TOY SOLDIER AND ITS RELATION TO PRICE

The price of a toy soldier depends not only on its desirability, but on its condition. In general, the 3¼" soldiers, which are the most sought after by collectors, will sell for $3 in good condition, $4 in very good, and $5 in mint. Rarer items, of course, go for more.

"Mint" means just that; the condition in which it was originally issued—perfect, regardless of age, not the slightest blemish. Needless to say this is a fairly rare state of affairs, but enough soldiers exist in mint condition to make it an employable term. Many people, hoping to dispose of toys, are tempted to term them "mint" when they are really "near mint", "very good" or sometimes even just "good". Inevitably this can result in unhappiness all around, and not infrequently, in a cancelled sale.

"Very Good" indicates a soldier which has obviously seen use; with signs of wear and aging, but with most of its paint remaining and in general having a freshness to its appearance that makes it seem attractive and collectible to all but the most discriminating.

"Good" signals a soldier that has seen considerable wear, but has at least one half to one third of its original paint, and is basically sound. A collector will collect it, but will often not be wholly satisfied with it as an example of his collection, and thus prices are well below that which the same item in mint can command.

Condition below good results in another drastic drop in price, generally to $1 or less, and figures with missing parts, although otherwise in excellent condition, will usually fall into this lower-priced category. At present, a BARCLAY soldier minus its tin helmet (signalled by a large round hole in the top of its head) is worth about half of what it would otherwise bring. Rust, even small spots of it on the cast iron soldiers, can seriously lower their price, as can repainting of any of the soldiers. "Near-Mint", "Fine", "Very Fine" and similar terms often found in sellers' descriptions, denote conditions between Mint and Very Good, and are priced accordingly.

The key to grading is to avoid wishful thinking. Grading can sometimes be a problem for the uninitiated, but common sense will usually prevail, and when possible a consultation with an expert in the field can often clear up lingering doubts. A toy in its original box is worth up to 10 to 20% more if the box is in mint condition, with the price dropping as condition lessens.

TOY SOLDIERS

BARCLAY: Barclay Mfg. Co. was the largest manufacturer of toy soldiers in the U.S. prior to World War II, selling millions of figures annually. The company, named after Barclay St. in West Hoboken, New Jersey (now 10th Street) was in business before 1925, owned by a Frenchman named Donzé (pronounced DON'-zee). However, the company did not become a major one until it was taken over around 1930 by Michael Levy (c. 1895-10/9/64), who had begun as an employee about five years before. His superb selling ability led to a partnership and then full ownership. Within a few years, from 30-50 employees in 1925, the company was employing 400 people, and moved several times as it was forced to expand. BARCLAY'S soldiers came in four styles prior to World War II. Little is known about the first, except that at least two of the figures had a moving arm. The second, with a separate tin helmet, seems to have been produced no earlier than 1934, and was probably by BARCLAY sculptor-tool worker Frank Krupp. This figure (the tin helmet was sub-contracted) was rather stiff and is known by collectors as "short stride", because its marching figures' feet were close together. The third style, again probably by Krupp, also had the separate tin helmet, but was more realistic, and is known as "long-stride". These were on sale as early as 1937. The fourth style, introduced when BARCLAY moved from slush casting to die casting, was probably by free-lance artist Olive Kooken (spelling phonetic) and is known as "cast helmet", as the soldiers featured helmets that were a part of the figure. The one sure way to identify a pre-war BARCLAY soldier is by its eye, which in the early years looked like this: , and later like this: . Although BARCLAY seems to have produced toy soldiers from the beginning, they appear to have made little noise until around 1934.

The figures were all made from an alloy of lead, zinc and tin to which antimony was added at the factory. When slush-molding was done, only one mold was made of each single figure. The lead would be poured into the mold, rocked, and immediately poured out through a second hole, thus providing a hollow figure. Later, the die-cast molds produced a number of the same figures at the same time. During the Second World War BARCLAY laid off all but four of its employees, and did sub-contract work. It was never as successful after the war, and, unable to afford the cost of a transition to the more competitive plastic, finally closed down in 1971, by this time employing only 50-75 people. Although BARCLAY assigned numbers to its figures from the beginning for its own records, many of the soldiers themselves bore no numbers. Figures listed with a question mark after the number are based on the memory of longtime BARCLAY employee George Fall, whose memory, judged against known BARCLAY numbers, is quite accurate, but not infallible. All short stride BARCLAYS have separate tin helmets.

BARCLAY SOLDIERS

Number is unknown where no number appears. Question marks **after** a number indicates the number is only a guess by a longtime Barclay employee.   (See Barclay introduction)

	G	VG	M
Paint Your Own Army Set No. 2003, circa 1935-1936, boxed (Photo pg. 147)	60.00	90.00	120.00
87? Mounted officer in peaked cap, with moving arm, holding sword.....	8.00	12.00	16.00
88? Mounted cowboy with lasso........	4.00	5.50	7.00
89? Mounted Indian, moving arm, rifle..	4.00	5.50	7.00
90? Mounted cowboy with pistol........	4.00	5.50	7.00
701 Flagbearer, short stride............	3.00	4.00	5.00
701 Flagbearer, long stride, tin helmet...	3.00	4.00	5.00
701 Flagbearer, cast helmet............	3.00	4.00	5.00
702 Machine-gunner, kneeling, short stride..........................	3.00	4.00	5.00
702 Machine-gunner, kneeling, tin helmet, long stride................	3.00	4.00	5.00
702 Machine-gunner, kneeling, cast helmet..........................	3.00	4.00	5.00
Machine-gunner, sitting, cast helmet (may not be BARCLAY).............	4.00	5.00	6.00
703 Kneeling, firing, short stride........	3.00	4.00	5.00
703 Kneeling, firing, tin helmet, long stride..........................	3.00	4.00	5.00
704 Marching, shoulder arms, short stride	3.00	4.00	5.00
704 Marching, shoulder arms, tin helmet, long stride......................	3.00	4.00	5.00
705 Port arms, short stride.............	3.00	4.00	5.00
705 Port Arms, cast helmet.............	3.00	4.00	5.00
706? Rifle across waist, short stride......	3.00	4.00	5.00
706 Advancing with leveled rifle, tin helmet, long stride................	3.00	4.00	5.00
706 Advancing with leveled rifle, cast helmet	3.00	4.00	5.00
707 Attention, rifle at order arms, cast helmet.......................	3.00	4.00	5.00
708 Officer with sword, short stride.....	3.00	4.00	5.00
708 Officer with sword, tin helmet, long stride	3.00	4.00	5.00

BARCLAY American Legionaire flagbearer (see page 140)
Photo by Bill Kaufman
Courtesy Al Rizzolo, THE RED PONY

	G	VG	M
708 Officer with sword, cast helmet.....	3.00	4.00	5.00
709 Bugler, short stride................	3.00	4.00	5.00
709 Bugler, tin helmet, long stride......	3.00	4.00	5.00
710 Drummer, short stride.............	3.00	4.00	5.00
710 Drummer, tin helmet, long stride....	3.00	4.00	5.00
711 Drum Major, short stride...........	3.00	4.00	5.00
711 Drum Major, long stride, tin helmet.	3.00	4.00	5.00
713? Cadet officer, short stride.........	3.00	4.00	5.00
714 Cadet with rifle, short stride........	4.00	5.00	6.00
714 Cadet with rifle, long stride........	3.00	4.00	5.00
Ethiopian with rifle, circa 1935-36.....	8.00	10.00	12.00
Ethiopian Officer, circa 1935-36......	7.00	9.00	11.00
Italian Officer, circa 1935-36........	7.00	9.00	11.00
Italian Infantryman, port arms, circa 1935-36	7.00	9.00	11.00
Japanese, rifle waist-high, circa 1937...	5.00	7.00	9.00
Japanese officer in flat cap, circa 1937..	7.00	9.00	11.00

L TO R: Drummer, short stride 710; Drummer, tin helmet 710; Bugler, short stride 709; Bugler, tin helmet 709; French horn, short stride 740; Fifer, tin helmet 739; Officer in garrison cap holding orders 773. Photo Courtesy Don Pielin

L TO RL: Rifle across waist, short stride 706?; Advancing, with raised rifle, tin helmet 764; Advancing with leveled rifle, cast helmet 706; Advancing with leveled rifle, tin helmet 706; Running with rifle, tin helmet 748; Running with rifle, cast helmet 748. Photo Courtesy Don Pielin

	G	VG	M
Chinese officer in steel helmet, circa 1937	8.00	10.00	12.00
Chinese rifleman, port arms, circa 1937	5.00	7.00	9.00
717 Standing Indian, rifle across body...	2.00	3.00	4.00
719 Marching sailor (in bell-bottoms or puttees, in blue or white), short stride and long stride	3.00	4.00	5.00
718? Sailor Flagbearer, long stride	3.00	4.00	5.00
720? Sailor Signalman, long stride	3.00	4.00	5.00
721 Naval Officer, short stride	3.00	4.00	5.00
721 Naval Officer, long stride	3.00	4.00	5.00
722 Marine, short stride	3.00	4.00	5.00
722 Marine, long stride	3.00	4.00	5.00
953 American Legionaire in overseas cap, tall, circa 1937	8.00	10.00	12.00

	G	VG	M
American Legionaire flagbearer, tall, cloth flag.........................	10.00	15.00	20.00
701 Cuban flag variation of flagbearer, not known if tin or cast helmet, long or short stride................	12.00	16.00	22.00
728 Prone machine-gunner, tin helmet...	3.00	4.00	5.00
728 Machine-gunner, prone, small cast helmet.........................	3.00	4.00	5.00
728 Machine-gunner, prone, larger cast helmet.........................	3.00	4.00	5.00
729? Crawling with rifle, tin helmet.....	3.00	4.00	5.00
730 Signalman, tin helmet.............	3.00	4.00	5.00
731 Kneeling with pigeons, tin helmet...	4.00	5.00	6.00
732 Kneeling with phone, tin helmet....	4.00	5.00	6.00

L TO R: Radio Operator with separate antenna, tin helmet 951; Cameraman, kneeling, tin helmet 758; Kneeling with phone, tin helmet 732; Kneeling with pigeons, tin helmet 731; Crouching with binoculars, cast helmet 783.   Photo Courtesy Don Pielin

L TO R: Walking, with dog, tin helmet 952; Signalman, tin helmet 730; Walking with boxes, tin helmet 734; Looking through rangefinder tin helmet 735; Leaning out, with field phone, cast helmet 782.   Photo Courtesy Don Pielin

	G	VG	M
733 Kneeling, with shell, tin helmet.....	3.00	4.00	5.00
734 Walking with boxes, tin helmet.....	3.00	4.00	5.00
735 Looking through rangefinder, tin helmet.........................	3.00	4.00	5.00
736 Sentry in overcoat, tin helmet.......	3.00	4.00	5.00
737 Tommy-gunner, tin helmet.........	3.00	4.00	5.00
737 Tommy-gunner, cast helmet........	3.00	4.00	5.00
738 Grenade thrower, rifle butt on ground, tin helmet................	3.00	4.00	5.00
738 Grenade thrower, rifle off ground, tin helmet.........................	3.00	4.00	5.00
738 Grenade thrower, rifle off ground, cast helmet.......................	3.00	4.00	5.00
739 Fifer, tin helmet.................	3.00	4.00	5.00
Motorcycle with sidecar with machine gun.............................	5.00	6.50	8.00
740 French horn, short stride..........	3.00	4.00	5.00
741 Pilot........................	3.00	4.00	5.00
Doctor with bag...................	3.00	4.00	5.00
Kneeling Nurse....................	3.00	4.00	5.00
744 Nurse, hand on hip..............	3.00	4.00	5.00
Prone, firing rifle, tin helmet........	3.00	4.00	5.00
Wounded, sitting, arm in sling........	3.00	4.00	5.00
747 Standing, firing rifle, short stride....	3.00	4.00	5.00
747 Standing, firing, tin helmet, long stride	3.00	4.00	5.00
747 Standing, firing, cast helmet........	3.00	4.00	5.00
748 Running with rifle, tin helmet......	3.00	4.00	5.00
748 Running with rifle, cast helmet.....	3.00	4.00	5.00

L TO R: Tall grenadier, tin helmet 762; Grenade thrower, rifle butt on ground, tin helmet 738; Grenade thrower, rifle off ground, 738; Grenade thrower, rifle off ground, cast helmet 738; Officer with gas mask and pistol, cast helmet 778. Photo, Courtesy Don Pielin

L TO R: Officer with sword, short stride (Marine or American Legion)708; Officer with sword, tin helmet 708; Marine, short stride 722; Marine, long stride 722; American Legionaire in overseas cap 953; cadet officer with sword, short stride 713; cadet with rifle, short stride 714; cadet with rifle 714.   Photo Courtesy Don Pielin

	G	VG	M
749 Charging with gas mask, rifle, tin helmet	3.00	4.00	5.00
749 Charging with gas mask, rifle, cast helmet	3.00	4.00	5.00
Motorcyclist in cap	4.00	5.00	6.00
Cowboy with tin hat brim	2.50	3.50	4.50
752 Cowboy with lasso	2.50	3.50	4.50
753 Cowboy with pistol	2.50	3.50	4.50
754? Indian with Tomahawk and shield . .	2.00	3.00	4.00
755 Indian kneeling with bow and arrow .	3.00	4.00	5.00
Indian standing with bow and arrow .	4.00	5.00	6.00
Cook holding roast	2.00	3.00	4.00
Indian with knife	2.00	3.00	4.00
758 Cameraman, kneeling, with tin helmet	3.00	4.00	5.00
759 Stretcher-bearer, closed hand	3.00	4.00	5.00
759 Stretcher-bearer, open hand	4.00	5.00	6.00

L TO R: Doctor with stethoscope 760; Nurse, hand on hip 744; Nurse, kneeling (page 141); Wounded on crutches 775; Doctor treating soldier (page 145); Doctor walking with bag, in khaki and white, (page 141).
Photo Courtesy Don Pielin

	G	**VG**	**M**
760 Doctor with stethoscope...........	3.00	4.00	5.00
761 Lying wounded, tin helmet.........	3.00	4.00	5.00
762 Tall grenadier, tin helmet..........	5.00	7.00	9.00
763 Advancing, with rifle, in crouch, tin helmet........................	3.00	4.00	5.00
764 Advancing, with raised rifle, tin helmet..........................	3.00	4.00	5.00
765 Thrusting with gun muzzle, tin helmet...........................	3.00	4.00	5.00
766 Clubbing with rifle, tin helmet......	3.00	4.00	5.00
766 Clubbing with rifle, cast helmet.....	3.00	4.00	5.00
Sitting with rifle, tin helmet..........	3.00	4.00	5.00
Prone with long binoculars, tin helmet.	4.00	5.00	6.00
Prone with short binoculars, tin helmet.	3.00	4.00	5.00

L TO R: Machine-gunner, kneeling, tin helmet, short stride 702; Machine-gunner, kneeling, tin helmet 702; Machine-gunner, kneeling, cast helmet 702; Machine-gunner, sitting, cast helmet (may not be Barclay), see page 137.

Photo: Courtesy Don Pielin

773 Officer in garrison cap holding orders............................	3.00	4.00	5.00
774 Soldier with AA gun, standing, tin helmet........................	4.00	5.00	6.00
774 Soldier with AA gun, standing, cast helmet.......................	4.00	5.00	6.00
775 Wounded on crutches.............	3.00	4.00	5.00
776 Standing at searchlight, cap, several different versions...................	4.00	5.00	6.00
777 Marching, shoulder arms, with pack, tin helmet........................	3.00	4.00	5.00
777 Marching, shoulder arms, with pack, cast helmet.......................	3.00	4.00	5.00
778 Officer with gas mask and pistol, cast helmet.......................	3.00	4.00	5.00

	G	VG	M
779 Standing, firing from behind wall, cast helmet........................	7.00	9.00	12.00
780 Falling, with rifle, cast helmet......	3.00	4.00	5.00
781 Digging, cast helmet.............	3.00	4.00	5.00
782 Leaning out, with field phone.......	3.00	4.00	5.00
783 Crouching with binoculars, cast helmet..........................	3.00	4.00	5.00
784 Parachutist landing.............	3.00	4.00	5.00
785 Skiier, in white, cast helmet; 1940, with separate metal skiis (Meant to be Finnish).........................	6.00	9.00	12.00
785 Skiier, in brown or white, no skiis....	3.00	4.00	5.00
785 Skiier, in red, same as two above, meant to be Russian, worth twice the price of the above.			
Two-man machine gun car...........	6.00	8.00	10.00
Two soldiers on raft, cast helmet......	5.00	7.00	9.00
Sitting, eating.....................	3.00	4.00	5.00
787 Diver with axe..................	6.00	8.00	10.00
788 Marching with slung rifle, cast helmet..........................	3.00	4.00	5.00
789 Soldier with AA gun, cast helmet, sitting............................	5.00	7.00	9.00
791 Two-man rocket team............	4.00	5.00	6.00

BARCLAY Train Mechanic 615; Little Boy (page 147); Detective with pistol 623; Train Conductor (page 147).

Photo by Bill Kaufman
Courtesy Al Rizzolo, THE RED PONY

	G	VG	M
792 Mechanic with airplane engine, prop spins	6.00	7.00	8.00
187? Mounted in khaki, cap	5.00	6.00	7.00
187? Mounted in colored jacket and cap, may be Chinese or Japanese	5.00	6.00	7.00
Soldier kneeling with **anti-tank** gun, cast helmet	7.00	9.00	11.00
Peeling potatoes	3.00	4.00	5.00
Doctor treating soldier	6.00	8.00	10.00
951 Radio operator with separate antenna	6.00	7.00	8.00
952 Walking with dog, tin helmet	4.00	5.00	6.00
961 Typist with table and typewriter	8.00	10.00	12.00
961 Typist alone	3.00	4.00	5.00
801? Knight with pennant, post 1934, by Krupp	2.00	3.00	4.00
802? Knight with shield, post 1934, by Krupp	2.00	3.00	4.00
624 Burglar	3.00	4.00	5.00
623 Detective with pistol	3.00	4.00	5.00
? Redcap with bags, black	4.00	5.00	6.00
? Railroad porter, black	4.00	5.00	6.00
618 Woman with pocketbook	2.00	3.00	4.00
611 Man with overcoat over arm	2.00	3.00	4.00
630 Army Chaplain	3.00	4.00	5.00
Woman with dog	2.00	3.00	4.00

BARCLAY Indian with bow and Arrow 755; Mounted Cowboy 90?.
Photo by Bill Kaufman

BARCLAY Newsboy 621; Little Girl 627; Shoeshine Boy 622; Little Girl 627; paint Variation.
Photo by Bill Kaufman
Courtesy Al Rizzolo, THE RED PONY

(see this page and page 147)

	G	VG	M
Fireman with axe	2.00	3.00	4.00
852 Fireman with hose	2.00	3.00	4.00
619 Old Man	2.00	3.00	4.00
Indian with rifle, long headdress	4.00	6.00	7.00
853 Mailman	2.00	3.00	4.00
Policeman, arm raised	2.00	3.00	4.00
Boy Scout frying eggs over fire	6.00	8.00	10.00
802 Boy Scout saluting	3.00	4.00	5.00
801 Boy Scout with staff	3.00	4.00	5.00
803 Boy Scout signaling	5.00	7.00	8.00
625 Bride	2.00	3.00	4.00
626 Groom	2.00	3.00	4.00
620 Minister	2.00	3.00	4.00
621 Newsboy	2.00	3.00	4.00
622 Shoeshine boy	2.00	3.00	4.00
Pirate, post 1934, by Krupp	2.00	3.00	4.00

BARCLAY Boy Scouts, saluting 802;
with staff 801; signaling 803.

Photo By Bill Kaufman .

BARCLAY Minister 620; Bride 625; Groom 626.
Photo by Bill Kaufman
Courtesy Al Rizzolo, THE RED PONY

	G	VG	M
627 Little girl in coat................	2.00	3.00	4.00
Little boy in jacket..................	2.00	3.00	4.00
Train conductor.....................	2.00	3.00	4.00
615 Train mechanic..................	2.00	3.00	4.00
Little girl in rocking chair............	3.00	4.00	5.00

POSTWAR BARCLAY SOLDIERS: Postwar BARCLAYS consisted of three types: The standard 3¼"soldiers, often in the same pre-war poses, but with WW II pot helmets. These sell for 3-4-5. The second type was smaller, and rather baby-like in appearance. These sell for 2-3-4. The third are known as "Pod Feet"—no stand at all, just slightly widened feet to serve as a base. These sell for 1-2-3. BARCLAY also produced a series of winter figures in a smaller size, and in general, these sell for 2-3-4.

BARCLAY Paint your own Army Set No. 2003. (see page 137).
Photo Courtesy Bill Kaufman

MANOIL SOLDIERS

MANOIL: The MANOIL Mfg. Co. Inc. was owned by Jack Manoil (1900-1955), began in the 1930s, and was located in Manhattan, and later Brooklyn, New York, in the 1930s, moving to Waverly, New York, in 1940. MANOIL (pronounced MAN-oil) was second only to BARCLAY in the production of hollow lead soldiers, although BAR-CLAY never seems to have regarded it as a serious threat, despite the fact that MANOIL'S figures were ubiquitous in the 5 & 10's of the period. Whereas BARCLAY'S soldiers tended to the heroic, MAN-OIL'S were generally more vital. Its early figures were rather bloated, but lively, and its later ones were often quite dynamic, with a small group of soldiers produced after the early figures probably being the most realistic-looking combat soldiers of all the figures produced by American companies. From the little evidence available, MANOIL made picture frames, bank premiums, lamp bases and toy vehicles first, not coming out with soldiers until 1935 at the earliest. MANOIL-like figures were produced in composition and some form of clay during the Second World War, but there is no evidence they were produced by MANOIL. After World War II the company introduced several new lines of soldiers, but they were no longer distributed nearly as widely, and by 1953-1954 MANOIL went out of the toy business. Early models of MANOIL and BARCLAY soldiers are being reproduced (see Leading Dealers and Collectors), some hollow-cast from the original molds.

MANOIL, L TO R: Charging with fixed bayonet 36; Rifle pointed, waist-high 37; Clubbing with rifle 38; Bayoneting upward 39; Camouflaged rifleman, prone 57.
Photo Courtesy Don Pielin

	G	VG	M
Officer with sword.................	3.00	4.00	5.00
Seated, rifle in lap................	3.00	4.00	5.00
Flagbearer with staff touching helmet, early version....................	3.00	4.00	5.00
7 Flagbearer......................	3.00	4.00	5.00
8 Marching with rifle, early version.....	3.00	4.00	5.00
Marching with rifle, scabbard, later version.........................	3.00	4.00	5.00
Bugler..........................	3.00	4.00	5.00
Drummer with horizontal drum, early version.........................	3.00	4.00	5.00
11 Drummer with vertical drum, later version.........................	5.00	7.00	9.00
12 Machine-gunner, prone, several versions........................	3.00	4.00	5.00
13 Cadet..........................	2.00	3.00	4.00
14 Sailor marching..................	3.00	4.00	5.00
15 Marine.........................	3.00	4.00	5.00
16 Ensign.........................	3.00	4.00	5.00
17 Sailor Signalman.................	4.00	5.00	6.00
18 Cowboy, pistol raised in air..........	2.00	3.00	4.00
18A Cowboy surrendering.............	2.00	3.00	4.00
20 Doctor in white or khaki............	3.00	4.00	5.00
21 Nurse with plate of liquid...........	3.00	4.00	5.00

MANOIL L TO R: Sentry, rifle slung, knee bent 93; Marching, rifle slung at angle from body 79; Marching, slung rifle upright 67; Marching with overseas cap (see page 153); Marching with overseas cap on side of head 66; Marine 16; Cadet 13.
Photo Courtesy Don Pielin

MANOIL, Indian 22; Cowboy Surrendering 18A; Cowboy, pistol in air 18.
Photo By Bill Kaufman

	G	VG	M
22 Indian chief	2.00	3.00	4.00
23 Machine-gunner, sitting, several variations	3.00	4.00	5.00
24 Soldier with shell	3.00	4.00	5.00
Kneeling, firing thick rifle	4.00	5.00	6.00
25 Kneeling, firing thin rifle	3.00	4.00	5.00
Kneeling, firing folding rifle	6.00	8.00	10.00
Standing, firing thick rifle	4.00	5.00	6.00
Standing, firing thin rifle	3.00	4.00	5.00
Standing, firing folding rifle	6.00	8.00	10.00
Advancing tommy-gunner, bloated figure	3.00	4.00	5.00
27 Advancing tommy-gunner, leaning forward	4.00	5.00	6.00
28 Kneeling observer with binoculars	3.00	4.00	5.00
31 Grenade-thrower, two grenades in pouch	3.00	4.00	5.00
31 Grenade-thrower, three grenades in pouch	5.00	6.50	8.00

L TO R: Firing flare pistol, in gas mask 63; Charging, rifle and gas mask 62; Grenade-thrower, two grenades in pouch 31; Grenade-thrower, three grenades in pouch 31; Hot Papa firefighter 92.
Photo Courtesy Don Pielin

150

	G	VG	M
32 Stretcher-bearer with medical kit.....	3.00	4.00	5.00
Stretcher-bearer, no medical kit.......	4.00	5.00	6.00
Lying wounded...................	3.00	4.00	5.00
34 Pilot............................	3.00	4.00	5.00
35 Hostess.........................	5.00	7.00	9.00
36 Charging with fixed bayonet........	4.00	5.00	6.00
37 Rifle pointed, waist-high...........	4.00	5.00	6.00
38 Clubbing with rifle................	4.00	5.00	6.00
39 Bayoneting upward................	3.00	4.00	5.00
Crawling with loops of rope over shoulder.......................	5.00	6.00	7.00
Crawling with rifle................	4.00	5.00	6.00
Wounded, arm in sling.............	3.00	4.00	5.00
Crawling with pistol...............	3.00	4.00	5.00
Crawling medic...................	5.00	6.00	7.00
Grenade-thrower, crouching, rifle slung	4.00	5.00	6.00
Crouching, with rifle...............	4.00	5.00	6.00
45 Lying with periscope..............	3.00	4.00	5.00
46 Firing AA gun up, kneeling.........	4.00	5.00	6.00
47 Standing with searchlight..........	4.00	5.00	6.00
48 Sailor firing deck gun.............	4.00	5.00	6.00
49 Policeman with club behind his back..	2.00	3.00	4.00
50 Bicyclist........................	4.00	5.00	6.00
51 One-man machine gun car..........	6.00	8.00	10.00
52 Motorcyclist, grass at base...........	4.00	5.00	6.00
52 Motorcyclist, no grass at base........	4.00	5.00	6.00
53 Seated, hands in lap...............	3.00	4.00	5.00
54 Seated eating....................	3.00	4.00	5.00
55 Seated at map table, on phone.......	3.00	4.00	5.00

L TO R: Seated, rifle in lap (page 149); Seated, hands in lap 53; Seated eating 54; Seated at map table, on phone 55; Playing banjo 84.

Photo. Courtesy Don Pielin

	G	VG	M
56 Paymaster......................	5.00	6.00	7.00
57 Camouflaged rifleman, prone........	3.00	4.00	5.00
58 Pilot parachuting, open chute above..	4.00	5.00	6.00
59 Writing letter and smoking, seated....	5.00	6.00	7.00
60 Cook...........................	3.00	4.00	5.00
61 Photographer....................	4.00	5.00	6.00
62 Charging, rifle and gas mask........	3.00	4.00	5.00
63 Firing flare pistol, in gas mask.......	3.00	4.00	5.00
Running with Mortar, wood or metal wheels	5.00	6.00	7.00
65 Diver, two slight variations in placement of number...................	3.00	4.00	5.00

L TO R: Hostess 35; Paymaster 56; Boxer 68; Photographer 61; Cook 60; Carrying propellor 86.
Photo. Courtesy Don Pielin

L TO R: Kneeling with mortar, wooden wheels 78; Kneeling with mortar, metal wheels, round shield 78; Kneeling with mortar, metal wheels, squared shield 78; Telephone linesman 77; Standing with antenna around head 88.
Photo Courtesy Don Pielin

L TO R: Firing heavy machine gun up 80; Firing AA gun up 46; Firing AA gun through viewer 82; Firing rocket 83; Standing with seachlight 47.
Photo Courtesy Don Pielin

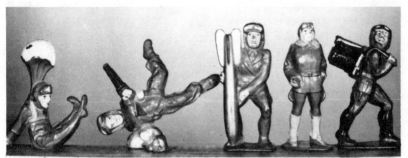

L TO R: Pilot parachuting, open chute above 58; Pilot parachuting, with weapon 102; Pilot with bomb 85; Pilot 34; Pilot walking with bombsight 87.
Photo Courtesy Don Pielin

	G	VG	M
66 Marching with overseas cap on side of head..........................	5.00	6.00	7.00
Marching with overseas cap..........	3.00	4.00	5.00
67 Marching, slung rifle upright........	3.00	4.00	5.00
68 Boxer..............................	3.00	4.00	5.00
Boxer, black......................	8.00	10.00	12.00
Fusing shell.......................	4.00	5.00	6.00
77 Telephone lineman, two pieces.......	6.00	8.00	10.00
78 Kneeling with mortar, several versions	5.00	6.00	8.00
79 Marching, rifle slung at angle from body..............................	4.00	5.00	6.00
80 Firing heavy machine gun up........	5.00	6.00	7.00
81 Two-man machine-gun team with open handle......................	4.00	5.00	6.00
81 Two-man machine-gun team with closed handle.....................	4.00	5.00	6.00

	G	VG	M
82 Firing AA gun through viewer......	4.00	5.00	6.00
83 Firing rocket....................	4.00	5.00	6.00
84 Playing banjo...................	5.00	6.00	7.00
85 Pilot with Bomb.................	3.00	4.00	5.00
86 Carrying propeller...............	3.00	4.00	5.00
Carrying propeller, propeller away from head.......................	6.00	8.00	10.00
87 Pilot walking with bombsight.......	3.00	4.00	5.00
88 Standing with antenna around head..	4.00	5.00	6.00
89 Lying with antenna...............	4.00	5.00	6.00
90 Soldier digging..................	4.00	5.00	6.00
91 Carrying roll of barbed wire........	3.00	4.00	5.00
92 Hot Papa firefighter, grey..........	4.00	5.00	6.00
92 Hot Papa firefighter, white.........	3.00	4.00	5.00
93 Sentry, rifle slung, knee bent.......	4.00	5.00	6.00
99 Ski trooper skiing, 1940...........	4.00	5.00	6.00
100 Ski trooper prone, firing machine gun, 1940......................	3.00	4.00	5.00
101 Paratroop, cloud base, wearing helmet........................	4.00	5.00	6.00
102 Pilot parachuting, with weapon.....	4.00	5.00	6.00

L TO R: Running with mortar, wooden wheels (see page 152); Running with mortar, metal wheels (see page 152); Lying with periscope 45.
Photo Courtesy Don Pielin

L TO R: Standing, firing folding rifle (see page 150); Crouching with rifle (see page 151); Ski trooper skiing 99.
Photo Courtesy Don Pielin

MANOIL "Happy Farm" figures (see this page)
Photo by Bill Kaufman
Courtesy Al Rizzolo, THE RED PONY

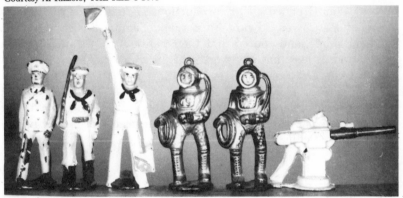

L TO R: Ensign 16; Sailor marching 14; Sailor signalman 17; Diver, "65" on chest 65; Diver (number 65 under base); Sailor firing deck gun 48.

Photo Courtesy Don Pielin

MANOIL produced several variations of post-WW II American toy soldiers, ranging from the standard 3¼" to smaller versions. Virtually all sell in the 3-4-5 range. In 1941, it began producing a line of civilian figures in a "Happy Farm" series. At least 41 pieces were made and tend to sell today in the 1-2-3 range. The exception would be No. 41-14, "Darky Eating Watermelon", which would sell for at least $8 in mint. A series of cowboy ranch pieces produced after the war in a smaller size would also sell in the 1-2-3 range.

GREY IRON: GREY IRON made the only 3¼" cast iron soldiers. The company began in 1840 as the Brady Machine Shop in Mount Joy, Pennsylvania, where it has remained to this day, and in 1881 was organized as the Grey Iron Casting Company, Limited. As early as 1903 it was manufacturing toy banks and stoves, cap pistols, wheeled toys and trains, as well as a number of non-toy items. On August 14, 1917, the company was granted two patents for their 40 mm. solid cast iron Grey Klip Armies, which they then manufactured through 1941, the last of the series emerging in 1938 as "Uncle Sam's Defenders", painted khaki rather than nickel-plated, as the earlier versions had been. The soldiers were not successful at first, but with the advent of a new distributor, the company was swamped with orders, and in January, 1933, introduced a new line of thirty-five different cast iron soldiers, in an approximately 3" size (four Revolutionary War soldiers; an infantryman, a foot officer, a flagbearer and a mounted officer, may have been introduced earlier, as they are numbered lower, but were not part of the 1933 announcement, and are rare). The figures tended to be slight, and while apparently successful, were superseded in July 1936 by Grey's "Iron Men" series, a slightly larger, more robust model, which continued to be sold until World War II ended all toy production. Designers for the soldiers were at least two; Edward Musser and Samuel S. Schmidt. The soldiers were hand-poured and then painted on an assembly-line basis, and at least initially were sold for a dime, while their competitors charged a nickel. Grey is still in business today as the John Wright division of Donsco, but except for some "Iron Men"– sized Continental Soldiers which were probably produced in the 1950s, manufactures no toy soldiers, producing instead mechanical banks, horse-drawn vehicles, etc.

GREY IRON SOLDIERS

	G	VG	M
1. Colonial soldier, private, port arms...	5.00	7.00	9.00
1. Colonial soldier, private, port arms, larger	3.00	4.00	5.00
1A Colonial foot officer, drawing sword..	5.00	7.00	9.00
1A Colonial foot officer, drawing sword, larger	3.00	4.00	5.00
1? Colonial flag-bearer	5.00	7.00	9.00
1? Colonial flag-bearer, larger, 1950s?...	3.00	4.00	5.00
1MA Colonial mounted officer	5.00	7.00	9.00
2 Cadet, early, port arms	3.00	4.00	5.00
2 Cadet, later, larger, rifle at slope	3.00	4.00	5.00

	G	VG	M
2A Cadet officer, early..............	3.00	4.00	5.00
2A Cadet officer, later, larger..........	3.00	4.00	5.00
3 U.S. Infantry, shoulder arms, early, campaign hat......................	3.00	4.00	5.00
3/1 U.S. Infantry, port arms, later, campaign hat.....................	3.00	4.00	5.00
3A U.S. Infantry Officer, early, peaked cap...........................	3.00	4.00	5.00
3A U.S. Infantry Officer, later, larger, peaked cap......................	3.00	4.00	5.00
3AR Red Cross officer, same as above, with armband....................	4.00	5.00	6.00
4 U.S. Infantry, port arms, early, campaign hat.......................	3.00	4.00	5.00
4A U.S. Doughboy Officer with field glasses..........................	3.00	4.00	5.00
4/1 U.S. Doughboy Signaling..........	3.00	4.00	5.00
4/2 U.S. Doughboy Combat Trooper, thrusting with rifle................	3.00	4.00	5.00
4/3 U.S. Doughboy with range finder....	5.00	6.00	7.00
4/4 U.S. Doughboy Ammunition Carrier.	3.00	4.00	5.00
4/5 U.S. Doughboy Sharpshooter, kneeling with rifle....................	3.00	4.00	5.00
4/6 U.S. Doughboy with Bayonet, thrusting downward...............	3.00	4.00	5.00
5 U.S. Infantry, charging, campaign hat, early......................	3.00	4.00	5.00
6 U.S. Doughboy, port arms, early......	3.00	4.00	5.00
6/1 U.S. Doughboy charging, later......	3.00	4.00	5.00
6/2 U.S. Doughboy sentry, in overcoat, at the slope.....................	3.00	4.00	5.00
6/3 U.S. Doughboy Bomber, crawling with pistol, bomb.................	3.00	4.00	5.00
6/4 U.S. Doughboy Grenade Thrower, rifle at 45° angle.................	3.00	4.00	5.00
7 U.S. Doughboy charging, early version.	3.00	4.00	5.00
8M U.S. Cavalryman, mounted, campaign hat, early.................	5.00	6.00	7.00
8M U.S. Cavalryman, mounted, later............................	5.00	6.00	7.00

GREYKLIP ARMY: Set 1, Co. A (attention), Bugler, Officer, Standard, Drummer, Rifleman
Photo Courtesy Karl Zipple   TOP and BOTTOM, (see page 162)

GREYKLIP ARMY: Set 2, Co. B (marching), Bugler, Officer, Standard, Drummer, Rifleman
Photo Courtesy Karl Zipple

	G	VG	M
8M U.S. Cavalry Color Bearer with Silk Flag, (mounted), early..........	8.00	10.00	12.00
8MA U.S. Cavalry Officer, mounted, peaked cap, early.................	5.00	6.00	7.00
8MA U.S. Cavalry Officer, mounted, peaked cap, later.................	5.00	6.00	7.00
9 U.S. Marine, port arms, early........	3.00	4.00	5.00
9 U.S. Marine, later, larger, port arms...	3.00	4.00	5.00
10 Royal Canadian Police, port arms, early.............................	3.00	4.00	5.00
10 Royal Canadian Police, port arms, later..............................	3.00	4.00	5.00
10M Royal Canadian Mounted Police, early.............................	5.00	6.00	7.00

L TO R: U.S. Cavalry Officer 8MA; U.S. Cavalry Officer, early 8MA; U.S. Cavalryman, early 8M; U.S. Doughboy Signaling 4/1.

	G	VG	M
10M Royal Canadian Mounted Police, later	5.00	6.00	7.00
11 Indian, with headdress, hatchet, early	2.00	3.00	4.00
11/1 Indian Brave, shielding eyes with hand	2.00	3.00	4.00
11/2 Chief Attacking, Indian with raised tomahawk	3.00	4.00	5.00
11M Indian Mounted, early	4.00	5.00	6.00
11M Indian Mounted, later, with rifle, lying on horse	5.00	6.00	7.00
11/1M Indian Scout Mounted, firing pistol rearward	5.00	6.00	7.00
12 Cowboy, early, hat front flattened	2.00	3.00	4.00
12 Cowboy, later, hands on hips	2.00	3.00	4.00
12/1 Hold-up Man, cowboy with two drawn pistols	2.00	3.00	4.00
12/2 Cowboy with lasso	3.00	4.00	5.00
12/3 Bandit, surrendering, cowboy	3.00	4.00	5.00
12M Cowboy Mounted, hatbrim turned up, early	4.00	5.00	6.00
12M Cowboy Mounted, bucking horse	4.00	5.00	6.00
12/1M Masked Cowboy Mounted	6.00	7.00	8.00
13 U.S. Machine Gunner, small, early	3.00	4.00	5.00
13 U.S. Machine Gunner, larger, later	3.00	4.00	5.00
13/1 U.S. Machine Gunner, prone, later	3.00	4.00	5.00
14 and 14W U.S. Sailor in blue or white, early	3.00	4.00	5.00

GREY IRON Continental Officer, 1A; Italian officer (page 161); Cowboy, hat front flattened 12; Cowboy with lariat 12/2.
Photo By Bill Kaufman

	G	VG	M
14 and 14W U.S. Sailor in blue or white, later	3.00	4.00	5.00
14A and 14AW U.S. Naval Officer in blue or white, early	3.00	4.00	5.00
14A and 14AW U.S. Naval Officer in blue or white, later	3.00	4.00	5.00
15/1 Boy Scout saluting, early	3.00	4.00	5.00
15/2 Boy Scout walking, early	3.00	4.00	5.00
16/1 Pirate Boy, all pirates circa 1935, though also sold later	4.00	5.00	6.00
16/2 Pirate with Pistols—captain, arms crossed	3.00	4.00	5.00
16/3 Pirate with Dagger	3.00	4.00	5.00
16/4 Pirate with hook, with sword	3.00	4.00	5.00
16/5 Pirate with Sword, sword horizontal at waist	3.00	4.00	5.00
17/1 Legion Drum major, early, American Legionaire	3.00	4.00	5.00
17/1 Legion Drum major, later	3.00	4.00	5.00
17/2 Legion Bugler, early, bugle at waist	3.00	4.00	5.00
17/2 Legion Bugler, later, bugle at hip	3.00	4.00	5.00

L TO R: U.S. Naval Officer, early, white 14AW; U.S. Naval Officer, early, blue, 14A; U.S. Infantry Officer, early, 3A; U.S. Infantry, Port Arms, early 4; U.S. Doughboy Officer, early, 6A; Royal Canadian Police 10; U.S. Cavalryman, 8M.
Photo Courtesy Don Pielin

DC 3 transport (see Aircraft)
Photo by Bill Kaufman Courtesy Al Rizzolo, THE RED PONY

BARCLAY Boy Scouts (See Soldiers)
Photo by Bill Kaufman

Buck Rogers Atomic Pistol (see Comic Character)
Photo Courtesy Jim Harmon

Texan pistol (see Guns)
Photo by Bill Kaufman Courtesy Al Rizzolo, THE RED PONY

Movie Komics and Komic Kamera (see Comic Character)
Photos by Bill Kaufman Courtesy Alan Levine

3A-7: Model Flat-Top (See Paper)

DOEPKE NO. 2006 Adams Diesel Road Grader (see Vehicles)
Photo courtesy Ray Funk

Little Orphan Annie Stove, 1930s (see
Comic Character)
Photo by Bill Kaufman Courtesy Alan
Levine

MANOIL Soldier. (See Soldiers) Photo by Bill Kaufman

Soldiers on Parade, MILTON BRADLEY (see Paper)
Photo by Bill Kaufman Courtesy Alan Levine

MANOIL, AUBURN and BARCLAY soldiers with vehicles, cannon and wooden fort of the period (see Soldiers)
Photo by Bill Kaufman

Cannon, TOOTSIETOY, approximately 3¾" long, MANOIL howitzer (see Miscellaneous)
Photo by Bill Kaufman

TOOTSIETOY Sedans and Roasters (see Vehicles)
Photo by Bill Kaufman Courtesy Al Rizzolo, THE RED PONY

ARCADE Tractor 273 (see Vehicles)
Photo by Bill Kaufman Courtesy Al Rizzolo, THE RED PONY

TOOTSIETOY Bulldog Mack (see Vehicles)
Photo by Bill Kaufman Courtesy Al Rizzolo, THE RED PONY

"Patrol Car No. 7" (see Tin Wind-up)
Photo by Bill Kaufman Courtesy Al Rizzolo, THE RED PONY

MARX "Chief-Fire Dept. No. 1" (see Vehicles)
Photo by Bill Kaufman Courtesy Al Rizzolo, THE RED PONY

BARCLAY American Legionaire in overseas cap, 1937, in ten color combinations
Photo by Bill Kaufman   (See Soldiers)

A. C. GILBERT Erector Set No. 2 (see Miscellaneous)
Photo by Bill Kaufman Courtesy Alan Levine

MECCANO Microscope Set (see Miscellaneous)
Photo by Bill Kaufman Courtesy Alan Levine

AUBURN RUBBER "Pursuit Ship. (See Aircraft), AUBURN Tank (See Vehicles) Photo by Bill Kaufman.

Captain Midnight Code-O-Graph Badge, 1942 (See Premiums) Photo courtesy Jim Harmon.

BARCLAY Chinese Rifleman and Japanese Officer, GREY IRON Ethiopian Chief (See Soldiers) Photo by Bill Kaufman.

Tom Mix Signal Arrowhead (see Premiums)

M.I.C. Toys Flat Bed Truck with removeable rack (see Vehicles). Photo courtesy Ray Funk

Western Thrills with Billy The Kid (see Comic Character)
Photo by Bill Kaufman Courtesy Alan Levine

Hoppy the Flying Marvel Bunny (see Comic Character)
Photo by Bill Kaufman Courtesy Alan Levine

Captain Marvel's Magic Eyes (see Comic Character)
Photo by Bill Kaufman Courtesy Alan Levine

Fun Farm (see Paper)
Photo by Bill Kaufman Courtesy Alan Levine

BARCLAY Paint Your Own Army Set No. 2003. (See Soldiers).
Photo courtesy Bill Kaufman

Three Flying Marvels (see Comic
Character)
Photo by Bill Kaufman Courtesy Alan
Levine

Flub a Dub (see Movies)
Photo by Bill Kaufman Courtesy Alan Levine

Aerial Ladder Truck (see Vehicles)
Photo by Bill Kaufman Courtesy Al Rizzolo, THE RED PONY

	G	VG	M
17/3 Legion Drummer, early...........	3.00	4.00	5.00
17/3 Legion Drummer, later...........	3.00	4.00	5.00
17/4 Legion Color Bearer, later........	3.00	4.00	5.00
18/1 Ethiopian Tribesman, large, with rifle, circa 1936...................	5.00	6.00	7.00
18/2 Ethiopian Chief, with sword and shield...........................	4.00	5.00	6.00
18/3 Ethiopian Soldier, Shoulder Arms, same as early No. 3................	4.00	5.00	6.00
18/3A Ethiopian Officer, same as early No. 3A.........................	4.00	5.00	6.00
18/5 Ethiopian Soldier, Charging, same as early No. 5......................	4.00	5.00	6.00

L TO R: Ethiopian Officer 18/3A; Ethiopian Soldier Charging 18/5; Ethiopian Soldier Shoulder Arms 18/3; Ethiopian Tribesman 18/1; Ethiopian Chief 18/2; Italian Rifleman; Italian Officer. (see this page)

L TO R: U.S. Sailor Blue Uniform, early, 14; U.S. Sailor, white uniform, early, 14W; U.S. Naval Officer, blue uniform 14A; U.S. Naval Officer, white uniform 14AW; U.S. Sailor, blue uniform, 14; U.S. Sailor, white uniform 14W; U.S. Sailor Signalman 14/1W; Traffic Officer 3AP; Knight in Armor 19.

Photos Courtesy Don Pielin

Italian Officer, sun helmet and pistol, circa 1936........................	6.00	7.00	8.00
Italian infantryman, sun helmet and rifle.............................	6.00	7.00	8.00

	G	VG	M
19 Knight in Armor...................	3.00	4.00	5.00
20 Red Cross Doctor, hatless...........	4.00	5.00	6.00
21 Stretcher Bearer...................	3.00	4.00	5.00
22 Stretcher with Patient.............	4.00	5.00	6.00
22/1 Wounded Sitting, Arm in White Sling............................	5.00	6.00	7.00
22/2 Wounded on Crutches...........	4.00	5.00	6.00
23 Nurse...........................	3.00	4.00	5.00
Ski Trooper, circa 1940.............	6.00	8.00	10.00
Greek Evzone....................	3.00	4.00	5.00
25 Aviator........................	3.00	4.00	5.00
75 Radio Set, Operator and Aerial, two pieces......................	10.00	15.00	20.00
75 Radio Operator with set, alone.......	4.00	5.00	6.00
D26 Nurse and wounded soldier, one piece............................	6.00	7.00	8.00
D27 Doughboy Supporting Wounded Soldier, one piece.................	6.00	7.00	8.00

NOTE: GREY figures in blue as foreign legion, same price, in grey or red and yellow as enemy, add $1.

GREYKLIP ARMIES: Although early, most of these pieces sell for about one or two dollars, with the large one-piece gun limber selling for about five. GREY also produced an "American Family" series before the war of civilian figures about 2¼" high. Prices average 1-2-3.

AUBURN RUBBER: Although AUBURN (also Aub-Rub'r) was founded in 1913, in Auburn, Indiana, as the Double Fabric Tire Corporation, making auto tubes and tires for Model T Fords, etc., it didn't produce its first toy until 1935, with five soldiers. The prototype was a Palace Guard, which AUBURN President and chief stockholder A. L. Murray had obtained in England. The model was taken to a local pattern-maker who made patterns from it, and then the company made the original molds from lead and molded sample toys for Murray. These samples were then taken to an artist and were decorated per Murray's instructions. Presented to buyers, they immediately caught on. The soldiers were molded in 24" rubber presses, each containing forty to sixty soldiers, with cure time approximately 6-12 minutes. The soldiers, once trimmed, were dipped in a base laquer (advertised as "pure vegetable dyes") and then sent down a decorating conveyor, where as many as 24 women, using small camel hair brushes, added finishing touches, painting the faces, shoes, belts, buttons, medals, and finally eyes. After drying, each was wrapped individually in waxed paper and packed three dozen to a chipboard carton and twelve dozen to a corrugated carton for shipment. Design of the soldiers was credited to Edward McCandish, a free-lance artist. The soldiers sold well from the beginning, with approximately 200 of the 400 AUBURN employees (AUBURN consistently made non-toy products as well) involved in them and other toys on a two-shift basis. Shortly after the soldiers were introduced, animals and wheeled vehicles, the first a Cord automobile, were marketed, all successfully. AUBURN produced no soldiers during the war, and few after, though it continued to make toys in great quantity (70,000 wheeled items a day in 1962, for example). In 1960 the toys portion of AUBURN was purchased by the town of Deming, New Mexico, where it remained until it went out of business in 1967 or 68. AUBURN'S soldiers, all approximately the standard 3¼" length, went through three stages. The first were frail-looking, with long, thin bodies; the second, which emerged as early as September, 1936, were stockier and larger-headed, and the third, introduced in 1941, were more well-proportioned and realistic. Unlike its competitors, AUBURN produced no cowboys, Indians, sailors or civilians, except for baseball and football players. Descriptions are AUBURN'S where known.

AUBURN TOY SOLDIERS

	G	VG	M
Marching at Port Arms, early version, came in various colors with blue being U.S. Marines	2.00	3.00	4.00
Marching at Port Arms, second version	2.00	3.00	4.00
Bugler, first version, came in several colors	2.00	3.00	4.00
Bugler, second version	2.00	3.00	4.00
Palace Guard Officer (also "Foreign Legion")	3.00	4.00	5.00
Palace Guard infantryman (also "Foreign Legion"), port arms	3.00	4.00	5.00

AUBURN, L TO R: Plane Shooter, Firing Soldier. (see next page)
Photo By Ed Poole

	G	VG	M
Ethiopian, black, carrying shield and spear...............................	4.00	6.00	8.00
Officer, first version..................	2.00	3.00	4.00
Officer, second version...............	2.00	3.00	4.00
Charging Soldier—running with tommy-gun, early version..................	3.00	4.00	5.00
Charging Soldier, running with tommy-gun, second version................	2.00	3.00	4.00
Cavalry Officer, mounted, long coat....	4.00	5.00	6.00
Machine Gunner, first version..........	3.00	4.00	5.00
Machine Gunner, second version........	2.00	3.00	4.00
Doctor	2.00	3.00	4.00
Nurse, white or khaki uniform..........	2.00	3.00	4.00
Stretcher-Bearer in overseas cap........	2.00	3.00	4.00
Soldier lying wounded................	2.00	3.00	4.00
Kneeling with Binoculars..............	2.00	3.00	4.00
Signalman with semaphore flags........	2.00	3.00	4.00
Crawling, arm outstretched, rifle slung over shoulder......................	2.00	3.00	4.00
Grenade Thrower, holding rifle on ground in front....................	2.00	3.00	4.00

AUBURN, Stretcher Bearers and Soldier Lying Wounded. (see this page)
Photo By Ed Poole

AUBURN, L TO R: Cavalry Officer, Motorcycle with sidecar. (see this page and next)
Photo By Ed Poole

AUBURN, Aircraft Defender. (see this page)
Photo By Ed Poole

AUBURN, L TO R: Searchlight, Sound Detector. (see this page)
Photo By Ed Poole

	G	VG	M
Aircraft Gunner, kneeling, firing AA gun upward	4.00	5.00	6.00
Motorcyclist, in khaki,or blue as policeman	3.00	4.00	5.00
Motorcycle with sidecar, machine gun	4.00	5.00	6.00
Aircraft Defender, standing, firing 50 Cal. AA gun upward; this and the following all introduced in 1941	5.00	6.50	8.00
Color Bearer	3.00	4.00	5.00
Marching Soldier, slope arms	3.00	4.00	5.00
Firing Soldier, kneeling, firing rifle	3.00	4.00	5.00
Plane Shooter No. 272, kneeling firing rifle upward	3.00	4.00	5.00
Sound Detector, standing with large three-eared sound detector	5.00	6.50	8.00
Searchlight, standing with large searchlight	5.00	6.00	7.00
Trench Mortar No. 296, kneeling, placing shell in mortar	3.00	4.50	5.50
Tank Defender? Firing submachine gun from shoulder, beret, jodphùrs, goggles	5.00	6.00	7.00

AUBURN Batter, Catcher, Runner, Fielder. (see page 167)
Photo By Bill Kaufman

165

TOP, AUBURN, L TO R: Machine Gunner, second version, Crawling. (see page 164)
Photo By Ed Poole

MIDDLE, AUBURN, L TO R: Trench Mortar, Grenade thrower, Charging soldier.
Photo By Ed Poole (see pages 164, 165)

BOTTOM, AUBURN L TO R: Signalman,
Kneeling with binoculars (see page 164).
Photo By Ed Poole

	G	VG	M
Tank Soldier? Running with box, in beret, scarf, goggles...............	4.00	5.00	6.00
Tank Soldier? Running, looking skyward, pilot helmet and goggles.......	5.00	6.00	7.00
Motor Scout, on motorcycle, pilot type helmet, goggles, rifle in sheath.......	6.00	7.00	8.00
Baseball Players were introduced around 1939, and consisted of Batter, Fielder, Runner, Catcher, Pitcher; price per each.	1.00	2.00	3.00
Football players may not have been produced till 1941, and consisted of Center on the Ball, Lineman on all fours, Crouching line backer, Running back with ball, Quarterback passing. Price per each.........................	1.00	2.00	3.00

ALL-NU

ALL-NU: Very little is known about other competitors in the pre-WW II period. ALL-NU, at 67 Irving Place, New York City, appears to have been in business for just the year 1941 and perhaps a few months of 1942, before the war ended its production of toy soldiers. Its all-girl marching band is its best-known product in the toy soldier field, although its horses and riders may be more ubiquitous (see Animal-Drawn and Miscellaneous). The latter, however, were not the same size as its soldiers. The soldiers it manufactured appear to be extremely rare. A photograph in Toys and Novelties Magazine (April, 1941) attests to their existence, but most seem to be unknown otherwise. ALL-NU, like BARCLAY, seems to be identifiable by its eye—which with ALL-NU was a single line, giving its figures a squint-eyed look.

METAL CAST, L TO R: Sucide Squad, Bomb Thrower (see page 170)
Photo By Bill Kaufman

	G	VG	M
ALL-NU "Newsreel" Camerman in helmet	5.00	6.50	8.00
ALL-NU seated machine gunner	5.00	6.50	8.00
ALL-NU Soldier advancing with tommy gun, solid puttees		extremely rare	
ALL-NU Grenadier, rifle slung over shoulder, solid puttees		extremely rare	
ALL-NU Bugler, solid puttees		extremely rare	
ALL-NU Signalman, solid puttees		extremely rare	
ALL-NU Girl's Marching Band; Major-ette, Color-bearer, Drummer, Fifer, Bugler, Saxophonist, price per each . . .	3.00	4.00	5.00
ALL-NU mounted cowboy	3.00	4.00	5.00

TOMMY TOY

TOMMY TOY: This company has so far baffled all researchers, perhaps was located in Newark, New Jersey, before the War. Its soldiers were slightly smaller in size, but well-sculpted and identified on the underside of the base. It also made a number of nursery rhyme figures.

TOMMY TOY, L TO R: "Hand Grenade"; "Wounded"; "Officer Gas Mask"; "Ground Arms".
Photo By Norbert Schachter

	G	VG	M
TOMMY TOY "Officer Gas Mask A Tommy Toy"	4.00	5.50	7.00

	G	VG	M
TOMMY TOY Nurse..................	4.00	5.00	6.00
TOMMY TOY "Wounded", holding helmet at side, arm in sling, head bandaged...........................	4.00	5.50	7.00
TOMMY TOY "Ground Arms", soldier in helmet at attention................	4.00	5.50	7.00
TOMMY TOY "Hand Grenade", soldier with rifle and grenade.............	4.00	5.50	7.00
TOMMY TOY "Kneeling, Firing Rifle"..	4.00	5.50	7.00
TOMMY TOY "Machine Gunner" holding tommy gun................	4.00	5.50	7.00
TOMMY TOY Nursery Rhyme Figures— at least ten produced, including Puss in Boots, Humpty Dumpty, Mother Hubbard, Jack and the Beanstalk, Little Bo Peep, Little Miss Muffet , Tom the Piper's Son, Witch on broomstick, Jack and Jill, Old King Cole , price per each	3.00	4.50	6.00

TOMMY TOY "Little Miss Muffet".
Photo By Bill Kaufman

METAL CAST PRODUCTS CO: This New York, New York company both manufactured soldiers and sold their slush cast molds to small businessmen. Thus there appears to be no way of knowing which were made by METAL CAST and which by other individuals or companies. Although little is known about this company, in 1946 all their helmeted soldiers were wearing pre-World War II helmets. Several resembled BARCLAY, MANOIL and GREY figures.

	G	VG	M
METAL CAST Flag Bearer, 21A........	2.00	3.00	4.00
METAL CAST Aviator 22A............	2.00	3.00	4.00
METAL CAST Pilot With Bomb 23A....	2.00	3.00	4.00
METAL CAST Suicide Squad—officer in gas mask with pistol 24A............	2.00	3.00	4.00
METAL CAST Signal Corps 25A with semaphore flags....................	2.00	3.00	4.00
METAL CAST Anti-Aircraft 26A, soldier with searchlight..................	2.00	3.00	4.00
METAL CAST Bomb Thrower 27A, gas mask, slung rifle, throwing grenade...	2.00	3.00	4.00
METAL CAST Wounded 28A, lying down, head on hand, arm in sling.....	2.00	3.00	4.00
METAL CAST Machine Gunner 29A, kneeling.........................	2.00	3.00	4.00
METAL CAST Motorcycle Officer 30A, on motorcycle, peaked cap..........	2.00	3.00	4.00

"JONES" SOLDIERS

JONES is a catch-all term currently used for the greatest number of otherwise unidentified toy soliders. The company is known to have manufactured several German figures, and is usually, in an informal way, credited by collectors for American soldiers (also painted in gray, as "enemy") who are basically distinguished by a simplified sculpture that seems to combine BARCLAY and MANOIL (sometimes actually copying their figures), and by a haphazard line-and-dot eye and eyebrow that appears to have been done with a clotted pen or too-thick brush. However, whether these were actually done by JONES is not yet known. Information received as this book was going to press suggests that the company's full name was J. E. JONES, was in business from 1930 into the 1960s, and was also known as METAL ARTS, METAL MINIATURES, MILITARY MINIATURES and WORLD MINIATURES.

	G	VG	M
German, kneeling with rifle............	4.00	5.50	7.00
German, charging with rifle..........	4.00	5.50	7.00
German, prone machine-gunner (similar to Barclay's)......................	5.00	6.50	8.00
Marching, shoulder arms (similar to Manoil's).........................	3.00	4.00	5.00
Observer with binoculars and rifle (similar to Manoil)...................	4.00	5.00	6.00
Wire-cutter, prone..................	6.00	8.00	10.00
Officer with sword, shot in neck.......	6.00	8.00	10.00
Stretcher-bearer (similar to Manoil's)....	3.00	4.00	5.00
Kneeling with AA Gun (similar to Auburn's)...........................	4.00	5.50	7.00
Charging, port arms.................	3.00	4.00	5.00

JONES Officer in Greatcoat, pointing holding pistol in other hand.
Photo By Ed Poole

	G	VG	M
Firing machine gun on tree stump.......	5.00	6.50	8.00
Grenade-thrower, no weapons.........	4.00	5.00	6.00
Seated, with rifle (similar to Barclay's)...	3.00	4.00	5.00
Officer in greatcoat, pointing, holding pistol in other hand................	8.00	10.00	12.00
Fat kneeling Cowboy (probably not Jones), masked, gun in air...........	3.00	4.00	5.00
Prone, with rifle, trunk upraised.......	6.00	8.00	10.00
Prone, firing double-barreled machine gun..............................	5.00	6.50	8.00
Kneeling, firing anti-tank gun (similar to Barclay's)..........................	5.00	6.50	8.00

	G	VG	M
Cook with frying pan, chef's hat (similar to Barclay's)	3.00	4.00	5.00
Ammunition Carrier	3.00	4.00	5.00
Doctor with Stethoscope (similar to Barclay's cast helmet with slung rifle)	4.00	5.50	7.00
Motorcyclist with machine gun mounted on motorcycle	6.00	8.00	10.00
Flagbearer (similar to Manoil)	3.00	4.00	5.00
Bugler (similar to Manoil)	3.00	4.00	5.00
Pilot (similar to Barclay, but smaller)	2.00	3.00	4.00
Kneeling with searchlight	5.00	6.50	8.00
Seated with phone	3.00	4.00	5.00
Kneeling, firing rifle, no stand (probably not Jones)	5.00	6.00	7.00
Charging, pack on back (probably not Jones)	5.00	6.00	7.00
Kneeling, firing (similar to Manoil)	4.00	5.00	6.00
Nurse with plate, towel over arm (may be Tommy Toy, rather than Jones)	4.00	5.00	6.00
Soldier with gas mask, plunging rifle down, smaller (probably not Jones)	3.00	4.00	5.00

LINCOLN LOG: These figures, about 2" high, were introduced in 1928 and include cowboys and Indians, foot and mounted, pioneer in coonskin hat, 1812 infantry, various train personnel and passengers, World War I soldiers, Revolutionary War soldiers, mounted George Washington, sailors, cadets and Royal Canadian Mounted Police. Prices average 3-4-5.

PLASTIC SOLDIERS: Plastic figures as yet, even the early ones, do not seem to hold much attraction for collectors, with $2 in mint being about the top price. Plastic soldiers were introduced at least as early as 1938, when BETON Soldiers, manufactured by BERGEN TOY & NOVELTY CO. INC. of Carlstadt New Jersey were sold. Figures in 1938 consisted of U.S. Infantry, U.S. Cadets in various colors, Indians, Cowboys, both foot and mounted.

TOOTSIETOY produced a line of flat 1½" high metal soldiers in the 1930s and early 1940s. These sell for about $1 in mint.

MARX produced a large number of 3½" flat tin lithographed soldiers in the 1930s and after which are attractive to collectors. At least 50 different figures are known, consisting of soldiers from all over the world.

	G	VG	M
MARX Soldiers of Fortune, set of eight with pop gun.....................	10.00	15.00	20.00
MARX Soldiers of Fortune, set of eight with cannon.....................	10.00	15.00	20.00
MARX Soldiers of Fortune, Fort Dix Barracks........................	15.00	22.50	30.00
MARX Soldiers of Fortune, set of 24 with pop gun.........................	15.00	22.50	30.00

PREMIUMS

TOYS FREE AS THE AIR
by
Jim Harmon

Many radio premiums were nearly as free as the wonderful radio shows that advertised them.

We did have to pay the electric bill (or our folks did) to run the radio, and to get the offered toys we did have to send in a box-top from the sponsor's product.

Sometimes it was only that, a proof of purchase (Orphan Annie and Captain Midnight were particularly generous in responding with gifts for labels or inner seals from Ovaltine drink mix) and other times, usually only a dime was required "to handle the cost of handling and mailing". (That's really all it did do—the cost of premium itself came from the advertising budget.)

The lure of the premium to kids then and for grown-up kids who are now collectors is difficult to explain to those who never lived through the era themselves. The ring or badge was more than the toy itself; it was our tangible link to those magical friends on the other side of the speaker cloth.

Those voices were wonderful out there—The rumbling bass of Brace Beemer as the Lone Ranger; the slightly "country" sound of Curley Bradley as Tom Mix; Bret Morrison, whom we recognized even as children was "sophisticated" as Lamont Cranston, alias The Shadow—but they were bodiless and yes, a bit remote.

It was the premium they offered, the same as the one they were using in the story, that put us in touch with them.

There were historic precedents for radio premiums. There were pictures of famous actresses in cigarette packages around the turn of the century, and early radio personalities, such as bandleader Vincent Lopez, offered their autographed pictures. But such footnotes to history aside, radio premiums began with **Little Orphan Annie** in 1931. The plucky little waif from the Sunday comics first gave away sheet music of her theme song ("Who's that little chatterbox with the pretty auburn locks?) and her own photo, but very shortly, she offered a drinking mug that could be used to shake-up Ovaltine powder with milk to make something resembling a soda fountain milk shake. The first significant radio premium, it was the only successful one that encouraged further use of the sponsor's product.

174

Many different models of the shake-up mug were offered by Annie, and later by Captain Midnight (on both radio and TV). So successful were the offers, shake-up mugs are not rare or high in dollar value. (The most sought-after is the orange and blue, embossed—not decaled—Midnight mug.)

It took two more years after Annie came to radio for the fledgling medium to develop its really classic adventure heroes. In 1933, there appeared the Lone Ranger, Tom Mix and Jack Armstrong. Unlike Annie, the two Westerners and the All-American Boy were still around until the 1950s, when television began driving out all radio drama. In those nearly twenty years, these shows offered hundreds of give-away toys, which inspired similar premiums on dozens of other shows.

Any small toy that could be manufactured inexpensively enough might turn up as a premium. Those concerned with the great outdoors were popular. We had compasses, pedometers, telescopes, flashlights, pocketknives, signal mirrors, portable telegraph sets.

The secret society of childhood had its emblems and tokens. So we had secret decoders and secret manuals of every size and description. It is these and other **paper** items that have the greatest dollar value. They were the most easily lost or used up in the rush to adulthood. A Captain Midnight Secret Manual is worth more than the metallic decoder it accompanied.

The rarest paper item is the Lone Ranger Frontier Town offered about 1947. To complete this model of a Western village, one had to get four different envelopes by mail, then augment this by buying several packages of Cheerios to cut out the model buildings from the packs. The complete set has been known to sell for hundreds of dollars, and today might bring $1,000.00, the highest dollar value premium.

Perhaps the most popular single type of premium was the ring. Rings let the listener show his loyalty to the fraternity of his favorite hero, but in a less officious and more "grown-up" way than the badge (although they were also highly popular). Besides . . . the rings looked neat, and many of them could **do** things—some of them pretty incredible things.

The rings began simply. In 1933, Tom Mix offered one made from a bent Horseshoe Nail. But personalizing was important. Tom put his TM-Bar brand on the next ring, and Orphan Annie had her face on her first one, both around 1934.

As with radio premiums in general, the Tom Mix show (and Ralston cereal's premium manufacturer, the Robbins Company) blazed the trail with ingenious ring designs. In 1937, Tom Mix Straight Shooters could get a Signet Ring with their own initial on it.

(Years later, Captain Midnight would offer a ring that would ink-stamp your initial.) By 1938, Tom had a ring that let you look in a peep-hole and see a magnified picture of himself and his horse. Tony. (Technology had progressed so much that by the fifties, Straight Arrow offered a similar ring that put your own photo, if supplied, alongside radio's great Indian hero.)

After World War II and the ease in metal rationing, Tom Mix offered a Magnet Ring (good for picking up paper-clips—like the one on the stolen plans to the atomic bomb, in Tom's case). His spinning siren whistle ring was neat (but admittedly borrowed in design from Jack Armstrong's 1937 Egyptian Whistle Ring). Tom's Sliding Whistle Ring that played different musical notes (about 1948) was unique, however. His Look-Around Ring concealed an inner mirror that let you see behind you (sort of), a design rustled for a later Tennessee Jed ring.

The final Tom Mix ring looked attractive, sporting a glowing cat's-eye, but the Tiger-Eye Ring was only lightweight plastic in 1949, a far cry from the well-crafted metal rings of a decade earlier. But then, the decade was nearly over, and so was the era, fading in the light of another glowing eye in the living room.

The Shadow's own Glow-in-the-Dark Ring in 1939 had a band composed of two sculpted Shadow figures holding up a jagged blue stone—a proxy lump of his sponsor's product, Blue Coal. One of the very few Shadow premiums and the best-looking, this ring has sold for a record $250.00.

One glowing plastic ring—the identical mold—was used for several different radio shows. The band had two crocodiles holding a setting in their mouths. The oval "stone" was **black** when it was Jack Armstrong's Dragon Eye Ring in 1940, and when it was the Shadow ring for Carey Salt in 1947 (not the rare Blue Coal model). The setting was **green** for **Terry and the Pirates** in the mid-forties, and **red** for Buck Rogers' Ring of Saturn in 1945. It is back to **black** in the slightly lumpy **counterfeit** being manufactured today, one of the handful of premiums of simple enough design to be faked for profit. The best way to authenticate these rings is by the accompanying paper instruc-

JIM HARMON is a writer of non-fiction (**The Great Radio Heroes**) and science fiction, magazine editor (**Monsters of the Movies**), and currently writer-producer-co-star with radio's Tom Mix in the 1977 **Curley Bradley, U.S. Marshal** radio and recording series.

tion sheets, naming the famous character whose prize it is.

These rings, as are all radio premiums, are worth whatever you will pay to possess them. A fair average price is $25.00 with $100.00 a top price for very rare, complex and fragile items. No one who is not very familiar with the whole field should pay more. Even though $100.00 or more may be easier to come by today than a dime and a box-top were in those days of yesteryear.

CONDITION OF A PREMIUM
AND ITS RELATION TO PRICE

The price of a premium depends not only on its desirability, but on its condition. A premium in mint condition is generally worth twice what that same premium would bring in good condition, with "very good" falling about equally in between good and mint.

"Mint" means just that; the condition in which it was originally issued—perfect, regardless of age, not the slightest blemish. Needless to say this is a fairly rare state of affairs, but enough premiums exist in mint condition to make it a pertinent term. Many people trying to dispose of items are tempted to call an item "mint" when it is really "near mint", "very good", or sometimes just "good". Inevitably this can result in unhappiness all around, and not infrequently, a cancelled sale. "Very Good" indicates a premium that has obviously seen some use, with some signs of wear and aging, but in general having a crispness to its appearance that makes it attractive and collectible to all but the most discriminating.

"Good" signals a premium that has seen considerable wear, shows its age, but is basically sound. A collector will collect it but will often not be wholly satisfied with it as an example of his collection, and thus prices are often drastically below that which the same item in mint can command.

Condition below good results in another drastic drop in price, and premiums with missing parts, although otherwise in excellent condition, will usually fall into this lower-priced category.

"Near Mint", "Fine", "Very Fine" and similar terms often found in sellers' descriptions denote conditions between Mint and Very Good, and are priced accordingly.

The key to grading is to avoid wishful thinking. Grading can sometimes be a problem to the uninitiated, but common sense will usually prevail, and when possible, a consultation with an expert in the field can often clear up lingering doubts. A premium in its original mailing envelope or box is worth up to 10 to 20% more, depending on the condition of the container.

PREMIUMS

	G	VG	M
ADMIRAL TELEVISION STUDIO GIVEAWAY—1953 paper punchout TV studio and characters, features Sky King, Flight to Mars, Walt Disney's Peter Pan and Three Little Pigs. 15x16"	40.00	60.00	80.00
AMOS & ANDY Pepsodent Give-away-Amos' Wedding....................	12.50	18.75	25.00
AMOS & ANDY Puzzle...............	10.00	15.00	20.00
ARCHIE COMICS Club Button.......	1.00	2.00	3.00
AUNT JEMIMA BREAKFAST CLUB Badge-metal	5.00	7.50	10.00
BARNEY BAXTER Junior Birdmen of America wings, metal, circa late 1930s.	7.50	11.25	15.00
BENDIX RADIO—5½" WWII military figures circa 1944. Color photos with stands. a. Lt. (jg) Navy; b. Marine 1st Lt. (dress uniform); c. Commander-Coast Guard; d. Army Air Force officer with parachute harness; e. 2nd Lt. with modern Mae West; f. Flier with flying suit; g. Capt. Army Airforce; h. Air officer with furlined jacket and helmet. Price per each....................	1.00	1.50	2.00
BETTY BOOP face mask—1931 theatre premium	3.50	5.25	7.00
BETTY BOOP pin "Roxy Theatre, New York", large.....................	2.25	3.50	4.50
BLONDIE & DAGWOOD GO TO LEISURELAND, 1940, Westinghouse....	9.00	15.50	18.00
BOBBY BENSON Code Rule 1935 cardboard decoder, HECKER H-O.......	40.00	60.00	80.00
BOBBY BENSON'S GAME CIRCUS, 1934	15.00	22.50	35.00

	G	VG	M
BUCK JONES Club Ring............	14.00	21.00	28.00
BUCK JONES Horseshoe Pin..........	4.00	6.00	8.00
BUCK JONES JR. Sheriff Badge........	5.00	7.50	10.00
BUCK ROGERS Bade, enameled.......	37.50	56.00	75.00
BUCK ROGERS Birthstone and initial ring.........	35.00	52.50	70.00
BUCK ROGERS Chief Explorer Badge..	25.00	37.50	50.00
BUCK ROGERS Flight Commander Whistle Badge...............	22.50	33.75	45.00
BUCK ROGERS Girl's charm bracelet...	27.50	41.00	55.00
BUCK ROGERS Helmet.............	35.00	52.50	70.00
BUCK ROGERS Knife..............	37.50	56.25	75.00
BUCK ROGERS Pendant............	25.00	37.50	50.00
BUCK ROGERS Pinback button, circa 1935, WHITEHEAD AND HOAG, Buck facing right, with inscription "Buck Rogers in the 25th Century"....	25.00	37.50	50.00
BUCK ROGERS Repeller Ray Ring (seal ring)..........	50.00	75.00	100.00
BUCK ROGERS Ring, glows in the dark, with red stone........	60.00	90.00	120.00
BUCK ROGERS Solar Scouts Badge, all brass color........	25.00	37.50	50.00
BUCK ROGERS Solar Scouts Spaceship Commander Badge, 1936 Cream of Wheat premium............	42.50	53.75	85.00
BUCK ROGERS Solar Scout Sweater Emblem............	25.00	37.50	50.00
BUCK ROGERS Telescope..........	42.50	53.75	85.00

JACK ARMSTRONG Secret Egyptian coder siren ring (see page 189).
Photo Courtesy Jim Harmon.

	G	VG	M
BUCK ROGERS items given away for Cream of Wheat Green Triangle (sold in stores also):			
BUCK ROGERS Films for projector.....	3.50	5.25	7.00
BUCK ROGERS Interplanetary Game...	45.00	67.50	90.00
BUCK ROGERS lead figures, hollow lead, Buck, Wilma, Huer, Robot, Kane, Ardala, price per each........	8.00	12.00	20.00
BUCK ROGERS Lite Blaster Flashlight..	8.00	10.00	25.00
BUCK ROGERS Movie Projector.......	20.00	25.00	30.00
BUCK ROGERS Printing Set (12 rubber stamps).........................	20.00	25.00	40.00
BUCK ROGERS Super Dreadnaught, balsa wood......................	4.00	8.00	12.00
BUCK ROGERS Uniform.............	20.00	50.00	75.00
BUFFALO BILL Bamby Bread Horseshoe Badge, late 1930s..................	5.00	7.50	10.00
BUSTER BROWN GANG (Smilin' Ed) Ring...........................	10.00	15.00	20.00
BUSTER BROWN GANG tab pins, assorted, price per each..............	2.00	3.00	5.00
CAPTAIN FRANKS AIR HAWKS RING.	15.00	22.50	30.00
CAPTAIN FRANKS AIR HAWKS Wings, circa late 1930s, POST'S 40% Bran Flakes Premium..................	6.00	9.00	12.00
CAPTAIN HAWK Sky Patrol Propellor Badge, circa late 1930s.............	7.50	11.25	15.00
CAPTAIN MARVEL Club button.......	12.50	18.75	25.00
CAPTAIN MIDNIGHT Aerial Torpedo Bomber (Airplane), 1941...........	30.00	45.00	60.00
CAPTAIN MIDNIGHT American Flag Loyalty Badge, 1940..............	20.00	30.00	40.00
CAPTAIN MIDNIGHT Aviation Wings Badge, 1941.....................	20.00	30.00	40.00
CAPTAIN MIDNIGHT Aviation Wings, 1942..........................	22.50	33.75	45.00

Captain Marvel Club Button (see page 181).
Photo Courtesy Jim Harmon.

	G	VG	M
CAPTAIN MIDNIGHT Code-O-Graph Decoder Pin, 1941, Eagle on top......	20.00	30.00	40.00
CAPTAIN MIDNIGHT Code-O-Graph Badge, 1942, with photo of Captain Midnight........................	30.00	45.00	60.00
CAPTAIN MIDNIGHT Code-O-Graph, 1945, magnifier...................	22.50	33.75	45.00
CAPTAIN MIDNIGHT Code-O-Graph, 1946, Mirromatic.................	22.50	33.75	45.00
CAPTAIN MIDNIGHT Code-O-Graph, 1947, works as whistle.............	20.00	30.00	40.00
CAPTAIN MIDNIGHT Code-O-Graph, 1948, round, with mirror...........	22.50	33.75	45.00
CAPTAIN MIDNIGHT Code-O-Graph, 1949, Key-O-Matic (with key)........	22.50	33.75	45.00
CAPTAIN MIDNIGHT Detect-O-Scope, 1941...........................	30.00	45.00	60.00
CAPTAIN MIDNIGHT Flight Commander Commission, 1956...........	20.00	30.00	40.00
CAPTAIN MIDNIGHT Flight Commander Flying Cross, 1942...........	17.50	26.25	35.00
CAPTAIN MIDNIGHT Flight Commander Ring, 1941.................	20.00	30.00	40.00
CAPTAIN MIDNIGHT Flight Commander Signet Ring, 1957...........	30.00	45.00	60.00
CAPTAIN MIDNIGHT Flight Commander Ring, 1959................	22.50	33.75	45.00

	G	VG	M
CAPTAIN MIDNIGHT Jumping Bean Target, 1939....................	6.00	9.00	12.00
CAPTAIN MIDNIGHT MJC-10 Plane Detector, 1942, distance-finder.......	17.50	26.25	35.00
CAPTAIN MIDNIGHT Magic Blackout Lite-Ups, 1942...................	15.00	22.50	30.00
CAPTAIN MIDNIGHT 1941 Manual for Decoder.......................	50.00	75.00	100.00
CAPTAIN MIDNIGHT 1942 Manual for Decoder.......................	50.00	75.00	100.00
CAPTAIN MIDNIGHT 1945 Manual for Code-O-Graph...................	25.00	37.50	50.00
CAPTAIN MIDNIGHT 1946 Manual for Code-O-Graph...................	25.00	37.50	50.00
CAPTAIN MIDNIGHT 1947 Manual for Code-O-Graph...................	30.00	45.00	60.00
CAPTAIN MIDNIGHT 1948 Manual for Code-O-Graph...................	17.50	26.25	35.00
CAPTAIN MIDNIGHT 1949 Manual for Code-O-Graph...................	22.50	33.75	45.00
CAPTAIN MIDNIGHT 1956 Manual for Decoder Badge...................	100.00	150.00	200.00
CAPTAIN MIDNIGHT 1957 Manual for Silver Dart decoder...............	100.00	150.00	200.00
CAPTAIN MIDNIGHT Marine Corps Ring, 1942......................	17.50	26.25	35.00
CAPTAIN MIDNIGHT Medal, brass, pictures of cast, secret word, spinner, 1940	4.50	6.75	9.00
CAPTAIN MIDNIGHT Mystic Eye Detector Ring, 1942..................	30.00	45.00	60.00
CAPTAIN MIDNIGHT Mystic Sun God Ring, 1946......................	87.50	131.25	175.00
CAPTAIN MIDNIGHT Printing Ring, 1948...........................	27.50	41.25	55.00
CAPTAIN MIDNIGHT Secret Squadron Decoder Badge, 1955...............	30.00	45.00	60.00
CAPTAIN MIDNIGHT Secret Squadron Decoder Badge, 1956..............	22.50	33.75	45.00

	G	VG	M
CAPTAIN MIDNIGHT Secret Squadron Insignia transfer, 1949	12.50	18.75	25.00
CAPTAIN MIDNIGHT Service Ribbon pin, 1944	17.50	26.25	35.00
CAPTAIN MIDNIGHT Silver Dart Decoder Badge, 1957	30.00	45.00	60.00
CAPTAIN MIDNIGHT Spy Scope, 1947	30.00	45.00	60.00
CAPTAIN MIDNIGHT Surprise Package, 1942	27.50	41.25	55.00
CAPTAIN MIDNIGHT 3-Way Mystic Dog Whistle, 1942	17.50	26.25	35.00
CAPTAIN MIDNIGHT Trick and Riddle Book, 1939 Skelly Oil Premium, 64 pages	20.00	30.00	45.00
CAPTAIN MIDNIGHT Weather Wings, 1940, Predicts weather	20.00	30.00	45.00
CAPTAIN MIDNIGHT Whirlwind Whistling Ring, 1941	22.50	33.75	45.00
CAPT. TIM IVORY CLUB Pin—IVORY SOAP, circa 1936	4.00	8.00	12.00
CAPTAIN VIDEO Flying Saucer Ring	12.50	18.75	25.00
CAPTAIN VIDEO Rite-O-Lite	42.50	63.75	85.00
CAPTAIN VIDEO Rocket Launcher and Ships, 1950s	25.00	37.50	50.00
CAPTAIN VIDEO Secret Seal Ring, 1950s	25.00	37.50	50.00
CAPTAIN VIDEO Space Fleet Ray Gun, 1952, TV premium—POWERHOUSE	12.50	18.75	25.00
CAPTAIN VIDEO X-9 Rocket Balloon, 1950s	10.00	15.00	20.00
CHANDU THE MAGICIAN Galloping Coin Trick, 1930s	35.00	52.50	70.00
CHANDU THE MAGICIAN Hindu Cones, 1930s	35.00	52.50	70.00
CHARLIE MCCARTHY Puppet Doll— 21" high, cardboard, CHASE & SANBORN mailer	17.50	26.25	35.00

	G	VG	M
CHARLIE MCCARTHY RADIO PARTY GAME—Giveaway by Standard Brands, 1938, 21 cardboard figures....	12.50	18.75	25.00
CINNAMON BEAR (annual Christmas show, circa 1940s) Silver Star.........	25.00	37.50	50.00
CISCO KID Badge, western hat on chain, 1950s	7.50	11.25	15.00
CISCO KID cardboard gun, 7" long, Harvest Bread giveaway, clicker sounds when handle squeezed..............	4.00	6.00	8.00
CISCO KID and **PANCHO** face masks, 1953, price per each...............	10.00	20.00	30.00
CISCO KID Triple S Club Kit..........	20.00	30.00	40.00
CISCO KID Picture Ring, 1950s........	30.00	45.00	60.00
COCO WHEATS RADIO CLUB BADGE shape of microphone...............	17.50	26.25	35.00
DAVID HARDING COUNTERSPY, Junior Agent Badge...................	12.50	18.75	25.00
DAVY CROCKETT Gold-plated ring...	3.00	4.50	6.00
DICK TRACY Air Detective Ring.......	27.50	41.25	55.00
DICK TRACY Badge, "Capt."..........	20.00	30.00	40.00
DICK TRACY Badge, "Crime Stoppers".	7.50	11.25	15.00
DICK TRACY Badge, "Detective", picture of Tracy and Junior.............	6.00	9.00	12.00
DICK TRACY Badge, "Lt."..........	20.00	30.00	40.00
DICK TRACY Badge—Republic Pictures	8.00	12.00	16.00
DICK TRACY Badge—"Sgt."..........	17.50	26.25	35.00

DICK TRACY Secret Service Patrol pin (see page 186).
Photo Courtesy Jim Harmon.

	G	VG	M
DICK TRACY Decoder, green (circa 1938?)	6.00	9.00	12.00
DICK TRACY Decoder, red (circa 1938?)	6.00	9.00	12.00
DICK TRACY Glider Airplane, 1938....	15.00	22.50	30.00
DICK TRACY Ring, in shape of Tracy's head	30.00	45.00	60.00
DICK TRACY Secret Compartment Ring	30.00	45.00	60.00
DICK TRACY Secret Service Patrol Member pin, early 1940s	12.50	18.75	25.00
DICK TRACY Secret Service 2nd Year Member pin	15.00	22.50	30.00
DICK TRACY'S Secret Detective Methods & Magic Tricks. 1939 QUAKER OATS, 68 pages	17.50	26.25	35.00
DON WINSLOW Decoder Torpedo.....	25.00	37.50	50.00
DON WINSLOW Honor Badge........	17.50	26.25	35.00
DON WINSLOW Magic Slate Secret Code Book	15.00	22.50	30.00
DON WINSLOW Ring...............	25.00	37.50	50.00
DONALD DUCK Punchout figure, circa late 1940s, DONALD DUCK BREAD.	2.50	3.75	5.00
DONALD DUCK Playboard, 1946, 9" high, Comics giveaway	9.00	13.50	18.00
FIGHTING DEVIL DOGS Ring, 1938, Republic Pictures serial ring, has bulldog head on top	12.50	18.75	25.00
FLASH GORDON Ring, 1949 POST TOASTIES CORN FLAKES	11.00	16.50	22.00
FORT APACHE (Rin Tin Tin) plastic, ring 1950s TV premium	4.00	6.00	8.00
FRANK BUCK Explorer's sun watch, post WW II (offered by Jack Armstrong)	17.50	26.25	35.00
FRANK BUCK Leopard Ring..........	30.00	45.00	60.00
G. E. Punchout Circus—65 pieces......	10.00	15.00	20.00
G.E. Rodeo Punchout—65 pieces.......	10.00	15.00	20.00
G-MAN Badge......................	.50	.75	1.00

	G	VG	M
G-MAN Official Signet Ring 1933-35, G-man radio program premium, metal	1.00	1.50	2.00
GABBY HAYES Antique Cars, 1950s, set for:	10.00	15.00	20.00
GABBY HAYES QUAKER Cannon Ring, 1950s	22.50	33.75	45.00
GABBY HAYES Western Gun Collection, 6 weapons, 3 pistols, 3 rifles, solid, non-working, 1950s	7.50	11.25	15.00
GABBY SCOOPS 1940-41 Press Card, Crackajack Comics	2.50	3.75	5.00
GANGBUSTERS PIN	14.00	21.00	28.00
GOOFY Playboard, 1946, 9" high, comics giveaway	9.00	13.50	18.00
GREEN HORNET Secret Compartment Ring, hornet seal, glows in dark	62.50	93.75	125.00
Gun, cardboard—Giveaway from Theatorium in Lykens, Pa. Pat'd Dec. 1914 by Spots Spec. Co. Lexington Ky. Swoop downward to produce bang. "The Bang Gun For Young America."	2.00	3.00	4.00
H.C.B. Club Kit, contains, badge, etc., early CREAM OF WHEAT	17.50	26.25	35.00
HOPALONG CASSIDY Face Ring	10.00	15.00	20.00
HOPALONG CASSIDY tin badge, POST RAISIN BRAN Giveaway, Circa 1950s	3.00	4.50	6.00
HOWDY DOODY Climber—Cardboard, with string, WELCH'S PREMIUM, 1950's	12.50	18.75	25.00
HOWDY DOODY Face Flashlight Ring, 1950s	30.00	45.00	60.00
HOWDY DOODY Flicker Key Chain— 3D picture of Howdy Doody flicks to Poll Parrot (POLL PARROT SHOES), 1950s	4.00	6.00	8.00
HOWDY DOODY Flicker Ring—POLL PARROT Premium, flicks from Howdy to Poll	6.00	9.00	12.00
HOWDY DOODY 8" Howdy Doody			

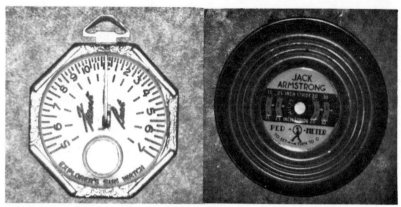

FRANK BUCK Explorer's Sun Watch (see page 186).   Photo Courtesy Jim Harmon.

JACK ARMSTRONG Ped-O-Meter (see this page).   Photo Courtesy Jim Harmon.

	G	VG	M
flexible cardboard figure—WONDER BREAD	7.50	11.25	15.00
HOWDY DOODY puppet, MARS CANDY, cardboard, 15" high, 1950s	5.00	7.50	10.00
HOWDY DOODY Princess dancing puppet, 13" high, joints moveable, 1950s SNICKERS premium	3.00	4.50	6.00
HOWDY DOODY Princess Spring etc. cardboard figure, 14" high	4.00	6.00	8.00
I AM A SPY SMASHER button, 1940, Fawcett Comics	7.00	10.50	14.00
INDIAN CHIEF tin badge, POST RAISIN BRAN, circa 1950s	2.00	3.00	4.00
INDIAN GUM CHIEF'S HEAD RING— GOUDEY GUM card premium, 1930s, silver	2.50	3.75	5.00
JACK ARMSTRONG Crocodile Ring, glows in dark, black stone	57.50	86.25	115.00
JACK ARMSTRONG Big 10 Football Game	37.50	56.25	75.00
JACK ARMSTRONG Explorer's Telescope	15.00	22.50	30.00
JACK ARMSTRONG Flashlight	20.00	30.00	40.00
JACK ARMSTRONG Ped-O-Meter (Blue or Silver models)	12.50	18.75	25.00
JACK ARMSTRONG Hike-O-Meter	12.50	18.75	25.00
JACK ARMSTRONG Magic Answer Box.	27.50	41.25	55.00

	G	VG	M
JACK ARMSTRONG, Secret Norden Bomb Sight, circa WW II, with three bombs, paper target ships	35.00	52.50	70.00
JACK ARMSTRONG Paper airplane models, many different, price per each	20.00	30.00	40.00
JACK ARMSTRONG Secret Whistle Code Card for Secret Egyptian Coder Siren ring	17.50	26.25	35.00
JACK ARMSTRONG Secret Egyptian Coder Siren Ring, late 1930s, WHEATIES	22.50	33.75	45.00
JACK ARMSTRONG 3-D viewer, film-strip	17.50	26.25	35.00
JEFF paper mask, 1933 SHELL OIL	6.00	9.00	12.00
JIMMIE ALLEN Colonial Gasoline Flying Cadet wings, late 1930s, bronze	6.00	9.00	12.00
JIMMIE ALLEN High-Speed Gasoline Flying Cadet wings, late 1930s, bronze	6.00	9.00	12.00
JIMMIE ALLEN Richfield Hi-Octane Flying Cadet wings, circa 1930s	6.00	9.00	12.00
JIMMIE ALLEN Richfield Hi-Octane Pilot's Identification Bracelet, late 1930s, all metal	22.50	33.75	45.00
JIMMIE ALLEN Skelly Oil Die-Cut Airplane cadet wings, late 1930s	10.00	15.00	20.00
JIMMIE ALLEN Skelly Oil Flying Cadet Wings, late 1930s, bronze	6.00	9.00	12.00
JOE E. BROWN pin	7.00	10.50	14.00
JUNIOR G-MAN Membership kit, circa mid-1930s	17.50	26.25	35.00

LONE RANGER Silver Bullets (see page 191).

Photo Courtesy Jim Harmon.

189

	G	**VG**	**M**
JUNIOR G-MEN OF AMERICA, late 1930s, gold-plated tin badge.........	5.00	7.50	10.00
JUNIOR TEXAS RANGER Badge, 1936 premium	7.50	11.25	15.00
KELLOGG'S Frogmen, 1950s, add baking soda and they swim under-water	7.50	11.25	15.00
KELLOGG'S KRUMBLES—Around-the-World paper dolls. Each cutout from box contains boy and girl, 10: Italy 11: Mexico 13: France 17: Czecho-slovakia. Price per each.............	1.00	1.50	2.00
KELLOGG'S Nautilus Nuclear Sub-marine, 1950s....................	5.00	7.50	10.00
KELLOGG'S PEP WARPLANES circa 1945, balsa wood models. Price per each	3.75	4.60	7.50
KELLOGG'S PEP WARPLANES circa 1945, balsa, with Superman ad on envelope........................	5.00	7.50	10.00
KELLOGG'S PEP WARPLANES—Circa 1944, cardboard. Price per each......	2.50	3.75	5.00
LITTLE ORPHAN ANNIE Necklace, circa 1936, metal enamel figure of LOA on metal chain...............	15.00	22.50	30.00
LITTLE ORPHAN ANNIE pinback button, "Little Orphan Annie, Member Funy Frosty's Club, mid-1930s.......	22.50	33.75	45.00
LONE RANGER, A Republic Serial—brass star badge...................	10.00	15.00	20.00
LONE RANGER, Atom Bomb Ring (very common)	9.00	13.50	18.00
LONE RANGER Blackout Kit 1942, KIX cereal glow in the dark material (two pieces), glow in the dark pledge to flag, glow in the dark Lone Ranger Volunteers armband, plus in-structions........................	32.50	48.75	65.00
LONE RANGER Bond Bread Safety Club Badge, 1938......................	8.00	12.00	16.00

	G	VG	M
LONE RANGER Clicker Pistol, black, 1939 movie giveaway, Lone Ranger on one side and ruby on other. Non-moveable silver cylinder............	15.00	22.50	30.00
LONE RANGER Deputy Shield—brass with secret compartment............	17.50	26.25	35.00
LONE RANGER Flashlight Ring.......	20.00	30.00	40.00
LONE RANGER Frontier Town—Full Set.............................	500.00	750.00	1000.00
LONE RANGER Glow-in-the-dark Belt, circa 1942......................	25.00	37.50	50.00
LONE RANGER Hiyo Silver pin, 1938...	5.00	7.50	10.00
LONE RANGER Lucky Piece—advertises 17th anniversary—1933-50..........	7.50	11.25	15.00
LONE RANGER Movie Film ring, late 1940s CHEERIOS premium.........	17.50	26.25	35.00
LONE RANGER Pedometer, 1943 CHEERIOS......................	10.00	15.00	20.00
LONE RANGER Rubber Band Gun and 6 different targets, 1938 MORTON SALT giveaway, cardboard..........	22.50	33.75	45.00
LONE RANGER Secret Compartment Ring, with picture of Lone Ranger and Silver.......................	20.00	30.00	40.00
LONE RANGER Silver bullet..........	3.75	4.60	7.50
LONE RANGER Silver bullet, Secret compartment Compass.............	20.00	30.00	40.00
LONE RANGER Silver Saddle Film Ring, late 1940s, CHEERIOS........	27.50	41.25	55.00

LONE RANGER Chief Scout Badge, SILVERCUP BREAD, early 1940s

LONE RANGER Secret Compartment Ring (see this page).
Photo Courtesy Jim Harmon.

	G	VG	M
premium, red, blue and gold.........	40.00	60.00	80.00
LONE RANGER Six-Shooter Ring, gun ring with plastic and metal gun attached to top. Turn wheel and flint sparks........................	15.00	22.50	30.00
LONE RANGER Victory Corps Badge, 1942, KIX Cereal.................	12.50	18.75	25.00
LONE RANGER Weather Ring—clear square stone on top with litmus paper. No markings to identify as Lone Ranger...........................	12.50	18.75	25.00
MAGIC SHOW Kit, 1946 GENERAL MILLS...........................	12.50	18.75	25.00
MAGICIAN'S BOOK OF CIGARETTE TRICKS, 1933, CAMEL CIGARETTES...........................	5.00	7.50	10.00
MAJOR BOWES—Home Microphone...	25.00	37.50	50.00
MALTEX HEALTH CLUB—pinback button	1.50	2.25	3.00
MELVIN PURVIS Junior G-Man Corps Badge, late 1930s.................	7.50	11.25	15.00
MELVIN PURVIS Junior G-Man Corps Roving Operative Badge, late 1930s...	7.50	11.25	15.00
MELVIN PURVIS Law and Order Ring.	22.50	33.75	45.00
MELVIN PURVIS Law & Order Patrol Lieutenant's Secret Operator Badge, mid-1930s	8.00	12.00	16.00
MELVIN PURVIS Law & Order Patrol Secret Operator Badge, late 1930's. ...	7.50	11.25	15.00
MELVIN PURVIS Secret Operator, Girl's Division	15.00	22.50	30.00
MICKEY AND DONALD'S RACE TO TREASURE ISLAND, 1939, 19x25" STANDARD OIL giveaway..........	25.00	37.50	50.00
MICKEY AND DONALD'S RACE TO TREASURE ISLAND, 1939, map of U.S. in full color 20x27", CALCO Gasoline giveaway, with stamps.........	100.00	150.00	200.00

	G	VG	M
MICKEY MOUSE CLUB Pinback Button, "Copyright 1928-30 by W. E. Disney", 1¼"	22.50	33.75	45.00
MICKEY MOUSE Globe-Trotters Map, 28x20", NBC Bread, 1937	25.00	37.50	50.00
MICKEY MOUSE Globe-Trotters Map, 28x22", NBC Bread, with all pictures pasted on	125.00	187.50	250.00
MICKEY MOUSE Globe-Trotters Map, 1930s, PEVELY MILK Premium	75.00	112.50	150.00
MICKEY MOUSE Official Money, 1930s MICKEY MOUSE CONES Giveaway, Denomination is "1" (each)	5.00	7.50	10.00
MICKEY MOUSE Playboard, 1946, 9" high, comics giveaway	9.00	13.50	18.00
MORTON SALT "Bat-O-Ball", 1939, features The Shadow (cartoon)	12.00	18.00	24.00
NABISCO Finger Puppet Rings, Slim Chants, horse Humbolt, gun, hand, Prairie Mary, Tagalong Boswell, Cold Deck Charlie, Sam Spiel, price per each figure	1.00	1.50	2.00
NABISCO Santa Fe Twin Unit Diesel Train, 1956, Includes engine, train, tracks, ground, background	4.00	6.00	8.00
NABISCO Sound-Jet Glider	5.00	7.50	10.00
NABISCO Trailblazers of America cards, six cards make up horse-drawn van and open van, 1956	4.00	6.00	8.00
NABISCO SHREDDED WHEAT Nabisco Flying Circus, 1948, designed by Wallace Rigby, 4x7" cards, planes, once cut out, can glide. Series of 24. Price per each	.35	.55	.75
THE NEBBS—Detroit Times series No. 27544 (comic strip)	3.75	4.60	7.50

	G	VG	M
NEW YORK WORLD'S FAIR CHILD-REN'S WORLD G-MAN Badge, give-away, 3-color brass badge..........	17.50	26.25	35.00
NEWSBOY BRAND Soups and Vegetables Official Booster Badge, late 1930s	3.00	4.50	6.00
PEP PINS—Superman...............	3.25	4.87	6.50
PEP PINS—Popeye and Olive Oyl—each.	3.00	4.50	6.00
PEP PINS—Flash Gordon and Felix the Cat—each	2.50	3.75	5.00
PEP PINS—The Phantom.............	2.00	3.00	4.00
PEP PINS—Others, includes Smitty, Inspector, Harold Teen, Skeezix, Corky, Judy, Min Gump, Wilmer, Smoky Stover, Tilda, Daisy, Ma Winkle, Tess Trueheart, Herbie, Mamie, Beezie, Pat Patton, Vitamin Flintheart, Maggie, Barney Google, Fat Stuff, Chief Brandon, Toots, Harold Teen, Nina, etc.	1.25	1.87	2.50
PILLSBURY-FARINA Complete Tel-A-Phone Set, 1938, two holders, mouthpieces, ear phones and 50 feet of line...	10.00	15.00	20.00
PINOCCHIO Playboard, 1946 Disney Comics sub. giveaway..............	9.00	13.50	18.00
POPEYE THE SAILOR MAN Button, ¾" copyright 1935, theatre giveaway.....	7.50	11.25	15.00
POPSICLE Movie Star coins—Aluminum coins circa early 1930s, includes Irene Dunne, Clark Gable, Marion Davies, Fredric March, Marie Dressler, Gary Cooper	1.50	2.25	3.00
PORCELAIN ENAMEL & MFG Co. 6" West Point Cadet on 3x6" card with PEMCO ad on back...............	.50	.75	1.00
POST GRAPE NUTS FLAKES Play-Filling Station, circa 1950s..............	2.00	3.00	4.00

	G	VG	M
POST TOASTIES 1939 Walt Disney cutout figures, on box, Mickey the Traffic Cop, two types of Pinocchio, etc. Price per each box......................	7.50	11.25	15.00
POST TOASTIES CORN FLAKES COMIC RINGS 1949, Fritz, Hans, Tillie the Toiler, Toots, Casper, etc.	3.75	4.60	7.50
POST'S CEREAL Junior Detective Club Sergeant Badge, late 1930s...........	7.00	10.50	14.00
POST'S Explorer Ring, 1947, includes compass, sun watch, sunset predicter and star finder, plastic dome........	15.00	22.50	30.00
POST Cereal Rings—1948, Perry Winkle, Winnie Winkle, Harold Teen, Skeezix, Lillums, Herbie, Smoky Stover, etc. ..	3.00	4.50	6.00
POST Cereal rings—1948—Dick Tracy..	5.00	7.50	10.00
POST RAISIN BRAN Sheriff Badge.....	1.00	1.50	2.00
RADIO ORPHAN ANNIE—Annie and Joe Corntassel button, 1931..........	5.00	7.50	10.00
RADIO ORPHAN ANNIE—Associated Membership Pin, 1934.............	5.00	7.50	10.00
RADIO ORPHAN ANNIE Bandana, 1934	20.00	30.00	40.00
RADIO ORPHAN ANNIE Birthstone Ring, 1935.......................	12.50	18.75	25.00
RADIO ORPHAN ANNIE Capt. Sparks Aviation Trainer..................	50.00	75.00	100.00
RADIO ORPHAN ANNIE Circus Cut-Outs, 1935......................	20.00	30.00	40.00
RADIO ORPHAN ANNIE Code Captain Belt and Buckle, 1940..............	40.00	60.00	80.00
RADIO ORPHAN ANNIE Code Captain Pin, 1939.......................	17.50	26.25	35.00
RADIO ORPHAN ANNIE Manual, 1934.	20.00	30.00	40.00
RADIO ORPHAN ANNIE 1935 Decoder Manual..........................	20.00	30.00	40.00
RADIO ORPHAN ANNIE 1936 Decoder Manual..........................	17.50	26.25	35.00
RADIO ORPHAN ANNIE 1937 Decoder Manual..........................	15.00	22.50	30.00

	G	VG	M
RADIO ORPHAN ANNIE 1938 Decoder Manual...........................	20.00	30.00	40.00
RADIO ORPHAN ANNIE 1939 Decoder Manual...........................	20.00	30.00	40.00
RADIO ORPHAN ANNIE 1940 Decoder Manual...........................	50.00	75.00	100.00
RADIO ORPHAN ANNIE 1942 Decoder Manual and cardboard decoder........	100.00	150.00	200.00
RADIO ORPHAN ANNIE Decoder Pin, 1935...............................	15.00	22.50	30.00
RADIO ORPHAN ANNIE Decoder Badge, 1936............................	7.50	11.25	15.00
RADIO ORPHAN ANNIE Decoder Badge 1937.............................	10.00	15.00	20.00
RADIO ORPHAN ANNIE Decoder Badge 1938.............................	7.50	11.25	15.00
RADIO ORPHAN ANNIE Decoder Badge 1939.............................	15.00	22.50	30.00
RADIO ORPHAN ANNIE Decoder Badge 1940.............................	30.00	45.00	60.00
RADIO ORPHAN ANNIE Foreign Coins, 1937.............................	10.00	15.00	20.00
RADIO ORPHAN ANNIE Goofy Circus, 1939.............................	10.00	15.00	20.00
RADIO ORPHAN ANNIE Identification Bracelet, 1934....................	15.00	22.50	30.00
RADIO ORPHAN ANNIE Identification Bracelet, 1935....................	10.00	15.00	20.00
RADIO ORPHAN ANNIE Identification Tag, 1939........................	12.50	18.75	25.00
RADIO ORPHAN ANNIE Magic Transfer Pictures, 1935....................	10.00	15.00	20.00
RADIO ORPHAN ANNIE Magic Transfer Picture, 1937....................	7.50	11.25	15.00
RADIO ORPHAN ANNIE Mask, 1933...	12.50	18.75	25.00
RADIO ORPHAN ANNIE Mystic Eye Ring, 1939.........................	12.50	18.75	25.00
RADIO ORPHAN ANNIE Package, 1942, includes Whirl-O-Matic Decoder, Whistle Badge, booklet and order blanks............................	60.00	90.00	120.00

	G	VG	M
RADIO ORPHAN ANNIE Pin, 1937	5.00	7.50	10.00
RADIO ORPHAN ANNIE Portrait Ring, 1934, ring has head of Annie embossed into top	12.50	18.75	25.00
RADIO ORPHAN ANNIE Premium Manual, 1937	25.00	37.50	50.00
RADIO ORPHAN ANNIE Premium Manual, 1938	37.50	46.00	75.00
RADIO ORPHAN ANNIE Punchouts, 1942	100.00	150.00	200.00
RADIO ORPHAN ANNIE Ring, 1934 . . .	12.50	18.75	25.00
RADIO ORPHAN ANNIE Ring, 1935 . . .	15.00	22.50	30.00
RADIO ORPHAN ANNIE Roller Skates, 1938	30.00	45.00	60.00
RADIO ORPHAN ANNIE Secret Egyptian Compass and Sundial, 1938	22.50	33.75	45.00
RADIO ORPHAN ANNIE Secret Society Pin, 1934	5.00	7.50	10.00
RADIO ORPHAN ANNIE Signet Ring, 1937	15.00	22.50	30.00
RADIO ORPHAN ANNIE Silver Star Pin, 1934	10.00	15.00	20.00
RADIO ORPHAN ANNIE Silver Star Pin, 1935	10.00	15.00	20.00
RADIO ORPHAN ANNIE Secret Society Silver Star Ring, 1936	30.00	45.00	60.00
RADIO ORPHAN ANNIE Silver Star Ring, 1937	20.00	30.00	40.00
RADIO ORPHAN ANNIE Silver Star Ring, 1938	17.50	26.25	35.00

RADIO ORPHAN ANNIE Decoder Badge 1936 (see page 195).
Photo Courtesy Jim Harmon.

	G	VG	M
RADIO ORPHAN ANNIE School Pin, 1939	3.00	4.50	6.00
RADIO ORPHAN ANNIE Secret Guard Clicker, 1942	15.00	22.50	30.00
RADIO ORPHAN ANNIE Shake-Up Game, 1931	6.00	9.00	12.00
RADIO ORPHAN ANNIE Sun Watch, 1938	12.50	18.75	25.00
RADIO ORPHAN ANNIE 3-Way Dog Whistle, 1940	20.00	30.00	40.00
RADIO ORPHAN ANNIE Treasure Hunt Game, 1933	7.50	11.25	15.00
RADIO ORPHAN ANNIE Treasure Hunt Game, 1935	7.50	11.25	15.00
RANGE RIDER & Dick West button, PETER PAN Bread, 1950s	2.50	3.75	5.00
RED RYDER Lucky Coin	1.00	1.50	2.00
RIN TIN TIN Ring, plastic, 1950s	4.00	6.00	8.00
RIP MASTERS (Rin Tin Tin) plastic rings, 1950s	4.00	6.00	8.00
ROCKY LANE'S Explorer's Sun Watch, 1951, CARNATION MILK	12.50	18.75	25.00
ROY ROGERS Branding Iron Ring	20.00	30.00	40.00
ROY ROGERS Deputy Badge	9.00	13.50	18.00
ROY ROGERS Microscope Ring, 1947, QUAKER OATS	17.50	26.25	35.00
ROY ROGERS Paint Set, 1950s	7.50	11.25	15.00
ROY ROGERS Signal Badge with mirror, secret compartment, and whistle	12.50	18.75	25.00
ROY ROGERS Silver Hat Ring	15.00	22.50	30.00
ROY ROGERS—Trigger's Lucky Horseshoe, full size, black rubber	7.50	11.25	15.00
ROY ROGERS Tuck-A-Way-Gun	5.00	7.50	10.00
SCOOP WARD NEWS OF YOUTH OFFICIAL REPORTER BADGE, late 1930s, Ward's Soft Bun Bread Giveaway	5.00	7.50	10.00
SECRET THREE Badge, with manual of secret codes	7.50	11.25	15.00

SHADOW ring (see this page).
Photo Courtesy Jim Harmon.

	G	VG	M
SGT. PRESTON Distance Finder.......	32.50	48.75	65.00
SGT. PRESTON Fire-Fighting Set......	32.50	48.75	65.00
SGT. PRESTON Flashlight—Signals, has two filters........................	15.00	22.50	30.00
SGT. PRESTON Klondike Land Pouch..	11.25	16.87	22.50
SGT. PRESTON Pedometer...........	12.50	18.75	25.00
SGT. PRESTON Police Whistle with Nylon Cord, brass, 1950............	12.50	18.75	25.00
SGT. PRESTON Skinning Knife........	15.00	30.00	45.00
SGT. PRESTON Totem Pole Set........	20.00	30.00	50.00
SGT. PRESTON Trail Kit (Probably the most complex of all premiums)....	30.00	50.00	100.00
SGT. PRESTON Yukon Village.........	150.00	225.00	300.00
SHADOW Ring, Glow in Dark, "blue coal" jewel on white ring............	125.00	187.50	250.00
SHADOW "Carey Salt" ring (identical to J. Armstrong crocodile ring except for paper instructions)..............	35.00	50.00	75.00
SHIELD G-Man Club Badge, 1942, Pep Comics premium, lithographed celluloid pinback......................	12.50	18.75	25.00
SKIPPY S.S.S.S. Captain, pinback button, all celluloid, 1930s.............	7.50	11.25	15.00
SKIPPY Compass, 1930s?.............	6.00	9.00	12.00
SKY BIRDS Propellor ring, brass and silver, 1930s GOUDEY GUM premium	2.50	3.75	5.00
SKY KING Aztec Indian Ring..........	25.00	37.50	50.00
SKY KING Detecto Microscope.........	20.00	30.00	40.00

	G	VG	M
SKY KING Detecto Writer.............	26.00	39.00	52.00
SKY KING Electronic Television Ring...	32.50	48.75	65.00
SKY KING Glow in the dark Signal Ring.	20.00	30.00	40.00
SKY KING Magni-Glo Ring............	12.50	18.75	25.00
SKY KING Mystery Picture Ring........	22.50	33.75	45.00
SKY KING Navajo Indian Ring.........	22.50	33.75	45.00
SKY KING—Small plastic statue of Penny from the show, dressed in cowgirl clothes (models of other characters also undoubtedly exist).............	7.00	10.50	14.00
SKY KING Signal Scope...............	25.00	37.50	50.00
SKY KING Stamp Kit.................	12.00	18.00	24.00
SKY KING Teleblinker Ring...........	25.00	37.50	50.00
SNOW WHITE Game, TEK TOOTH-BRUSH.........................	25.00	37.50	50.00
SPACE PATROL Binoculars, circa 1950s.	22.50	33.75	45.00
SPACE PATROL Buckle decoder.......	12.50	18.75	25.00
SPACE PATROL Diplomatic Pouch, Contains money, stamps, etc.........	25.00	37.50	50.00
SPACE PATROL Goggles.............	10.00	15.00	20.00
SPACE PATROL Ring, with secret powder compartment, circa early 1950s	50.00	75.00	100.00
SPACE PATROL Smoke Gun, 1950s....	45.00	67.50	90.00
SPACE PATROL Space Helmet, circa 1950s	20.00	30.00	40.00
SPACE PATROL Space Ship, circa 1950s.	50.00	75.00	100.00
SPACE PATROL Walkie Talkie, circa 1950s	30.00	45.00	60.00
SPEED GIBSON'S Flying Police Badge, DREIKORN'S BREAD..............	15.00	22.50	30.00
STRAIGHT ARROW Indian Head Ring, circa early 1950s.................	22.50	33.75	45.00
STRAIGHT ARROW Picture Ring, circa early 1950s.......................	20.00	30.00	40.00
STRAIGHT ARROW Tom-Tom, circa early 1950s.......................	12.50	18.75	25.00
STRAIGHT ARROW Wrist Bracelet with secret compartment—circa early 1950s	12.50	18.75	25.00
SUPERMAN Crusader Ring...........	37.50	56.25	75.00

Superman of America Button (see this page).

Photo Courtesy Jim Harmon.

	G	VG	M
SUPERMAN KELLOGG'S Gy Rocket...	35.00	52.50	70.00
SUPERMAN KELLOGG'S Silver Jet Airplane Ring, plane flies off............	20.00	30.00	40.00
SUPERMAN PIN, 1940s, "Read Superman Action Comics Magazine".......	8.00	12.00	16.00
SUPERMAN Planes from PEP cereal, set of 8, 1948....................	12.50	18.75	25.00
SUPERMAN Premium Club Set—Certificate, Button and Decoder...........	50.00	75.00	100.00
SUPERMAN Tim Club Ring...........	35.00	52.50	70.00
SUPERMAN'S Secret Code, circa 1939...	20.00	30.00	40.00
SUPERMEN OF AMERICA Button—1939 version, 1-3/8" pinback button...	17.50	26.25	35.00
TARZAN Gift Statues, FOULDS, 1930s, Tarzan, Jane, Kala, etc. Price per set..............................	400.00	600.00	800.00
TARZAN Jungle Map and Treasure Hunt WESTON BISCUIT, 1933......	50.00	75.00	100.00
TENNESSEE JED Look Around Ring, 1940s	27.50	41.25	55.00
TENNESSEE JED Paper Gun, circa 1940s	20.00	30.00	40.00
TERRY AND THE PIRATES Glow in the Dark ring, crocodiles on sides.....	20.00	30.00	40.00
TERRY AND THE PIRATES Gold Detector Ring...................	20.00	30.00	40.00
TEXAS LONGHORN tin badge, POST RAISIN BRAN, circa 1950s..........	2.00	3.00	4.00

TOM MIX Tiger Eye Ring (see page 207).

Photo Courtesy Jim Harmon.

TERRY & THE PIRATES Glow in the dark ring (see page 201).

Photo Courtesy Jim Harmon.

	G	VG	M
TOM CORBETT SPACE CADET Badge, early 1950s	7.50	11.25	15.00
TOM CORBETT SPACE CADET Belt Buckle Decoder, early 1950s	25.00	37.50	50.00
TOM CORBETT Decoder, cardboard, 1950s	2.50	3.75	5.00
TOM CORBETT SPACE CADET Space Cadet Girl Uniform plastic ring, 1952 KELLOGG'S PEP	4.00	6.00	8.00
TOM CORBETT SPACE CADET Space Cadet Insignia Ring, plastic, KELLOGG'S PEP 1952	12.50	18.75	25.00
TOM MIX Airplane and Parachute	50.00	75.00	100.00
TOM MIX Badge—Ranch Boss	32.50	48.75	65.00
TOM MIX Badge—Whistles	22.50	33.75	45.00
TOM MIX Belt Buckle with Secret Compartment, belt glows in dark (offered only on cereal boxes after radio show ended)	50.00	75.00	125.00
TOM MIX Bandana, has TM Brand	25.00	37.50	50.00
TOM MIX Baseball	17.50	26.25	35.00
TOM MIX Baseball bat	17.50	26.25	35.00
TOM MIX Baseball cap	17.50	26.25	35.00
TOM MIX Blowdart Game	35.00	52.50	70.00
TOM MIX Branding Iron, TM Brand	20.00	30.00	40.00
TOM MIX Bullet Telescope, bird-call device comes with it. approx. 4" long	17.50	26.25	35.00

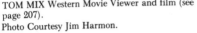

TOM MIX Western Movie Viewer and film (see page 207).
Photo Courtesy Jim Harmon.

TOM MIX Postal Telegraph Signal set, back view (see page 205).
Photo Courtesy Jim Harmon.

	G	VG	M
TOM MIX Charm Bracelet with charms-steer head, gun, horseman, TM brand.	20.00	30.00	40.00
TOM MIX Compass Magnifying Glass, 1937, silver color (Note: Originals have "Japan" written on the back. Imitations have the words "Comet-Japan" on the back)..............	21.00	31.50	42.00
TOM MIX Compass—Magnifying Glass 1939, brass.......................	26.00	39.00	52.00
TOM MIX Compass—Magnifying Glass circa 1948, glows in the dark, plastic..	17.50	26.25	35.00
TOM MIX Decoder Badge 1940—moveable 6-shooter points to symbols..	22.50	33.75	45.00
TOM MIX Decoder Buttons Instruction Sheet, 1946, Ralston................	7.50	11.25	15.00
TOM MIX Decoder Pins—Tom, Tony, Jane, Sheriff, Wash. Price per pin.....	3.00	4.50	6.00
TOM MIX Flashlight.................	27.50	41.25	55.00
TOM MIX Gold Ore Badge...........	7.50	11.25	15.00
TOM MIX Gold Ore Charm, 1940, RALSTON, contains genuine gold ore under plastic dome................	17.50	26.25	35.00
TOM MIX "Good Luck" Spinner.......	21.00	31.50	42.00
TOM MIX Horseshoe nail ring, 1933 (can be verified only by Accompanying papers)...................	25.00	37.50	50.00
TOM MIX Identification Bracelet.......	20.00	30.00	40.00
TOM MIX Initial Ring, 1935...........	25.00	37.50	50.00

TOM MIX Six-Shooter (see page 206).
Photo Courtesy Jim Harmon.

TOM MIX Whistle Ring (see page 207).

Photo Courtesy Jim Harmon.

TOM MIX Straightshooters Medal (see page 207).
Photo Courtesy Jim Harmon.

CAPTAIN MIDNIGHT Medal, 1940 (see page 183).
Photo Courtesy Jim Harmon.

	G	VG	M
TOM MIX Look-Around Ring, circa post 1945	30.00	45.00	60.00
TOM MIX Lucky Wrist Band, 1936 Ralston Premium, Metal, TM bar brand, with leather strap and buckle	37.50	56.25	75.00
TOM MIX Magnet Gun and Signal Arrowhead bracelet, gun and arrowhead glow in the dark	30.00	45.00	60.00
TOM MIX Magnet Ring, 1945	21.00	31.50	42.00
TOM MIX Makeup kit (two grease-paint model, plus five grease-paint model)	75.00	112.50	150.00
TOM MIX 1941 Manual	30.00	45.00	60.00
TOM MIX 1944 Manual	27.50	41.25	55.00
TOM MIX 1946 Manual	27.50	41.25	55.00
TOM MIX Mask, cardboard	32.50	48.75	65.00
TOM MIX Mystery Picture Ring, 1939, with "look-in" picture of Tom Mix and Tony, viewed through one side of the ring	75.00	112.50	150.00

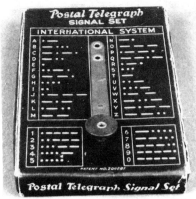

TOM MIX Postal Telegraph Signal Set 1940 (see this page).
Photo Courtesy Jim Harmon.

TOM MIX Look-Around Ring (see page 204).
Photo Courtesy Jim Harmon.

TOM MIX Magnet Ring (see page 204).
Photo Courtesy Jim Harmon.

TOM MIX TM brand ring (see page 207).
Photo Courtesy Jim Harmon.

	G	VG	M
TOM MIX Periscope	35.00	52.50	70.00
TOM MIX Postal Telegraph Set— Blue, metal clicker, 1938	37.50	56.25	75.00
TOM MIX Telegraph Set—Red, uses batteries, 1940	100.00	150.00	200.00
TOM MIX Ralston Straight Shooters Pocket Knife, 1940	17.50	26.25	35.00
TOM MIX Ralston Straight Shooters Walkie-Talkie, 1½" round	17.50	26.25	35.00
TOM MIX RCA TV set—shows photographs or comic strips (brown model, or reddish model)	15.00	22.50	30.00
TOM MIX PARACHUTE—1936 RALSTON premium	37.50	56.25	75.00

	G	VG	M
TOM MIX Secret Code Manual........	27.50	41.25	55.00
TOM MIX Sharpshooters Medal, glows in the dark.....................	27.50	41.25	55.00
TOM MIX Sheriff of Dobie County Siren Badge, 1946 RALSTON........	20.00	30.00	40.00
TOM MIX Signal Arrowhead with compass, magnifying glass, whistle....	15.00	22.50	30.00
TOM MIX Signal Flashlight............	26.00	39.00	52.00
TOM MIX Signature Ring, pre WW II...	27.50	41.25	55.00
TOM MIX Siren Ring, 1945............	22.50	33.75	45.00
TOM MIX Six-Shooter—wooden, barrel breaks and cartridge drum spins— 1933............................	25.00	37.50	50.00
TOM MIX Six-Shooter—wooden, barrel spins, 1936.......................	21.00	31.50	42.00
TOM MIX Six-Shooter—wooden, no moving parts, 1939.................	17.50	26.25	35.00

TOM MIX Decoder Badge (see page 203).

Photo Courtesy Jim Harmon.

TOM MIX Sharpshooters Medal (see this page).

Photo Courtesy Jim Harmon.

TOM MIX Mystery Picture Ring ad. (see page 204).
Photo Courtesy Jim Harmon.

TOM MIX Compass-Magnifying Glass, 1939 (see page 203).
Photo Courtesy Jim Harmon.

TOM MIX Compass-Magnifying Glass, 1937 (see page 203).
Photo Courtesy Jim Harmon.

	G	VG	M
TOM MIX Spinning Rope, 1936, RAL-STON, hemp with wood handle......	32.50	48.75	65.00
TOM MIX Spurs—Metal, with plastic glow-in-the-dark rowels. Late........	42.50	63.75	85.00
TOM MIX "Square and Fair" Spinner...	20.00	30.00	40.00
TOM MIX Straight Shooters Campaign Medal, gold......................	20.00	30.00	40.00
TOM MIX Straight Shooters Campaign Medal, silver.....................	22.50	33.75	45.00
TOM MIX Sundial Watch.............	27.50	41.25	55.00
TOM MIX Telephone Set.............	26.00	39.00	52.00
TOM MIX Telescope, TM brand on side.	26.00	39.00	52.00
TOM MIX Tiger Eye Ring, 1949, RALSTON......................	45.00	67.50	90.00
TOM MIX TM Brand ring, circa 1933...	22.50	33.75	45.00
TOM MIX Western Movie Viewer— shows scenes from Tom Mix films, 1935............................	30.00	45.00	60.00
TOM MIX Whistle Ring, 1945..........	20.00	30.00	40.00
TOM MIX Wrangler Badge, 1936, RALSTON......................	25.00	37.50	50.00
TRIGGER Button, 7/8", POST GRAPE NUT FLAKES....................	2.00	3.00	4.00
WHEATIES Jogometer..............	10.00	15.00	20.00
WHEATIES Pedometer, circa late 1940s	6.00	9.00	12.00
WILD BILL HICKOCK Treasure Map & Guide, 1952, KELLOGG'S..........	17.50	26.25	35.00

COMIC CHARACTER

(see also Premiums, Paper, Vehicles-Arcade, Hubley, Tootsietoy)

Comic character toys are extremely popular today with collectors, boosted by the surge in interest in comic books and strips which began in the middle 1960s. Although the bloom seems to be coming off the comic-collecting rose, there is as yet no sign that the relative amount of inertia current in that field has affected toy prices. However it is a state that may be worth casting a wary eye on.

"The Yellow Kid" is generally credited as the first American comic strip and comic character, beginning February 16, 1896. Within three years it had inspired what are presumably the first comic character toys.

In addition to the Yellow Kid, characters considered the most collectible include Popeye, Buck Rogers, Flash Gordon, Tarzan, Superman, Batman, Felix the Cat, Barney Google and Happy Hooligan. "Toonerville Trolley" also produced a number of sought-after toys, but probably as much because of the companies which made them, and the inherent charm of the toys themselves as for any strong interest in the strip itself. Dick Tracy toys sell well, but at generally lower prices, presumably because there were so many of them, and because few of the Tracy toys possessed the qualities that seize the imagination of collectors.

Since comic character toys draw collectors from different fields—toys, comic strips and comic books, radio and movies, prices are high due to the increased competition. Comic character toys also draw interest because they are almost invariably eye-catching and colorful, no doubt because of the medium from which they spring.

CONDITION OF A TOY
AND ITS RELATION TO PRICE

The price of a toy depends not only on its desirability, but on its condition. A toy in mint condition is generally worth twice what that same toy would bring in good condition, with "very good" falling about equally in between good and mint.

"Mint" means just that; the condition in which it was originally issued—perfect, regardless of age, not the slightest blemish. Needless to say this is a fairly rare state of affairs, but enough toys exist in mint condition to make it an employable term. Many people hoping to dispose of toys are tempted to call an item "mint" when it is really "near mint", "very good", or sometimes even just "good". Inevitably this can result in unhappiness all around, and not infrequently, a cancelled sale.

"Very Good" indicates a toy which has obviously seen use, with signs of wear and aging, but in general having a freshness to its appearance that makes it attractive and collectible to all but the most discriminating.

"Good" signals a toy that has seen considerable wear, shows its age, but is basically sound. A collector will collect it, but will often not be wholly satisfied with it as an example of his collection, and thus prices are often drastically below that which the same item in mint can command.

Condition below good results in another drastic drop in price, and toys with missing parts, although otherwise in excellent condition, will usually fall into this lower-priced category. Rust, even small spots of it, can seriously lower the price of a toy. "Near Mint", "Fine", "Very Fine" and similar terms often found in sellers' descriptions denote conditions between Mint and Very Good, and are priced accordingly.

The key to grading is to avoid wishful thinking. Grading can sometimes be a problem to the uninitiated, but common sense will usually prevail, and when possible, a consultation with an expert in the field can often clear up lingering doubts. A toy in its original box is worth up to 10 to 20% more if the box is in mint condition, with the price dropping as condition lessens.

LEHMANN "The Powerful Katrinka" (toonerville trolley) 6½" long (see page 218).
Photo Courtesy PB84

POPEYE in Barrel, Chein (see page 216).

COMIC CHARACTER

	G	VG	M
ALBERT ALLIGATOR (Pogo) plastic, 1969	2.00	3.00	4.00
ANDY GUMP bisque doll, small	7.50	11.25	15.00
BARNEY GOOGLE—stuffed cloth	35.00	52.50	70.00
BARNEY GOOGLE tin wind-up, circa 1923	325.00	487.50	650.00
BARNEY GOOGLE and SPARK PLUG, tin wind-up by NIFTY	300.00	450.00	600.00
B.O. PLENTY holding SPARKLE PLENTY, circa mid-1940s, tin wind-up, MARX	25.00	37.50	50.00
BATMAN glasses, 1966	.75	1.13	1.50
BATMAN Thingmaker set, 1960s	10.00	15.00	20.00
BATMAN Utility Belt, 1941, with belt-radio buckle	60.00	90.00	120.00
BEAUREGARD (Pogo), plastic, 1969	2.00	3.00	4.00
BILLY BATSON (Capt. Marvel) Magic Box	15.00	22.50	30.00
BLONDIE paint tin, 1952	1.50	2.25	3.00
BRINGING UP FATHER, hingee, 1944	7.00	10.50	14.00
BUCK ROGERS Atomic Pistol, 1946, U-235, sparks and pops, DAISY	32.50	48.75	65.00
BUCK ROGERS Battle Cruiser, TOOTSIETOY, 1937, two grooved wheels on top to run on string	20.00	30.00	40.00
BUCK ROGERS Chemical Laboratory, GROPPER TOYS, 1937	150.00	225.00	300.00
BUCK ROGERS Disintegrator pistol, 1936, DAISY	45.00	67.50	90.00
BUCK ROGERS Flash Attack Ship, TOOTSIETOY, 1937, two grooved wheels on top to run on string	20.00	30.00	40.00

BUCK ROGERS lead figures—These are generally new, from early casting sets. Sell for $2.50, painted and mounted.

	G	VG	M
BUCK ROGERS Police Patrol rocket, wind-up, MARX 1939	50.00	75.00	100.00
BUCK ROGERS "Pop" pistol, 1930s	9.00	13.50	18.00
BUCK ROGERS Rocket Pistol, XZ-31, 1934, DAISY, 9½" long	18.00	27.00	36.00
BUCK ROGERS rubber stamps, set of 7, 1930s	25.00	37.50	50.00
BUCK ROGERS Sonic Ray Gun, yellow plastic, uses bulb and battery	12.50	18.75	25.00
BUCK ROGERS Super-Scope, 1953, NORTON-HONER MFG CO., 8½" long, adjustable plastic telescope	10.00	15.00	20.00
BUCK ROGERS Rocket Ship, MARX wind-up, 1934	100.00	150.00	200.00
BUCK ROGERS Strato Kite, 1946	17.50	26.25	35.00
BUCK ROGERS U-238 Atomic Pistol & holster set, 1948	50.00	75.00	100.00
BUCK ROGERS U-238 Atomic Pistol & holster set, with box, adventure book, and coupon, 1948, DAISY	62.50	93.75	125.00
BUCK ROGERS Venus Duo Destroyer, TOOTSIETOY, two grooved wheels on top to run on string, 1937	20.00	30.00	40.00
BUCK ROGERS Water Pistol, Liquid Helium, XZ-44, DAISY, 1936	50.00	75.00	100.00
BUSTER BROWN in cart pulled by TIGE, cast iron	100.00	150.00	200.00
BUSTER BROWN and TIGE ring, brass, 1930s	11.00	16.50	22.00
CAPTAIN MARVEL Buzz Bomb	2.25	3.38	4.50
CAPTAIN MARVEL Magic Flute, copyright 1946, picture of Captain Marvel on side	10.00	15.00	20.00
CAPTAIN MARVEL Lightning race car, 1948, FAWCETT, tin wind-up, 4" long	7.00	10.50	14.00
CAPTAIN MARVEL Toss Bag	8.00	12.00	16.00
CAPTAIN MARVEL JR. Ski Jump, 7x10", circa 1946, paper, REED & ASSOCIATES, CHICAGO	2.00	3.00	4.00

	G	VG	M
CAPTAIN MARVEL'S Magic Picture, circa 1944, REED...............	2.25	3.38	4.50
CAPTAIN MARVEL'S Magic Eyes, circa 1945, REED....................	2.25	3.38	4.50
CAPTAIN MARVEL'S Rocket Raider, circa 1944-47, REED..............	2.25	3.38	4.50
CHESTER GUMP small bisque doll.....	7.50	11.25	15.00
CHESTER GUMP Cart, ARCADE, 1920s, horse, open two-wheel cart, Chester driving...................	185.00	277.50	370.00
CHING CHOW bisque doll, small......	7.50	11.25	15.00
COMIC STRIP RINGS, 1953, KING FEATURES, Phantom, Blondie, Barney Google, etc................	5.00	7.50	10.00
CHURCHY (Pogo) plastic, 1969........	2.00	3.00	4.00
DAGWOOD AEROPLANE, 1935, MARX	100.00	150.00	200.00
DAN DUNN Det. Corps Secret Operative 28 tin badge, circa 1930s............	15.00	22.50	30.00
DICK TRACY Air Detective Wings, circa late 1930s.......................	12.50	18.75	25.00
DICK TRACY click pistol, MARX No. 36	10.00	15.00	20.00
DICK TRACY detective badge with secret compartment, late 1930s, large, metal, leather pouch on back..............	20.00	30.00	40.00
DICK TRACY Electronic Wrist Radio...	12.50	18.75	25.00
DICK TRACY Insector General badge...	45.00	67.50	90.00
DICK TRACY Pen-Lite, 1940s?........	4.00	6.00	8.00
DICK TRACY Riot Car, circa 1946, MARX, heavy tin or sheetmetal litho, 7½" long, friction motor...........	15.00	22.50	30.00
DICK TRACY Siren Pistol, red with blue siren, circa late 1930s..............	15.00	22.50	30.00
DICK TRACY Siren Police Whistle No. 64, MARX, tin....................	5.00	7.50	10.00
DICK TRACY Sparkling Pop Pistol, tin litho, MARX No. 96...............	12.50	18.75	25.00

	G	VG	M
DICK TRACY Squad Car, convertible, heavy tin or sheetmetal, 20" long, MARX, circa 1948, friction motor with siren and battery-powered flashing light, Dick Tracy and Sam Catchum in plastic......................	17.50	26.25	35.00
DICK TRACY Target Game, MARX G25............................	12.50	18.75	25.00
DICK TRACY Target Game, MARX G34............................	7.50	11.25	15.00
DICK TRACY tin wind-up police car, 1949..........................	12.00	16.00	24.00
DICK TRACY viewer, 1940s, two films..	8.00	12.00	16.00
DICK TRACY JR. Click Pistol No. 78, MARX, aluminum.................	6.00	9.00	12.00
DICK TRACY'S HANDCUFFS FOR JUNIOR, circa 1946, JOHN HENRY PRODUCTS No. 700..............	7.50	11.25	15.00
ELMER FUDD Handpuppet, 1950s.....	1.00	1.50	2.00
FAVORITE FUNNIES large size rubber print set, Dick Tracy, Orphan Annie, etc. 14 stamps, pad, booklet.........	15.00	22.50	30.00
FELIX THE CAT, 1923, 2" high cast iron.............................	25.00	37.50	50.00
FELIX THE CAT, 2" pot metal nodding head figure, copyright Pat Sullivan on bottom of feet....................	12.50	18.75	25.00
FELIX THE CAT, 2½" high cast iron, circa 1930.......................	25.00	37.50	50.00
FELIX THE CAT, 1925, SCHOENHUT, jointed wood, 4" high..............	25.00	37.50	50.00
FELIX THE CAT, 1924, wooden, 6" high, GEORGE BORGFELDT CO., standup leather ears, jointed.........	37.50	56.25	75.00
FELIX THE CAT, 1940s, 9" high, wood, jointed, with rubber head......	22.50	33.75	45.00
FELIX THE CAT, China Set...........	25.00	37.50	50.00
FELIX THE CAT flasher ring, plastic...	6.00	9.00	12.00
FELIX THE CAT on fire truck, gong bell pull toy......................	30.00	45.00	60.00

	G	VG	M
FELIX THE CAT on tricycle, gong bell pull toy......................	55.00	82.50	110.00
FELIX THE CAT "Speedy Felix", in car.	50.00	75.00	100.00
FLASH GORDON aluminum pistol, 10" long, shoots blast of air using rubber diaphragm.......................	15.00	22.50	30.00
FLASH GORDON Arresting Ray, MARX, 1936? picture of Flash on handle......	50.00	75.00	100.00
FLASH GORDON belt, many illos, large plastic buckle showing rocket ship in flight	4.00	6.00	8.00
FLASH GORDON jet-propelled kite....	20.00	30.00	40.00
FLASH GORDON Radio Repeater clicker pistol, No. 58, MARX...............	12.50	18.75	25.00
FLASH GORDON Rocket Fighter, MARX wind-up, 1939...............	100.00	150.00	200.00
FLASH GORDON signal pistol, tin litho, MARX, No. 74....................	25.00	37.50	50.00
FLASH GORDON water gun, plastic....	5.00	7.50	10.00
Flying CAPTAIN MARVEL, 1944-47, REED, 7x10", paper................	2.25	3.38	4.50
HAPPY HOOLIGAN walking toy, CHEIN wind-up, 1932, 6" high.......	130.00	195.00	260.00
HER NAME IS MAUD tin watch fob, 1905................................	12.00	18.00	24.00
HERBY small bisque doll.............	7.50	11.25	15.00
HI-WAY HENRY, wind-up, 1920s, jalopy with man, woman, laundry above roof	800.00	1200.00	1600.00
HOPPY THE FLYING MARVEL BUNNY, circa 1944-47, REED, paper.	1.75	2.63	3.50
HUMPHREY MOBILE (Joe Palooka) tin wind-up, circa mid-1940s...........	40.00	60.00	80.00
"I Go POGO" button, 1952............	1.50	2.25	3.00
JEFF bendable figure, 1946............	60.00	90.00	120.00
JEFF small bisque doll................	7.50	11.25	15.00
JIGGS 3" high, hard plastic, 1960s......	2.00	3.00	4.00
JOAN PALOOKA doll...............	10.00	15.00	20.00
JOE PALOOKA, 4" high, wood-jointed..	10.00	15.00	20.00
KOMIC KAMERA—all metal viewer circa mid-1930s, used to view 35 mm film strips. With set of five film strips..	37.50	56.25	75.00

	G	VG	M
KOMIC KAMERA, without film strips..	25.00	37.50	50.00
KRAZY KAT tin wind-up, 1920s........	50.00	75.00	100.00
LIL ABNER AND HIS DOGPATCH BAND, 1945, UNIQUE, wind-up.....	60.00	90.00	120.00
LITTLE ORPHAN ANNIE tin wind-up, 5" high.........................	140.00	210.00	280.00
LITTLE ORPHAN ANNIE and SANDY, tin wind-up, MARX...............	175.00	262.50	350.00
LITTLE ORPHAN ANNIE stove, 8" high, circa 1930s..................	25.00	37.50	50.00
LITTLE ORPHAN ANNIE paint and crayon set, early 1930s, MILTON BRADLEY No. 4488...............	4.00	6.00	8.00
MAGGIE 3" hard plastic, 1960s........	2.00	3.00	4.00
MAMIE (Moon Mullins) 8" high bisque..	35.00	52.50	70.00
MANDRAKE THE MAGICIAN Magic Kit, 1949, TRANSOGRAM..........	11.00	16.50	22.00
MIGHTY MOUSE, rubber, 9" high, no mfr. listed....................	7.50	11.25	15.00
MOON MULLINS bisque doll, small....	7.50	11.25	15.00
MOON MULLINS and KAYO on Hand Car, circa 1940, 6" long, MARX tin wind-up......................	125.00	187.50	250.00
MOVIE KOMICS, reels of film for toy viewers, circa 1940s................	12.50	18.75	25.00
MUTT bendable figure, 1946..........	60.00	90.00	120.00
MUTT plaster figure, 1920s............	20.00	30.00	40.00
MUTT & JEFF terra cotta figurines, incense burners, circa 1910. Price for pair.............................	100.00	150.00	200.00
OLIVE OYL, rubber squeeze toy, 1950s.	7.00	10.50	14.00
OLIVE OYL and SWEEPEA HAND CAR, MARX.....................	75.00	112.50	150.00
PETE (the Tramp?) 1930s composition doll, strung......................	20.00	30.00	40.00
PETUNIA PIG, 1948, ceramic.........	4.00	6.00	8.00
POGO plastic, 1969..................	2.00	3.00	4.00
POPEYE "Bifbat" paddle toy, 1929.....	14.00	21.00	28.00
POPEYE "Bo Lo Paddle", 1929.........	3.00	4.50	6.00

	G	VG	M
POPEYE doll, "Cameo", hard rubber, jointed at neck, hips, shoulders, 14" high	37.50	56.25	75.00
POPEYE carrying parrots in cages, MARX wind-up, 1935, 7¾" high	40.00	60.00	80.00
POPEYE cast iron, 3½" high, circa 1930	30.00	45.00	60.00
POPEYE Express—MARX, overhead airplane, 1935	100.00	150.00	200.00
POPEYE Express—MARX, Popeye pushing box with parrot, wind-up, 1935	75.00	112.50	150.00
POPEYE handpuppet	2.50	3.75	5.00
POPEYE in a barrel, CHEIN, 7" high	30.00	45.00	60.00
POPEYE the Pilot, 1930, MARX wind-up	100.00	150.00	200.00
POPEYE in a Rowboat, 1935, HOGE	200.00	300.00	400.00
POPEYE on house, tin wind-up, 1930s	75.00	112.50	150.00
POPEYE Pirate, click pistol, MARX No. 68	7.50	11.25	15.00
POPEYE rubber squeeze toy, 1950s	8.00	12.00	16.00
POPEYE Whistle Pipe, NORTHWEST PRODUCTS OF ST. LOUIS, 3½" long, cardboard bowl with illos of Popeye characters, metal stem with whistle at base	5.00	7.50	10.00
POPEYE Yazoo Pipe, NORTHWESTERN PRODUCTIONS, ST. LOUIS MO., 1934	4.00	6.00	8.00
PORKY (Pogo) plastic, 1969	2.00	3.00	4.00
PORKY PIG squeeze toy, SUN RUBBER, Approx. 6" high, hollow with squeaker, has hands behind back, circa 1940	8.00	12.00	16.00
PORKY PIG hand puppet, 1950s	.50	.75	1.00
PRINCE VALIANT Shield, tin litho	9.00	13.50	18.00
PRINCE VALIANT Sword and tin scabbard, 1950s, MATTEL	10.00	15.00	20.00
RED RYDER gun and holster set, DAISY	10.00	15.00	20.00
RED RYDER Pop-Um shooting game, DAISY	12.50	18.75	25.00

	G	VG	M
RED RYDER Molding set............	12.50	18.75	25.00
RED RYDER Target Game, 1939.......	17.50	26.25	35.00
SCRAPPY Modeling clay, PETERSON MFG. circa early 1930s.............	7.50	11.25	15.00
SCHROEDER (Peanuts) rubber squeeze toy, circa 1960....................	2.50	3.75	5.00
SKEEZIX bisque, small...............	7.50	11.25	15.00
SKEEZIX oilcloth doll, cotton-stuffed, 1920s?...........................	37.50	56.25	75.00
SKIPPY bisque, approx. 2" high, painted, circa 1930s......................	2.50	3.75	5.00
SMOKEY STOVER, hard plastic, 3" high, 1960s......................	2.50	3.75	5.00
SNIFFLES THE MOUSE, 1948, ceramic.	3.50	5.25	7.00
SNOOPY rubber squeeze toy, 1958......	4.50	6.75	9.00
SPARKLE PLENTY molded soap figure, LIGHTFOOT SCHULTZ, 4½" high..	7.50	11.25	15.00
SPARKPLUG (Barney Google), stuffed cloth..........................	35.00	52.50	70.00
SUPERMAN holding airplane, MARX tin wind-up, 1940.................	75.00	112.50	150.00
SUPERMAN Krypto-Ray Gun, DAISY No. 94, 1939, with seven film strips....	125.00	187.50	250.00
TARZAN, mask of Akut the Ape, NORTHERN PAPER MILLS, 1933...	20.00	30.00	40.00
TARZAN, mask of Numa the Lion, paper, 1933 by NORTHERN PAPER MILLS...........................	20.00	30.00	40.00
TARZAN, mask of Tarzan, 1933 NORTHERN PAPER MILLS, paper..	25.00	37.50	50.00
TARZAN In The Jungle dart board game, 1935, large.................	75.00	112.50	150.00
THREE FLYING MARVELS (Captain, Jr., Mary), paper, circa 1944-47, REED............................	2.50	3.75	5.00
TOONERVILLE TROLLEY tin wind-up, "copyright 1922 by Fontaine Fox", 7½" high, Skipper driving..........	200.00	300.00	400.00
TOONERVILLE TROLLEY, 1921, STRAUSS wind-up................	250.00	375.00	500.00

"Popeye the Pilot" (see page 216)
Photo Courtesy PB84.

MARX, "Dagwood Aeroplane" (see page 212).
Photo Courtesy PB84

	G	VG	M
TOONERVILLE TROLLEY, 1-7/8" high, sometimes called Crackerjack size	160.00	240.00	320.00
TOONERVILLE TROLLEY—DENT, box only	5.00	7.50	10.00
TOONERVILLE TROLLEY, "Powerful Katrinka", 6½" long, pushing boy in wheelbarrow tin wind-up, LEHMANN, 1923	350.00	525.00	700.00
TWEETY BIRD rubber squeeze toy, 1950s	4.00	6.00	8.00
UNCLE WALT small bisque	7.50	11.25	15.00
UNCLE WIGGILY, MARX	50.00	75.00	100.00
WALTER LANTZ ink stamp character set, 12 different rubber stamps	2.50	3.75	5.00
Western Thrills with BILLY THE KID, character from Funny Animals Comics, circa 1944-47, REED, paper toy	1.25	1.88	2.50

Buck Rogers Atomic Pistol
(see page 210)
Photo Courtesy Jim Harmon.

	G	VG	M
WILLIE THE WORM and SAMMY in Car Trouble, paper toy, Fawcett Comics characters, REED, circa 1944-47	1.25	1.88	2.50
WILLIE THE WORM and SAMMY Flying Machine	1.25	1.88	2.50
WILLIE THE WORM and SAMMY Fish'n Fun	1.25	1.88	2.50
WIMPY 3" hard plastic figure, 1960s	2.00	3.00	4.00
WIMPY handpuppet	3.00	4.50	6.00
WIMPY pin, 1930s, 1¼", cut-out of Wimpy with hamburger, heavy metal, enameled	5.00	7.50	10.00
WIMPY rubber squeeze toy, 1950s	8.00	12.00	16.00
WOODY WOODPECKER, 6½" high, rubber, "Walter Lantz"	2.50	3.75	5.00
YELLOW KID papier mache and wood, SCHOENHUT, 11" high, early 1900s	60.00	90.00	120.00
YOGI BEAR sitting on log, rubber squeeze toy, 1960s	2.00	3.00	4.00

L TO R: Popeye carrying parrots in cages,
MARX (see page 216).
"Li'l" Abner and his dogpatch band (see page 215).

Photo Courtesy Garth's Auctions Inc.

MOVIES, RADIO, TELEVISION

(see also Paper, Premiums, Miscellaneous, Comic Character)

Toys based on people and characters from movies, radio and television are extremely popular, and attract collectors who otherwise would not bother with toys, and who are used to paying premium prices in their primary fields of interest, so prices here are generally high. Although usually toys from the period after World War II have minimal interest for collectors, the advent of television has made an impact on this category, and interest (as well as price) is high for such characters as Howdy Doody and Tom Corbett, indicating that plastic may be as much of a turn-on for future collectors as iron and tin are for today's.

CONDITION OF A TOY
AND ITS RELATION TO PRICE

The price of a toy depends not only on its desirability, but on its condition. A toy in mint condition is generally worth twice what that same toy would bring in good condition, with "very good" falling about equally in between good and mint.

"Mint" means just that; the condition in which it was originally issued—perfect, regardless of age, not the slightest blemish. Needless to say this is a fairly rare state of affairs, but enough toys exist in mint condition to make it an employable term. Many people hoping to dispose of toys are tempted to call an item "mint" when it is really "near mint", "very good", or sometimes just "good". Inevitably this can result in unhappiness all around, and not infrequently, a cancelled sale.

"Very Good" indicates a toy which has obviously seen use, with signs of wear and aging, but in general having a freshness to its appearance that makes it attractive and collectible to all but the most discriminating.

"Good" signals a toy that has seen considerable wear, shows its age, but is basically sound. A collector will collect it, but will often not be wholly satisfied with it as an example of his collection, and thus prices are often drastically below that which the same item in mint can command.

Condition below good results in another drastic drop in price, and toys with missing parts, although otherwise in excellent condition, will usually fall into this lower-priced category. Rust, even small spots of it, can seriously lower the price of a toy. "Near-Mint", "Very Fine", "Fine" and similar terms often found in sellers' descriptions denote conditions between Mint and Very Good, and are priced accordingly.

The key to grading is to avoid wishful thinking. Grading can sometimes be a problem for the uninitiated, but common sense will usually prevail, and when possible, a consultation with an expert in the field can often clear up lingering doubts. A toy in its original box is worth up to 10 to 20% more if the box is in mint condition, with the price dropping as its condition lessens.

Joe Penner, MARX (see page 225).

MARX, "Mortimer Snerd's Tricky Auto" (see page 225).

MARX, "Milton Berle Car" (see page 225).

MOVIES, RADIO, TELEVISION

	G	VG	M
AMOS tin wind-up....................	50.00	75.00	100.00
AMOS and ANDY wood jointed dolls, 6" high, price for pair.................	100.00	150.00	200.00
AMOS & ANDY FRESH-AIR TAXI, tin wind-up, MARX, 1929, 8" long....	150.00	225.00	300.00
BEATLES, Ringo, John, Paul, George, 5" vinyl figures, 1964. Price per each	2.50	3.75	5.00
BETTY BOOP character doll, jointed, 9½" tall, 1930s....................	15.00	22.50	30.00
BETTY BOOP pinback button........	3.50	5.25	7.00
BOB BURNS Bazooka, brass kazoo-like toy, patterned after radio-movie comic Burns' famous musical invention (the Army weapon gets its name from it), metal sliding tube, M.M. POCHAPIA TOYS, 13" long when not extended, 1930s	12.50	18.75	25.00
BUFFALO BILL JR. belt buckle (TV)...	5.00	7.50	10.00
CAPTAIN KANGAROO badge, tin shield	1.00	1.50	2.00
CHARLIE CHAPLIN, 4¾" high with soapstone finish, "Copyright by M.N.C."	12.00	18.00	24.00
CHARLIE CHAPLIN in cowboy outfit, SCHUCO.......................	35.00	52.50	70.00
CHARLIE CHAPLIN tin wind-up......	190.00	285.00	380.00
"CHARLIE MCCARTHY" written on top hat, standing erect, tin wind-up, circa 1938	50.00	75.00	100.00
CHARLIE MCCARTHY metal charm, 1930s, head moves.................	9.00	13.50	18.00
CHARLIE MCCARTHY BAND wind-up, MARX 1935.....................	112.50	168.75	225.00
CHARLIE MCCARTHY in his BENZINE BUGGY, MARX..................	57.50	86.75	115.00
CHARLIE MCCARTHY CAR wind-up, MARX, 1935....................	100.00	150.00	200.00

	G	VG	M
CHARLIE MCCARTHY chalk figure, colorful	15.00	22.50	30.00
CHARLIE MCCARTHY lapel pin	7.50	11.25	15.00
CHARLIE MCCARTHY rubber doll, Effanbee	20.00	30.00	40.00
CISCO KID neckerchief with nickel sombrero slide	10.00	15.00	20.00
DALE EVANS holster outfit	20.00	30.00	40.00
DRAGNET Jack Webb black police whistle	7.50	11.25	15.00
DRAGNET St. Los Angeles Police No. 714 badge	3.00	4.50	6.00
FLUB-A-DUB (Howdy Doody) small plastic figure	2.50	3.75	5.00
FROGGIE THE GREMLIN hollow rubber doll, squeeze toy 5" high, of the Buster Brown radio and TV show, squeeze and tongue sticks out, 1950s	12.50	18.75	25.00
HAROLD LLOYD "Funny Face", MARX wind-up walker, 1929	125.00	187.50	250.00
HOOT GIBSON lariat	15.00	22.50	30.00
HOPALONG CASSIDY compass	4.00	6.00	8.00
HOPALONG CASSIDY dart board, 14x17", stagecoach holdup and target practice, 1950	5.00	7.50	10.00
HOPALONG CASSIDY knife, circa mid-1940s, 3½" long	12.50	18.75	25.00
HOPALONG CASSIDY Photo Ring, circa late 1940s	5.00	7.50	10.00
HOPALONG CASSIDY Shooting Gallery	20.00	30.00	40.00
HOPALONG CASSIDY Signet Ring, all metal, late 1940s	7.50	11.25	15.00
HOPALONG CASSIDY woodburning set, 1950, AMERICAN TOY AND FURNITURE CO.	20.00	30.00	40.00
HOPALONG CASSIDY Zoomerang Gun, shoots paper, TIGRETT ENTERPRISES, CHICAGO	8.00	12.00	16.00
HOWDY DOODY, Clarabell's horn, 1950s	9.00	13.50	18.00

	G	VG	M
HOWDY DOODY, Cowboy Gloves, leather, 1950s....................	9.00	13.50	18.00
HOWDY DOODY hand puppets, no date no mfr., rubber heads, cloth bodies....	4.50	6.75	9.00
HOWDY DOODY Life Preserver, plastic, 1950s, shows Howdy, Mr. Bluster, etc.	10.00	15.00	20.00
HOWDY DOODY marionette, 17" high, wooden arms and legs, composition head...........................	30.00	45.00	60.00
HOWDY DOODY Mask, rubber........	4.00	6.00	8.00
HOWDY DOODY Piano, Howdy plays it	62.50	93.75	125.00
HOWDY DOODY plastic puppet toys, with levers in back of head to move mouths. Consists of Howdy, Bluster, Clarabell, Princess, Dilly Dally, TEE-VEE TOYS No. 549. Price for set.....	10.00	15.00	20.00
HOWDY DOODY plastic ukulele, EMENEE, 1950s...................	10.00	15.00	20.00
HOWDY DOODY "Put-In-Head", similar to Mr. Potato⁻ Head, but with Howdy characters, Howdy, Bluster, Clarabell, Princess. Price for set......	11.00	16.50	22.00
HOWDY DOODY, riding a cart, LINT TOYS 8½" long, 7" high...........	70.00	105.00	140.00
HOWDY DOODY Squeeze toy, 7" high..	7.50	11.25	15.00
HOWDY DOODY TV set with paper filmstrips, LEGO, 1950s...........	12.50	18.75	25.00
HOWDY DOODY tin wind-up, MARX, circa 1950, 5" high, Howdy plays banjo and moves head.............	30.00	45.00	60.00
HOWDY DOODY tin wind-up, circa 1950, Howdy does jig and Clarabell sits at piano, MARX, 5½" high.......	70.00	105.00	140.00
HOWDY DOODY wood-jointed doll, 12" high........................	37.50	56.25	75.00
HUCKLEBERRY HOUND as FIREMAN, rubber, squeeze toy, 1960s...........	2.00	3.00	4.00
HUCKLEBERRY HOUND with top hat, rubber squeeze toy, 1960s...........	2.00	3.00	4.00
HUCKLEBERRY HOUND For President badge..........................	.75	1.12	1.50

	G	VG	M
JOE PENNER tin wind-up, MARX, circa 1930s, 8" high, tips hat, walks, "Wanna Buy a Duck?"	60.00	90.00	120.00
LONE RANGER and SILVER composition figure, 1938	12.50	18.75	25.00
LONE RANGER Chuck Wagon Lantern	25.00	37.50	50.00
LONE RANGER flashlight	9.00	13.50	18.00
LONE RANGER harmonica, MAGNUS, 1950	5.00	7.50	10.00
LONE RANGER "Hiyo Silver, the Lone Ranger" tin wind-up, copyright 1938, Lone Ranger on Silver with lasso	30.00	45.00	60.00
LONE RANGER Official First Aid Kit with contents, 1938, tin litho	10.00	15.00	20.00
LONE RANGER Paint Box	2.00	3.00	4.00
LONE RANGER Picture Printing Set, 1939, 8 rubber stamps	15.00	22.50	30.00
LONE RANGER RIDES AGAIN movie viewer, 1939	15.00	22.50	30.00
LONE RANGER Shoulder Bag with color picture of Lone Ranger and Tonto, decorated with studs, jewels, and fringe, 1940s	8.00	12.00	16.00
LONE RANGER Signal Siren, 1950, with silver bullet secret code, UNITED STATES ELECTRIC MFG. CO	7.50	11.25	15.00
LONE RANGER Silver Bullet Knife, length 3", closed	14.00	21.00	28.00
LONE RANGER Target Game, 1938, MARX	20.00	30.00	40.00
MATT DILLON, U.S. Marshall badge (Gunsmoke)	2.50	3.75	5.00
MILTON BERLE CAR, two large wheels, two small, MARX, 1950s, "What the Hey", etc. written on car	25.00	37.50	50.00
MORTIMER SNERD Band, MARX wind-up, 1935	110.00	165.00	220.00
"MORTIMER SNERD'S TRICKY AUTO", 1939, MARX	65.00	97.50	130.00
OUR GANG, bisque of Joe, 3" high	12.00	18.00	24.00

	G	VG	M
RIN TIN TIN and RUSTY Knife, 1950s..	18.00	27.00	36.00
ROBIN HOOD Money Pouch, six foreign coins from Richard Greene TV series, 1953-54	3.75	5.62	7.50
ROBIN HOOD Money Pouch, fifteen foreign coins, from Richard Greene TV series.	5.00	7.50	10.00
ROY ROGERS bandana, large.	3.00	4.50	6.00
ROY ROGERS Double R Bar Ranch, 1950s, tin litho ranch house, MAR Toys, 6" high by 11" long by 6" wide.	17.50	26.25	35.00
ROY ROGERS Lantern, metal, hurricane type with plastic chimney.	5.00	7.50	10.00
ROY ROGERS Mineral City, town with hotel, music hall, cafe, bank, barber shop, trade goods, etc., tin.	12.50	18.75	25.00
ROY ROGERS Nellie Belle Jeep.	22.50	33.75	45.00
ROY ROGERS pocket flashlight.	5.00	7.50	10.00
ROY ROGERS Quickshooter hat.	14.00	21.00	28.00
ROY ROGERS Riders Lucky Piece.	4.00	6.00	8.00
ROY ROGERS Signal Flashlight.	4.50	6.75	9.00
ROY ROGERS and TRIGGER pocket knife.	14.00	21.00	28.00
SMALL FRY CLUB KIT, 1949, button, etc., Dumont TV show (may be premium).	7.50	11.25	15.00
SPANKY OF OUR GANG 1930s pinback button	6.00	9.00	12.00
TALES OF THE TEXAS RANGERS Deputy badge.	2.50	3.75	5.00
THREE STOOGES handpuppet, Moe, Curley and Larry, price per each.	7.00	10.50	14.00
TOM CORBETT SPACE CADET, 14 different figures, MARX, 1950s. Price per set.	4.50	6.75	9.00
TOM CORBETT, 7 different figures, same as above, price per set.	3.00	4.50	6.00
TOM CORBETT Cosmic Vision Space Helmet, one-way vision, plastic, early 1950s	20.00	30.00	40.00

	G	VG	M
TOM CORBETT SPACE CADET Field Glasses	25.00	37.50	50.00
TOM CORBETT Plaster Casting Set	20.00	30.00	40.00
TOM CORBETT SPACE CADET Flashlight with built-in signal siren, 7" long, metal, US ALITE Corp	7.00	10.50	14.00
TOM CORBETT SPACE CADET wind-up Polaris Rocket Ship, MAR Toys, 1952, 12" long, Tom, Astro and Roger looking out of cockpit	37.50	56.25	75.00
TOM CORBETT SPACE CADET Official Space Pistol, MARX No. 105, 1950s	10.00	15.00	20.00
TOM CORBETT SPACE CADET Rifle, MARX No. 0239	15.00	22.50	30.00
TOM CORBETT Space Station	40.00	60.00	80.00
TOM MIX Rodeorope, 1928, comes with box and instructions	37.50	56.25	75.00
WILD BILL HICKOCK Marshal Star Badge with picture of Hickock and Jingles in center	7.00	10.50	14.00

DISNEY

(see also Paper, Premiums)

Disneyana comprises one of the most popular areas of toy-collecting. The list of toys inspired by the Disney organization is virtually endless, and its collectors are perhaps the most diverse of all; mainline toy collectors, animation freaks, movie nuts, comic strip and comic book aficionados, straight Disney fanatics. As a result, competition by so many for Disney items has caused considerable inflation, with no sign of it stopping. Further, with Disney still heavily involved in movies, television, and comic strips, there is little likelihood of this happening in the foreseeable future. Although virtually all areas of Disney inspire interest, it is the comic characters who generate the most avidity, and in particular Donald Duck and Mickey Mouse, in that order.

Ducks are big these days. Donald was always big; recently the discovery that the "good" Donald Duck artist in Walt Disney comic books was a man named Carl Barks has caused interest in Donald to soar even further, the enthusiasm for Barks' work spilling over to the character himself. The emergence on the scene of Marvel Comics' Howard the Duck in comic books and strips has further stimulated interest in the original Duck (so much so, I am informed, that all sorts of old duck toys tend to sell quickly these days, no matter how divorced they may be from movies and comics). Mickey Mouse, though second most popular, was the first major Disney creation, and spawned countless toys. Mickey toys from the 1930s are the most pursued, since collectors seem to agree that he was esthetically at his most interesting during that period.

Although Walt Disney was involved in animation as early as 1920, his first really notable character was Oswald the Rabbit, introduced in 1927. However, Disney did not own the rights, which eventually fell into the hands of another animator, Walter Lantz. Mickey Mouse first appeared in the 1928 short "Plane Crazy", but the third Mickey cartoon, "Steamboat Willie", seems to have been the first released, on November 18, 1928, and Mickey was a success from that point on. Minnie Mouse also appeared in the latter film, with Pluto emerging in 1930, though not called that till 1931, Goofy debuting in 1932, and the terrible-tempered Donald Duck in 1934. Mickey Mouse toys were first produced in 1930, and since then the stream of Disneyana has been unending, and apparently all of it deemed collectible.

As a result, of all toys in this book, the important Disney collectibles are probably the least likely to suffer a collapse in interest.

Though there is no sure hedge against inflation and deflation, Disneyana gives strong evidence of being able to compete handily with the most blue-chipped of commodities on the New York Stock Exchange, and is certainly a great deal more pleasurable.

CONDITION OF A TOY AND ITS RELATION TO PRICE

The price of a Disney toy depends not only on its desirability, but on its condition. A toy in mint condition is generally worth twice what the same toy would bring in good condition, with "very good" falling about equally in between good and mint.

"Mint" means just that; the condition in which it was originally issued—perfect, regardless of age, not the slightest blemish. Needless to say this is a fairly rare state of affairs, particularly with the early Disney toys, but these items do exist, which means that full value must be given the term, or unhappiness all around will result.

"Very Good" indicates a toy that has obviously seen use, with some signs of wear and aging, but in general having a freshness to its appearance that makes it attractive and collectible to all but the most discriminating.

"Good" signals a toy that has seen considerable wear and shows its age, but is otherwise basically sound. A collector will collect it, but will often not be wholly satisfied with it as an example of his collection, and thus prices are often drastically below that which the same item in mint can command.

Condition below good results in another drastic drop in price, and toys with missing parts, although otherwise in excellent condition, will usually fall into this lower-priced category. "Near Mint", "Fine", "Very Fine" and similar terms often found in sellers' descriptions denote conditions between Mint and Very Good, and are priced accordingly.

The key to grading is to avoid wishful thinking. Grading can sometimes be a problem to the uninitiated, but common sense will usually prevail, and when possible, a consultation with an expert in the field can often clear up lingering doubts. A toy on its original card or in its original box is worth up to 10 to 20% more.

DISNEY

	G	VG	M
BASHFUL bisque, 3" high, circa 1935...	7.50	11.25	15.00
BASHFUL bisque, 4" high, circa 1939...	12.50	18.75	25.00
BASHFUL Party Mask, 1937..........	6.00	9.00	12.00
BIG BAD WOLF celluloid pinback, 1¼"............................	12.50	18.75	25.00
CLEO THE GOLDFISH (Pinocchio) SUN RUBBER squeeze toy..........	9.00	13.50	18.00
DAVY CROCKETT AUTO-MAGIC PICTURE GUN...................	17.50	26.25	35.00
DAVY CROCKETT BADGE, 1950s.....	7.50	11.25	15.00
DAVY CROCKETT doll, 8" high, FORTUNE TOY, 1950s............	5.00	7.50	10.00
DAVY CROCKETT handgun, pop-action, tin litho, 1950s.............	4.00	6.00	8.00
DAVY CROCKETT PLAY KNIFE, 1950s	3.50	5.25	7.00
DISNEY FERRIS WHEEL—circa late 1956, CHEIN....................	25.00	37.50	50.00
DOC bisque, 3" high, circa 1939........	7.50	11.25	15.00
DOC bisque, 4" high, circa 1939........	12.50	18.75	25.00
DOC, 11½" high, stuffed molded oil-cloth face, IDEAL................	40.00	60.00	80.00
DOC party mask, 1937................	6.00	9.00	12.00
DONALD DUCK, 1¾" bisque, early, long-billed......................	11.00	16.50	22.00
DONALD DUCK bisque, riding rocking horse, circa 1935..................	10.00	15.00	20.00
DONALD DUCK bisque, strutting, 1930s	5.00	7.50	10.00
DONALD DUCK CAMERA, 1947, HERBERT GEORGE CO...............	20.00	30.00	40.00
DONALD DUCK CHOO CHOO No. 450	2.00	3.00	4.00
DONALD DUCK DUET, small Donald, large Goofy, circa 1945, MARX tin wind-up........................	50.00	75.00	100.00
DONALD DUCK MOUSEKETEERS HAT..............................	2.50	3.75	5.00
DONALD DUCK Mechanical figure playing a metal drum, 6" high..........	20.00	30.00	40.00

	G	VG	M
DONALD DUCK pulltoy, FISHER-PRICE, 6½" long, long-billed, on platform........................	30.00	45.00	60.00
DONALD DUCK pull toy, FISHER-PRICE No. 400, 1940, 10" tall, 7½" long, wooden figure with move-able arms and legs, composition head..	20.00	30.00	40.00
DONALD DUCK pull toy-wagon, circa 1940, FISHER-PRICE No. 544.......	15.00	22.50	30.00
"DONALD DUCK RAILROAD CAR" with Pluto, Doghouse, 10" long, LIONEL No. 1107................	225.00	337.50	450.00
DONALD DUCK Rubber Boat, SUN RUBBER CO., circa 1940s..........	5.00	7.50	10.00
DONALD DUCK stuffed doll, 16" high, long bill, 1930s..................	100.00	150.00	200.00
DONALD DUCK, 10" high, SUN RUBBER......................	12.50	18.75	25.00
DONALD DUCK Teapot, OHIO ART...	5.00	7.50	10.00
DONALD DUCK and PLUTO in red roadster, SUN RUBBER, 1930s, about 6½" long........................	20.00	30.00	40.00
DONKEY (Pinocchio) bisque, 2" high NATIONAL PORCELAIN CO., 1940, glazed...........................	6.00	9.00	12.00
DOPEY bisque, 3" high, circa 1939.....	7.50	11.25	15.00
DOPEY bisque, 4" high, circa 1939.....	12.25	18.75	25.00
DOPEY party mask, 1937.............	6.00	9.00	12.00
DOPEY 10" rubber squeeze toy, 1950s...	3.25	5.88	6.50
DOPEY tin wind-up, MARX, 1938......	30.00	45.00	60.00
ELMER ELEPHANT pull toy, FISHER-PRICE, 1936....................	15.00	22.50	30.00
FERDINAND THE BULL, bisque, 3" high, 1930s, Ferdinand sitting and sniffing a handful of flowers........	10.00	15.00	20.00
FERDINAND THE BULL, copyright 1938, MARX, tail whirls, body shakes. Wind-up	30.00	45.00	60.00
FERDINAND THE BULL, late 1930s, SEIBERLING LATEX PRODUCTS hard rubber, 6" long, 3½" high......	10.00	15.00	20.00

	G	VG	M
"FERDINAND'S MOTHER", 1937, LAGUNA POTTERY, ceramic, 10" long	20.00	30.00	40.00
FIGARO (Pinocchio) bisque figure, NATIONAL PORCELAIN CO., 1940, 2½" high.	7.00	10.50	14.00
FIGARO tin wind-up, MARX, 1940.	20.00	30.00	40.00
GIDEON bisque figure, GEORGE BORGFELDT CORP., 3" high, painted, 1940.	10.00	15.00	20.00
GOOFY bisque, 2-3/8" high.	2.50	3.75	5.00
GRUMPY bisque, 3" high, circa 1939. . . .	7.50	11.25	15.00
GRUMPY bisque, 4" high, circa 1939. . . .	12.50	18.75	25.00
GRUMPY, 11½" high, stuffed, molded oilcloth face, IDEAL.	40.00	60.00	80.00
GRUMPY PARTY MASK, 1937.	6.00	9.00	12.00
GRUMPY rubber squeeze toy, 1950s.	3.50	5.25	7.00
HAPPY bisque, 3" high, circa 1939.	7.50	11.25	15.00
HAPPY bisque, 4" high, circa 1939.	12.50	18.75	25.00
HAPPY marionette, MADAME ALEX-ANDER, 9½" high, 1938.	37.50	56.25	75.00
HAPPY party mask, 1937.	6.00	9.00	12.00
HAPPY rubber squeeze toy, 1950s.	3.50	5.25	7.00
J. WORTHINGTON FOULFELLOW, bisque, 3" high.	12.00	18.00	24.00
JIMINY CRICKET bisque figure, 1940, 3" high, glazed, NATIONAL PORCE-LAIN CO.	6.00	9.00	12.00
JIMINY CRICKET molded soap figurine, LIGHTFOOT SCHULTZ CO., 1940. .	11.00	16.50	22.00
LUDWIG VON DRAKE rubber squeeze toy, 1960s.	3.00	4.50	6.00
MICKEY AND DONALD in fire truck, late 1930s, rubber.	17.50	26.25	35.00
MICKEY AND MINNIE MOUSE TEA SET, circa 1935, 13 pieces.	75.00	112.50	150.00
MICKEY MAGICIAN, battery toy.	110.00	165.00	220.00

	G	VG	M
MICKEY MOUSE, first toy made by BORGFELDT of NY in 1930, wooden Mickey with jointed hands, arms, legs and wire tail, leather ears. "Copyright 1928-1930 by Walter E. Disney".	150.00	225.00	300.00
MICKEY MOUSE, 31" high, all felt dressed, opening in back for storing things, black jacket with yellow buttons, red pants, bells on toes of yellow shoes......................	11.00	16.50	22.00
MICKEY MOUSE AIRMAIL, rubber....	10.00	15.00	20.00
MICKEY MOUSE BEVERAGES felt soda jerk hat, shows Mickey from shoulders up saying "have one on me", 5x11", circa 1930........................	30.00	45.00	60.00
MICKEY MOUSE bisque with walking stick, circa 1935....................	20.00	30.00	40.00
MICKEY MOUSE BUBBLE BUSTER GUN, metal Mickey standing at gun sight. Cast iron...................	12.50	18.75	25.00
MICKEY MOUSE cardboard mask, circa 1935............................	7.50	11.25	15.00
MICKEY MOUSE molded soap 4½" high, CASTILE, circa 1936..........	37.50	56.25	75.00
MICKEY MOUSE celluloid charm, 1" high, early......................	6.00	9.00	12.00
MICKEY MOUSE child's ring, multicolored Mickey in relief, 1940s........	7.50	11.25	15.00
MICKEY MOUSE CIRCUS TRAIN SET, LIONEL No. 1536, Engine, tender, containing Mickey, three carriage cars, dining car, Mickey Mouse Circus, Mickey Mouse Band, composition Mickey, and track..................	500.00	750.00	1000.00
MICKEY MOUSE CIRCUS TRAIN, Mickey shoveling tender, three Disney Circus cars, wind-up train, red, circa 1931	300.00	450.00	600.00
MICKEY MOUSE, 9½" high, "DELL", rubber	7.50	11.25	15.00
MICKEY MOUSE Hand Car...........	125.00	187.50	250.00

	G	VG	M
MICKEY MOUSE holding flag, cast iron, 1930s	60.00	90.00	120.00
MICKEY MOUSE JAZZ DRUMMER, finger-activated tin toy, NIFTY, 4¾" high	40.00	60.00	80.00
MICKEY MOUSE KNICKERBOCKER doll, 1935, 22" high	275.00	412.50	550.00
MICKEY MOUSE lead cast figure, 1930s	2.50	3.75	5.00
MICKEY MOUSE ORGAN GRINDER, Minnie Mouse dancing on organ pushed by much larger Mickey	1500.00	2250.00	3000.00
MICKEY MOUSE Pocket Knife, 1935	24.00	36.00	48.00
MICKEY MOUSE Puppet, approx. 10" high, "GUND"	4.00	6.00	8.00
MICKEY MOUSE rubber, 6" high, circa 1935	25.00	37.50	50.00
MICKEY MOUSE, rubber	25.00	50.00	75.00
MICKEY MOUSE, 8" high, SUN RUBBER	10.00	15.00	20.00
MICKEY MOUSE with saxophone, 3½" bisque	15.00	22.50	30.00
MICKEY MOUSE stuffed toy, 12" high, rubber shoes, felt ears, circa 1935	50.00	75.00	100.00
MICKEY MOUSE, TUMBLING, 1947, MARKS BROS., 8" high	15.00	22.50	30.00
"MICKEY MOUSE METEOR FIVE-CAR TRAIN, WALT DISNEY'S", tin litho, MARX, 43" long	175.00	262.50	350.00
MICKEY MOUSE piano, wooden, grand, with decal showing Mickey playing, Minnie listening, circa 1935	45.00	67.50	90.00
MICKEY MOUSE PROJECTOR, 1935	30.00	45.00	60.00
MICKEY MOUSE "SANTA CAR WITH MICKEY MOUSE AND HIS GIFT PACK" hand car, LIONEL No. 1105, 1935	450.00	675.00	900.00
MICKEY MOUSE Statue, 1½ feet high, old	12.50	18.75	25.00
MICKEY MOUSE felt doll, STEIFF, 6" high, 1935	150.00	225.00	300.00

	G	VG	M
MICKEY MOUSE 10" high, SUN RUBBER, 1940s..................	2.00	3.00	4.00
MICKEY MOUSE with red shirt and yellow pants, squeeze toy, SUN RUBBER, 1950...................	4.00	6.00	8.00
MICKEY MOUSE larger-size squeeze toy with clothes, 1950, SUN RUBBER	5.00	7.50	10.00
MICKEY MOUSE Tin flute...........	10.00	15.00	20.00
MICKEY MOUSE Tin Washboard set, circa 1935.......................	25.00	37.50	50.00
MICKEY MOUSE Tool Chest, 1935, HAMILTON METAL.............	30.00	45.00	60.00
MICKEY MOUSE VIEWER, with film of "Brave Little Tailor", 1946.........	9.00	13.50	18.00
MICKEY MOUSE WASHER, 1932, or 33, OHIO ART CO., tin litho washing machine, 7" high, two scenes with Mickey, Minnie, Pluto.............	40.00	60.00	80.00
MICKEY MOUSE, wooden, jointed arms and legs, circa 1933...............	37.50	56.25	75.00
MICKEY MOUSE Xylophone, tin wind-up, 1930s......................	27.50	56.25	75.00
MICKEY MOUSE CLUB Bow and Arrow Set, circa 1955...................	4.25	6.38	8.50
MICKEY MOUSE CLUB Snap-on ears, plastic, 1950s....................	1.00	1.50	2.00
MICKEY'S AIRMAIL, 1930s, SUN RUBBER	20.00	30.00	40.00
MICKEY'S TRACTOR, 1930s, SUN RUBBER, Mickey's head turns, 4½" long	14.00	21.00	28.00
MINNIE MOUSE with accordion, 3½" high bisque.....................	15.00	22.50	30.00
MINNIE MOUSE with mandolin, 3½" high bisque.....................	15.00	22.50	30.00
MINNIE MOUSE with umbrella, bisque, circa 1935.......................	20.00	30.00	40.00
MINNIE MOUSE bisque, 4" high, 1930s.	7.50	11.25	15.00

	G	VG	M
MINNIE MOUSE cardboard mask, circa 1935	7.50	11.25	15.00
MINNIE MOUSE cowgirl, Knicker-bocker, 18" high, 1936	225.00	337.50	450.00
MINNIE MOUSE handpuppet	2.00	3.00	4.00
MINNIE MOUSE lead cast, 1930s	2.50	3.75	5.00
MINNIE MOUSE ROLYPOLY	9.00	13.50	18.00
MINNIE MOUSE WASHING MACHINE, 1950, PRECISION SPECIALTIES, INC	30.00	45.00	60.00
MINNIE MOUSE, wooden, jointed, approx. 3" high	10.00	15.00	20.00
MOUSKETEERS HAT, 50% wool, 50% rayon, by DENAYALUEE, 1950s	6.00	9.00	12.00
OSWALD THE RABBIT, circa 1927, 6½" long celluloid crib toy	55.00	82.50	110.00
PANCHITO, 5" ceramic	7.00	10.50	14.00
PETER PAN Tea Set, circa 1953, 23 pieces	17.50	26.25	35.00
PINOCCHIO Handpuppet	2.00	3.00	4.00
PINOCCHIO tin wind-up, MARX, stand-ing erect, eyes skyward, circa 1940 . . .	30.00	45.00	60.00
PINOCCHIO molded soap figurine, 1940, LIGHTFOOT SCHULTZ CO., painted	11.00	16.50	22.00
PINOCCHIO molded wood fiber figure, MULTI PRODUCTS, 1940, 2¼" high .	5.00	7.50	10.00
PINOCCHIO molded wood fiber figure, MULTI PRODUCTS, 1940, 5" high . . .	9.00	13.50	18.00
PINOCCHIO THE ACROBAT, "Watch Him Go!" tin wind-up, circa 1940	50.00	75.00	100.00
PINOCCHIO EXPRESS, pull-toy, FISHER-PRICE, 1940, 11" long	16.00	24.00	32.00
PINOCCHIO ON DONKEY, pull-toy, FISHER-PRICE, 1940, bell-ringer	12.50	18.75	25.00
PINOCCHIO Ring-Toss Game, 1940, DE-WARD CO., MISS	9.00	13.50	18.00
PLUTO hand puppet	2.50	3.75	5.00
PLUTO lead cast, 1930s	2.50	3.75	5.00
PLUTO, 7½" long, SEIBERLING RUBBER	20.00	30.00	40.00

	G	VG	M
PLUTO, tin wind-up, LINE MAR TOYS, 5" long, tail winds, rubber ears and nose	9.00	13.50	18.00
PLUTO, wooden, 3" bendable legs, circa 1934	17.50	26.25	35.00
PLUTO, wooden, hand base, string-operated, many joints, marionette-type	20.00	30.00	40.00
PLUTO ON ROCKERS, wooden, circa 1930s	20.00	30.00	40.00
PLUTO "Watch Me Roll Over", MARX, 1939	25.00	37.50	50.00
PLUTO wood-jointed toy by FISHER-PRICE, 1936	8.00	12.00	16.00
PLUTO, sitting position, rubber squeeze toy, 1960s	3.00	4.50	6.00
Sand Pail, 1938, OHIO ART tin litho, Mickey, Minnie and Goofy pictured	15.00	22.50	30.00
SLEEPY bisque, 3" high, circa 1939	7.50	11.25	15.00
SLEEPY bisque, 4" high, circa 1939	12.50	18.75	25.00
SLEEPY party mask, 1937	6.00	9.00	12.00
SLEEPY 5" rubber, SEIBERLING, late 30s	10.00	15.00	20.00
SNEEZY bisque, 3" high, circa 1939	7.50	11.25	15.00
SNEEZY bisque, 4" high, circa 1939	12.50	18.75	25.00
SNEEZY party mask, 1937	6.00	9.00	12.00
SNEEZY rubber squeeze toy, 1950s	3.25	5,88	6.50
Snow Shovel, 26" long, shows Mickey and Pluto building snowman	75.00	112.50	150.00
SNOW WHITE bisque, 2¾" high	10.00	15.00	20.00
SNOW WHITE bisque, 4" high, circa 1939	10.00	15.00	20.00
SNOW WHITE bisque, 5" high, circa 1939	15.00	22.50	30.00
SNOW WHITE Party Mask	6.00	9.00	12.00
SNOW WHITE statue, 1949, LEEDS CHINA	5.00	7.50	10.00
THREE LITTLE PIGS, pig with drum, 3½" high bisque	10.00	15.00	20.00
THREE LITTLE PIGS, pig with flute, 3" high bisque	7.50	11.25	15.00

	G	**VG**	**M**
THREE LITTLE PIGS, fifer, 3½" high bisque, 1934, distributed by GEO. BORGFELDT CORP..............	10.00	15.00	20.00
THREE LITTLE PIGS, pig with violin, 3½" high bisque..................	10.00	15.00	20.00
THREE LITTLE PIGS, pig with violin, 4½" high bisque, 1930s............	10.00	15.00	20.00
THREE LITTLE PIGS, wooden pig, circa 1933, BORGFELDT, fiber arms and legs, 3¼" high................	17.50	26.25	35.00
TIMOTHY MOUSE (Dumbo), stuffed, 17" high, CHARACTER NOVELTY, 1942...........................	75.00	112.50	150.00
WENDY (Peter Pan) handpuppet.......	2.50	3.75	5.00
WITCH (Snow White) party mask......	6.00	9.00	12.00
ZORRO ring, black top with Z and Zorro name......................	4.50	6.75	9.00

GUNS
(see also Premiums, Comic Character)

SOME THOUGHTS ON
TOY GUN COLLECTING
by
Charles W. Best

Amid all the various toys in the world, the toy gun stands out as the one type most distinctly American and native to the United States, and with good reason. From the earliest days of our history up through the late 19th century, firearms were the primary tool that enabled us to survive, settle, explore, and subdue this land. Firearms gave us our freedom in 1776 and were instrumental in preserving that freedom throughout our first hundred turbulent years. Those years, as we now know, were to become an era of "romantic" wars when boys and young men dreamed of attaining fame and glory on the battlefield or out on the Western Frontier. The War of 1812, the Mexican War, the Civil War, and numerous Indian conflicts were all fought, basically, with small arms, so it is small wonder then that when toys first began to be mass produced after the Civil War, toy guns were among the first to appear on the market. Their success was instantaneous and toy guns remained among our most popular-selling toys until as recently as the 1960's.

Although toy guns were patented in the late 1850's they were not manufactured in any quantity until a decade later due to the wartime shortages. These early toy guns were, for the most part, pea shooters and cork poppers and were usually made of wood with metal hardware although iron and lead types may occasionally be found among them. As you might suspect, these early examples are quite hard to find today and most are known only through their patent drawings. By 1870, inventors, trying to add realism to these toy guns, began using paper caps, a then new invention which had been developed just

---

CHARLES W. BEST is a leading authority on toy weapons, and has been collecting them in earnest since 1966. His collection is regarded as one of the finest and most comprehensive in existence, and has won many awards at various gun shows. In addition to writing a number of articles on the subject in such magazines as Gun Report and Antique Toy World, he is the author of "Cast Iron Toy Pistols" (see Bibliography).

prior to the Civil War and was known as the Maynard Tape Primer. This tape primer was originally intended to detonate muzzle loading arms and closely resembled a roll of modern day paper caps. Now, for the first time, toy guns could make a loud noise yet still be relatively safe and harmless. Naturally, this spurred the demand for these new toys and designers worked overtime to create new and appealing guns. Their output was prolific and, today, the period from 1870 to 1900 is regarded as the "golden age" of the toy gun and especially the toy cap pistol, in America.

By 1880, the cast iron cap pistol had become the most popular type of toy gun by far the various toy makers, primarily J. & E. Stevens and Ives, were competing among themselves to see who could produce the most unique and appealing designs. A glance at any collection of these early day toy pistols will show that, in those days, realism was secondary to artistic imagination. Many pistols from this period were literally covered with ornamentation and, in some cases, any resemblance to a real gun was purely coincidental. Leaf and scroll designs were the most popular but pistols can also be found with numerous other designs, including both two and three dimensional figures. Those guns with moving figures are now known as "animated" pistols and even though not as rare as some, are worth much more to a collector than an ordinary-looking pistol from the same period.

Another very desirable pistol from this same era is now known as the "head" pistol and featured a head, either animal or human, which was placed at the breech end of the barrel with the mouth open to receive the cap. Over two dozen varieties of head and animated pistols are known to exist but are so much in demand that they are seldom offered for sale.

The most popular material used to make these early toy pistols was, of course, cast iron, which continued to be used heavily into the 20th century, until the demands of World War II cut off the supply. Many varieties of old toy guns were, however, made of other materials than iron. I have seen examples made from such diverse materials as paper, wood, steel, tin, lead, rubber, zinc, glass, and even wax. During the Second World War, to meet the heavy demand, toy guns were even made of molded sawdust mixed with glue. After the war a few cast iron pistols were produced and assembled, using both new and old parts, but the cost proved to be prohibitive, and makers soon turned to less expensive metals such as steel and die cast zinc. By 1950, most toy pistols were being made of the die cast material and also plastic, both of which continue to be used today.

From almost the very beginning, toy gun makers have felt the need to personalize their products and literally hundreds of different names can be found embossed on these little guns. Some examples that come to mind are: EXCELSIOR, VICTOR, AMERICAN BULLDOG, ACORN, SUN, BOOM, DARB, ACE, DAISY, COWBOY KING, POLO, TRIUMPH, TERROR, etc. Many names were used only once on one particular gun and then dropped while others have reappeared time and again on different guns over the years. This custom of naming toy guns still goes on today and a visit to any toy store will turn up names such as: COWHAND, TOP GUN JR., 007, etc. Many of these names seem to reflect current events or personalities while on others, the meaning has become obscure.

For the toy collector, or would-be collector, the collecting of toy guns and especially pistols, not only offers a large diversity of models and styles but, because of their tremendous popularity in the past, also the opportunity to find and acquire interesting and unusual examples at an affordable price. Guns from as far back as the 1920's and '30's can still be found at flea markets, garage sales, and second hand stores, often at a price that is only a fraction of what other toys from these same years will sell for. At the moment, toy guns are the most overlooked and under-collected of all old toys but, as more books and articles are published, this situation is bound to change. Interest in real antique guns has skyrocketed in recent years and I predict that the toys will not be far behind.

. . . .

NOTE: Measurements given, in general , are from one end of the gun to the other, rather than on a diagonal from grip to muzzle. Much of the information on manufacturers, measurements, etc., comes from Charles W. Best's excellent book "Cast Iron Toy Pistols" (see bibliography). Dates of manufacture can vary within five years, though most of the later dates are considerably more accurate. Names found on the weapon are in capital letters, as is the manufacturer's name.

CONDITION OF A TOY GUN
AND ITS RELATION TO PRICE

The price of a toy gun depends not only on its desirability, but also on its condition. Since condition in toy guns varies much less than in most toys, prices in "Good" are much closer to "Mint" than is usually the case.

However, "Mint" means just that; the condition in which it was originally issued—perfect, regardless of age, not the slightest blemish.

"Very Good" indicates a toy which has obviously seen use, with signs of wear and aging, but in general having a freshness to its appearance that makes it attractive and collectible to all but the most discriminating.

"Good" signals a weapon that has seen considerable wear, shows its age, but is basically sound. In cast iron pistols, which are hardy to begin with, and have no paint to wear off, a "good" pistol is worth more comparably to its mint version than a black-painted tin pistol would be to its mint version.

Condition below good results usually in a drastic drop in price, and guns with missing parts, although otherwise in excellent condition, will usually fall into this lower-priced category. Rust, even small spots of it, can seriously lower the price of a gun. "Near Mint", "Very Fine", "Fine" and similar terms often found in sellers' descriptions denote conditions between Mint and Very Good, and are priced accordingly.

The key to grading is to avoid wishful thinking. Grading can sometimes be a problem for the uninitiated, but common sense will usually prevail, and when possible, a consultation with an expert in the field can often clear up lingering doubts. A toy in its original box is worth up to 10 to 20% more if the box is in mint condition, with the price dropping as its condition lessens. A holster in mint condition can be worth as much as 50-100% of its gun's value.

GUNS

	G	VG	M
ACE cast iron cap pistol, STEVENS "Made in U.S.A." 5" long, 1930.......	8.00	10.00	12.00
ACE cast iron cap pistol, 5" long, 1935.............................	8.00	10.00	12.00
ACME steel cap automatic, repeater, circa 1930........................	3.00	5.00	6.00
ACORN cast iron pistol...............	10.00	12.50	18.00
ADMIRAL DEWEY cast iron cap **bomb**.	30.00	40.00	60.00

	G	VG	M
AEROMATIC GLIDER GUN, steel automatic, circa 1940, shoots balsa airplanes............................	5.00	7.50	10.00
AIM TO SAVE, circa 1909.............	100.00	125.00	150.00
AIR RAID WARNING signal pistol.....	15.00	20.00	25.00
AMERICA cap pistol, with shield, pat. 1873............................	35.00	50.00	60.00
AMERICAN cast iron cap pistol, KILGORE, 1940, 9-5/8"............	7.00	8.50	10.00
AMERICAN BULLDOG cast iron .22 cal. blank shooter, 1910, 4½" long, second trigger tips barrel to load, KENTON, handle projects outward...	12.00	16.00	20.00
AMERICAN BULLDOG cast iron .22 blank shooter, 1920, 4½" long, KENTON, second trigger tips barrel to load, handle curves inward........	10.00	14.00	16.00
Animated Cap Pistol Cannon...........	140.00	210.00	280.00
ARMY cast iron cap pistol, 1910........	10.00	12.00	15.00
ARMY 45 cast iron cap automatic, HUBLEY 1940 "Made in U.S.A." 6-5/8"...........................	7.00	8.50	10.00
ARMY 45 diecast zinc cap automatic, HUBLEY 1940, plastic grips, "Made in U.S.A.", 6½" long..............	7.00	8.50	10.00
Army pistol with revolving cylinder, tin litho, MARX No. 625.............	3.00	4.00	5.00
Army sparkling pop gun, MARX No. 197.............................	3.00	4.00	5.00
ATOMIC DISINTEGRATOR cap pistol, HUBLEY........................	30.00	40.00	50.00
AUTO MAGIC PICTURE GUN, projects film onto wall. 1936. Comes with film and instructions, in box.............	20.00	28.00	35.00
Automatic Repeater Paper Pop Pistol No. 74, MARX, aluminum...........	3.00	4.50	6.00
BANG cast iron cap pistol, KILGORE, "Made in U.S.A.", 6" long...........	5.00	6.50	8.00
BANG-O cast iron cap pistol, STEVENS 1938, "Made in U.S.A.", 7" long......	5.00	6.50	8.00

	G	VG	M
BANNER, blank-shooting mechanical cast iron pistol....................	12.00	15.00	20.00
Bell Pistol, WYANDOTTE.............	2.00	4.00	5.00
BIFF cast iron cap automatic, KENTON, 1935, "Made in U.S.A. Pat. Apld. For", 4½"......................	5.00	6.50	8.00
BIFF JR. cast iron cap automatic, KENTON 1935, "Made in U.S.A. Pat. Apld For", 4-1/8" long.............	4.00	5.00	6.00
BIG BILL cast iron cap pistol, large hammer, "Made in U.S.A." KILGORE 1935, 4-7/8"......................	4.00	5.00	6.00
BIG BILL cast iron cap pistol, large hammer, "Made in U.S.A.", KILGORE 1930, 5¾".............	4.00	7.00	10.00
BIG BUSTER cast iron cap automatic, KILGORE 1915, "Patd Jul 2 1907, Made in U.S.A.", 5", two-piece trigger	14.00	17.00	20.00
BIG CHIEF cast iron cap pistol, KILGORE, 1935, 6" long...........	4.00	5.00	6.00
BIG CHIEF cast iron cap pistol, KILGORE, 1935, has star and "K", 6"	5.00	6.50	8.00
BIG CHIEF cast iron cap pistol, early-looking, but made in 1930, 3½", DENT "Made in U.S.A."..............	7.00	8.00	10.00
BIG CLIP cast iron cap pistol, STEVENS 1930, "Made in U.S.A." 6¾".........	5.00	6.00	7.00
BIG HORN cast iron cap pistol, revolving cylinder, KILGORE 1939, 8-3/8"...........................	7.00	10.00	12.00
BIGGER BANG large hammer cast iron cap pistol, KILGORE 1930, 6" long...	3.00	4.00	5.00
BILLY THE KID cast iron cap pistol, KILGORE, 1930, 6¾",.............	5.00	6.50	8.00
BLACK JACK cast iron cap pistol, long barrel, KENTON 1930, "Pat. Sept. 11-23", 11"......................	6.00	8.00	10.00

	G	VG	M
BLAZE AWAY Dart Pistol, MARX No. G23.............................	2.50	4.00	5.00
BOB cast iron cap pistol, KILGORE, 1930, 5" long.....................	5.00	6.50	8.00
BORDER PATROL cast iron cap automatic, KILGORE, 1930, 4¼" long....	5.00	6.50	8.00
BORDER PATROL cast iron cap automatic, KILGORE, 1935, "Pat. Apld. For, Made in U.S.A.", 4½" long......	5.00	6.00	7.00
BOY'S DELIGHT Pat. June 1891, cast iron cap pistol.....................	60.00	75.00	90.00
BRAT cast iron cap pistol, original DENT sample.....................	15.00	20.00	25.00
BRONC cast iron cap pistol, KENTON 1935, "Kenton, Made In U.S.A.", 6"..............................	4.00	5.00	6.00
BUC-A-ROO cast iron cap pistol, KILGORE 1940, 7¾"..............	6.00	7.50	9.00
BUCK cast iron cap pistol, HUBLEY 1930, looks earlier, 3¼".............	2.00	3.00	4.00
BUCK JONES SPECIAL DAISY PUMP REPEATER RIFLE, with compass and sun dial in stock, 1937..............	40.00	55.00	70.00
BUDDY cast iron cap pistol...........	12.00	20.00	26.00
BUFFALO BILL cast iron cap pistol, KENTON, 1925, "Pat. Sept. 11-23", 11-3/8", very long barrel............	6.00	7.00	8.00
BUFFALO BILL cast iron cap pistol, KENTON, 1930, "Pat. Sept. 11-23", 13½", perhaps the longest-barreled cap pistol	12.00	16.00	20.00
BUFFALO BILL cast iron cap pistol, STEVENS, 1940, "Made in U.S.A.", 7¾" long........................	5.00	6.00	7.00
BULL cast iron cap pistol, HUBLEY, 1940, "Pat. Appld. for, Pat. Mch. 25, '24, 6¼"....................	4.00	5.00	6.00
BULL DOG cast iron cap pistol, HUBLEY, 1935, "Pat. 1,488,046", 6¼" long........................	5.00	6.00	7.00

	G	VG	M
BULLDOZER cast iron cap pistol, six-shooter, July 1874	35.00	42.00	50.00
BULL'S EYE cast iron cap pistol, KENTON, 1940, "Gene Autry" signature on grips, 6½"	4.00	5.00	6.00
BULLSEYE SAFETY cast iron pistol, flare barrel, with spring	35.00	45.00	55.00
BUTTING MATCH mechanical pistol, cast iron	200.00	250.00	300.00
Cap Bomb, cast iron, head shape	40.00	65.00	80.00
Cap Bomb, dog's head	30.00	40.00	45.00
Cap Pistol, cast iron, ornate, 1878	30.00	40.00	50.00
Cap Pistol, cast iron, revolving cylinder, 1887	30.00	40.00	50.00
Cap Pistol, cast iron, six-shot, dated 1895	30.00	40.00	50.00
Cast iron pistol, ornate, six-shot, 1895	20.00	25.00	30.00
Cast iron pistol, six-shot, pat. Jan. 1895	24.00	30.00	38.00
Cast iron pistol, shoots caps, embossed	20.00	25.00	30.00
Cast iron pistol, shoots caps, plated barrel	15.00	20.00	25.00
Cap pistol, steel, repeating, red, WYANDOTTE, 8" long	4.00	7.00	10.00
CAPTAIN cast iron cap automatic, KILGORE, 1940, 4¼" long	3.00	4.00	5.00
CAVALIER cast iron cap automatic, KILGORE, 1935, "Pat. Appld. For, Made in U.S.A.", 4½"	5.00	7.00	9.00
CHIEF cast iron .22 cal. blank shooter, KENTON 1915, 6" long, second trigger tips up barrel to load	10.00	12.00	15.00
CHIEF cast iron cap pistol, HUBLEY 1930, "Pat. 1,488,046", 6-1/8"	4.00	5.00	6.00
CHIEF cap pistol, aluminum single shot, HUBLEY	4.00	6.00	8.00
CHIEFTAIN cast iron cap pistol, NATIONAL, 1920, 11" long	4.00	6.00	8.00
CHINESE MUST GO mechanical cap pistol	200.00	250.00	325.00
"Click Pistol" MARX No. 32	1.00	2.00	3.00

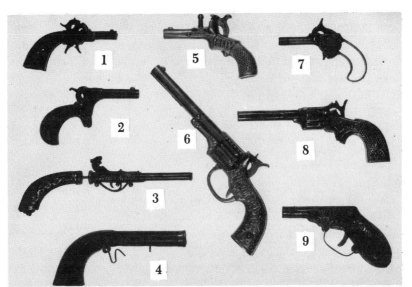

A variety of early toy pistols. 1. "ROB ROY" c.1875, a small, cast iron double barrelled cap shooter. 2. "STAR" c.1878, cast iron single shot. 3. A French made cork shooter c.1900. Has a tin handle with a lead and brass barrel. 4. "YOUNG SPORTSMAN" c.1868. A very early pea shooter made of wood and brass. 5. "RIP" c.1909, cast iron cap shooter with unusual peg on top to hold a roll of caps. 6. "COLUMBIA" c.1890, cast iron with ornate design. 7. "SHOOFLY" c.1873, early cast iron cap shooter with skeleton handle. 8. "PRINZ" c.1905, tin cap shooter with iron hammer, made in Germany. 9. "ROYAL LIQUID PISTOL" c.1915, tin squirt pistol with iron trigger.

	G	VG	M
Click Pistol, tin litho, MARX No. 36	1.00	2.00	3.00
Clicker Pistol, plain black, late 1930s, early 1940s	.50	.75	1.00
CLIP JR. cast iron cap pistol, STEVENS, 1935, 5¼"	3.00	4.00	5.00
CLIPPER cast iron cap automatic, KILGORE, 1935, 4-1/8"	4.00	5.00	6.00
Clown and Mule animated pistol	400.00	500.00	600.00
COLT cast iron cap pistol, STEVENS 1920, "Patented June 17, 1890, Made in U.S.A.", 5½"	4.00	5.00	6.00
COLT cast iron cap pistol, STEVENS 1935, 6½"	5.00	6.50	8.00
COLUMBIA 1885 cast iron cap pistol	20.00	30.00	40.00
COLUMBIA 1890 cast iron cap pistol	15.00	20.00	25.00
COLUMBIA cast iron cap pistol, pat. June 1891	8.00	10.00	14.00
COP cast iron cap pistol HUBLEY 1930 "Pat. 1,488,046" or "Pat. Mch. 25 '24", 5"	3.00	4.00	5.00

	G	VG	M
Cork-popper pistol, WYANDOTTE, spur trigger	4.00	6.50	8.00
Cork-shooting rifle, MARX No. 206.....	3.00	4.00	5.00
Corn Shooter cap pistol..............	35.00	42.00	50.00
COWBOY cast iron cap pistol, STEVENS, 1935, "Made in U.S.A.", 3½"	5.00	6.50	8.00
COWBOY cast iron cap pistol, long barrel, STEVENS, 1930, "Made in U.S.A."	7.00	8.50	10.00
COWBOY cast iron cap pistol, HUBLEY 1940 "Made in U.S.A.", 8"...........	5.00	6.50	8.00
DAISY air rifle, cast iron and brass, early, 31" long....................	42.00	65.00	80.00
DAISY air rifle target, 1935, 4½x5".....	.75	1.00	1.25
DAISY cast iron cap pistol, Pat. Apr. 1873	20.00	30.00	35.00
DAISY cast iron cap pistol, HUBLEY 1935, 4-1/8"......................	4.00	5.00	6.00
DAISY CINEMATIC PICTURE PISTOL, circa mid-1940s..................	25.00	35.00	40.00
DAISY DOUBLE DUTY PISTOL, pops and shoots water from separate barrel, very similar to Buck Rogers pistol (see Comic Character)..............	20.00	25.00	30.00
DAISY ZOOKA "POP" Pistol, similar to Buck Rogers pistol.................	10.00	12.00	16.00
DANDY cast iron cap pistol, HUBLEY, 1935, can have variety of markings, 5¾"	4.00	5.00	6.00
DARB cast iron cap pistol, KENTON 1930, "Pat. Sept. 11-23", 5½" long....	5.00	6.50	8.00
Dart Pistol, WYANDOTTE, colorful, fancy lithographing...............	3.50	5.00	7.00
DERBY cast iron cap pistol, HUBLEY 1930, 7".........................	5.00	6.50	8.00
DETROIT cast iron cap pistol, 1910, 6-5/8" long.......................	14.00	17.00	20.00
DICK cast iron cap pistol, HUBLEY 1930, 6".........................	4.00	5.00	6.00

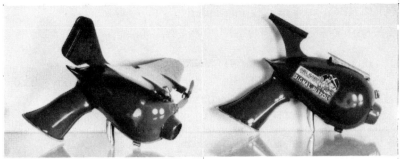

L TO R: Siren Sparkling Airplane Pistol (see page 258); Air Raid Warning Signal Pistol (see page 243).

	G	VG	M
DICK cast iron cap automatic, HUBLEY 1940, "Made in U.S.A.", 4-1/8"	3.00	4.00	5.00
DIG INJUN, hammerless	27.00	35.00	40.00
DIK cast iron cap pistol, KENTON 1935, "Pat. Sept. 11-23", 4¾"	3.00	4.00	5.00
DIXIE cast iron cap pistol, KENTON 1935, "Made in U.S.A. Pat. Appld. For", 6¼"	5.00	6.00	7.00
DOC cast iron cap pistol, KENTON 1940, "Pat. Sept. 11-23, 4½"	3.00	4.00	5.00
Dolphin animated cap pistol (may actually be Sea Serpent)	100.00	140.00	170.00
Double-barrel cast iron cap pistol, dated 1880	25.00	35.00	45.00
Double-barrel pop gun-rifle, MARX No. 230	4.00	6.00	8.00
Double cap pistol, cast iron	35.00	50.00	65.00
Double-faced cap bomb, cast iron	25.00	35.00	45.00
Double trigger cast iron cap pistol, large, STEPHENS, PA. 1873	45.00	60.00	75.00

L TO R: Army Pistol with revolving cylinder (see page 243); Lone Ranger Sparkling Pop Pistol (see page 254).

	G	VG	M
DOUGHBOY cast iron cap automatic, KILGORE 1920, "Made in U.S.A.", 5"	9.00	12.00	15.00
DUDE cast iron cap pistol, STEVENS 1887, "Pat. Mar. 22 '87", 3½"	15.00	20.00	25.00
DUDE cast iron cap pistol, plastic grips, 1941, KENTON, 6½"	7.00	8.50	10.00
EAGLE cast iron cap pistol, STEVENS, 1895, "Pat. June 17, 1890", 7½"	12.00	16.00	20.00
EAGLE, circa 1940	15.00	20.00	30.00
ECHO cap pistol, six-shooter cast iron, 1881	35.00	55.00	75.00
ECHO cast iron cap pistol, STEVENS 1920, 4¼"	5.00	6.50	8.00
ECHO cast iron cap pistol, STEVENS 1930, "Made In U.S.A.", 4½"	4.00	5.00	6.00
1895 cast iron six shot cap pistol	30.00	40.00	50.00
EXCELSIOR cast iron cap pistol, STEVENS, 1875, "Pat'd Apr. 22, '73, 5¼"	12.00	16.00	20.00
FEDERAL cast iron cap automatic, KILGORE 1940, 4-7/8", has removeable clip to hold caps	9.00	12.00	15.00
FEDERAL cast iron cap pistol, KILGORE 1920, "Pat. Dec. '14; Made in U.S.A."	8.00	10.00	12.00
FEDERAL—KILGORE No. 1 cast iron cap pistol, 1925, 5¼", KILGORE	5.00	6.50	8.00
FEDERAL No. 2 cast iron cap pistol, KILGORE 1925, 6-3/8"	7.50	9.00	11.00
Firecracker pistol, filigree handle, cast iron	10.00	12.50	14.00
Five-barrel firecracker pistol, iron and brass, 1877	450.00	600.00	750.00
5-STAR steel dart pistol, WYANDOTTE	4.00	6.50	8.00
FLASH cast iron cap pistol, HUBLEY 1934, "Pat'd" 6¼"	12.00	15.00	20.00
FOUR WAY cast iron cap pistol, KENTON 1930, "Pat. Appld. For", shoots pea or dart, rubber band and cap, all at same time	12.00	15.00	20.00

	G	VG	M
49-ER cast iron cap pistol, STEVENS 1940, 9"..........................	6.00	8.00	10.00
FOX cast iron cap pistol, HUBLEY 1935, 4½"........................	3.00	4.00	5.00
FRONTIER cast iron cap pistol, IVES 1890, "Pat. June 21, 1887 and June 17, 1890", Dog's head atop the barrel facing the hammer.................	25.00	32.00	40.00
G-MAN cast iron cap automatic, KILGORE 1935, 6", looks like German Luger, removeable magazine holds caps	12.00	16.00	18.00
G-MAN bakelite-framed cap automatic, KILGORE, 1940, 6".................	6.50	8.00	10.00
G-MAN clicker pistol, tin, black........	8.00	10.00	12.00
G-MAN wind-up steel spark pistol, painted finish.....................	8.00	10.00	12.00
G-MAN wind-up steel spark pistol, nickel finish with jewels on grip............	8.00	10.00	12.00
G-MAN automatic sparkling pistol, MARX No. 43 aluminum............	2.50	3.75	5.00
G-MAN automatic sparkling pistol, MARX No. 44 aluminum............	3.00	4.50	6.00
G-MAN automatic sparkling pistol, MARX No. 85, aluminum...........	2.50	3.75	5.00
G-MAN gun, MARX No. 707...........	2.50	3.75	5.00
G-MAN Silent Alarm Pistol, MARX No. 54, tin............................	3.50	4.75	7.00
GEM cast iron cap pistol, STEVENS, 1900, 3"...........................	3.00	4.00	5.00
GENE AUTRY cast iron cap pistol, KENTON 1939, 8-3/8"..............	12.00	16.00	20.00
GENE AUTRY cast iron cap pistol, KENTON 1939, "Made in U.S.A. Pat. Appld. For", 6½"..................	10.00	13.00	16.00
GENE AUTRY cast iron cap pistol, KENTON 1940, "Made in U.S.A.", 6½", red grips....................	12.00	16.00	20.00
GENE AUTRY cast iron pistol (doesn't fire caps), KENTON, 1940, "Made in U.S.A.", 6½"....................	5.00	6.50	8.00

	G	VG	M
GUARD cast iron cap pistol, KILGORE, 1935, "Made in U.S.A.", 6¼"........	8.00	10.00	12.00
H-BAR-O cast iron cap pistol, KILGORE 1925, "Made In U.S.A.", 7½"........	6.00	8.00	10.00
HAMMERLESS cast iron cap pistol, STEVENS, 1892, "Pat. Appld. For", 7¼", four revolving triggers, hammer concealed.........................	15.00	20.00	25.00
HANSON-LINDSBORG K.S. cast iron firecracker pistol, 1905, HANSON "Pat. Appld. For.", 6-3/8", fires fire cracker......................	30.00	40.00	50.00
HERO cast iron cap pistol, STEVENS, 1937, 5¼"......................	3.50	4.50	6.00
HI-HO cast iron cap pistol, STEVENS, 1940, "Made In U.S.A.", 7"..........	6.00	8.00	10.00
HI-HO cast iron pistol, can fire caps, STEVENS 1940, "Made In U.S.A.", 7"...............................	3.50	4.50	6.00
HI-HO cast iron cap pistol, KILGORE, 1940, 6½"......................	5.00	6.50	8.00
HIO cast iron cap pistol, KENTON 1940, "Pat. Sept. 11-23", 5-1/8"......	3.00	4.00	5.00
HI-RANGER cast iron cap pistol, STEVENS 1940, 7¾"...............	5.00	6.50	8.00
HUB cast iron cap pistol, HUBLEY, 1940, 6¼"......................	5.00	6.50	8.00
HUSTLER cast iron pistol.............	5.50	7.50	9.00
IDEAL.............................	1.50	2.25	3.00
INDIAN............................	1.50	2.25	3.00
INVINCIBLE cast iron cap pistol, KILGORE 1935, 5¼", "Pat. Dec. 14"...............................	6.00	7.25	9.00
JACK ARMSTRONG airplane gun, DAISY, 1936.....................	27.50	41.25	55.00
JAX cast iron cap pistol, KENTON, 1930, "Pat. Sept. 11-23", 4"..........	3.00	4.00	5.00
JUMBO cast iron cap pistol, "Pat. June 17, 1890; Made in U.S.A.", 9½" STEVENS 1895..................	12.00	16.00	20.00

	G	VG	M
JR. POLICE CHIEF, cast iron cap automatic, KENTON, 1938, "Made In U.S.A.", 3-7/8"....................	4.00	5.00	6.00
JUNIOR: POLICE 32 cast iron cap pistol, HUBLEY, 1940, "Hubley; Pat'd. 2088891", 5¼"....................	4.00	5.00	6.00
JUNIOR SIX-SHOOTER cast iron cap pistol, KILGORE, 1935, 5½"........	8.00	10.00	12.00
KIDO cast iron cap pistol, KENTON, 1936, "Kenton, Made In U.S.A.", 5-3/8"...........................	3.00	4.00	5.00
KING cast iron cap pistol, Pat. Aug. 1879...........................	16.00	20.00	24.00
KING cast iron cap pistol, STEVENS, 1925, "Made In U.S.A.", 4¾"........	5.00	6.50	8.00
KIT CARSON cast iron cap pistol, KENTON, 1928, "Pat. Sept. 11-23", 9"...............................	14.00	18.00	22.00
LIBERTY, circa 1912................	10.00	15.00	25.00
LASSO 'EM BILL cast iron cap gun, red rubies in handle, cylinder turns, 1930, 9"........................	12.00	16.00	20.00
LAWMAKER cast iron cap pistol, KENTON, 1941, 8-3/8".............	8.00	10.00	12.00
LIGHTNING EXPRESS, mechanical cap pistol, train slides forward along barrel to explode cap at end, 5", 1913, Arcade or Kenton..................	90.00	120.00	150.00
Lion head cast iron cap pistol, Pat. 1890, 5¼", STEVENS.............	35.00	50.00	65.00
LITTLE BILL cast iron cap pistol, KILGORE 1925, 5"................	4.00	5.50	7.00
LITTLE CHIEF FIRE-FIGHTER, water squirt gun.......................	1.50	2.00	2.50
LONE EAGLE cast iron cap pistol, KILGORE, 1929, 5¼".............	10.00	13.00	16.00
LONE RANGER cast iron cap pistol, KILGORE 1938, 8½".............	15.00	20.00	25.00
LONE RANGER cast iron cap pistol, KILGORE 1940, 8½".............	12.00	16.00	20.00

	G	VG	M
LONE RANGER 45 Flasher Flashlight Pistol, MARX....................	10.00	15.00	20.00
LONE RANGER Sparkling Pop Pistol, tin litho, MARX No. 096............	12.50	18.75	25.00
LONE RANGER tin pop gun, 1950s, picture of Lone Ranger on handles....	7.50	11.25	15.00
LONG BOY cast iron cap pistol, KILGORE, 1922, 11" long, "Made in U.S.A."	6.00	8.00	10.00
LONG TOM cast iron cap pistol, KILGORE, 1939, 10-3/8"...........	20.00	25.00	30.00
LOOK OUT dog's head cast iron cap pistol	40.00	60.00	75.00
M&L water pistol, die-cast, rubber ball..	11.00	16.50	22.00
MACHINE GUN, cast iron cap automatic, KILGORE, 1938, comes with crank, which when turned, fires the caps rapidly, "Ra-Ta-Ta-Tat", 5".....	10.00	14.00	18.00
MAGIC cast iron .22 cal. blank pistol, KENTON 1900, "Pat'd. Oct. 17 '99, 6¼" long, ornate, has second trigger to open barrel for loading............	35.00	45.00	60.00
MASCOT cast iron cap automatic, KILGORE, 1936, 3-7/8"............	5.00	6.50	8.00
MASTER cast iron cap automatic, KILGORE, 1930, 4-5/8"............	6.00	8.00	10.00
ME AND MY BUDDY, animated pistol with figure, steel, WYANDOTTE.....	5.00	7.50	10.00
MINUTE MAN cast iron cap rifle, KILGORE 1936, "Pat. Appld. For , Made in U.S.A.", 20"...............	80.00	100.00	120.00
MODEL, Pat. 1890, cast iron, 5-3/8"....	10.00	14.00	18.00
Monkey and coconut animated cap pistol, 1878, 4¼", STEVENS..............	170.00	210.00	250.00
NATIONAL cast iron cap automatic, NATIONAL, 1925, "Made in U.S.A.", 5¼"	9.00	12.00	15.00
NAVY cast iron cap pistol, KENTON 1930, "Pat. Sept. 11-23", 5½"........	4.00	5.00	6.00
NAVY double barrel cap pistol........	18.00	25.00	30.00
NIGGER HEAD cap pistol, cast iron,			

	G	VG	M
IVES, 1887, 4½"..................	50.00	65.00	80.00
NOVELTY cast iron cap pistol, STEVENS, 1885, "Pat. Appld. For", 5"	55.00	75.00	90.00
OFFICER PISTOL, cast iron cap automatic, KILGORE, 1940, 6", modeled after German Luger................	15.00	20.00	25.00
Official Detective-Type Sub-Machine Gun, MARX, No. 2146..............	5.00	7.50	10.00
OH BOY automatic cap, KILGORE, 1933, "Made in U.S.A.; Pat'd. Aug. 8, 1933", works both as automatic and as crank-operated rapid-fire gun, 4-1/8"............................	20.00	25.00	30.00
OHIO cast iron cap pistol, KENTON 1930, "Pat. Sept. 11-23", 5-1/8"......	5.00	6.00	7.00
OK cast iron cap automatic, maker unknown, 1935, 3¾"..............	8.00	10.00	12.00
OLD IRONSIDES cast iron cap pistol, 10¾"..........................	25.00	30.00	40.00
P-38 steel clicker pistol, circa 1945......	3.00	4.50	6.00
Padlock cap pistol, and key, HUBLEY, 4¼"..........................	28.00	37.50	50.00
PAL cast iron cap pistol, KILGORE, 1930, 4"........................	4.00	5.50	7.00
PAL cast iron cap automatic, KILGORE, 1930, 4"........................	5.00	6.50	8.00
PAT cast iron cap pistol, KENTON, 1935, "Pat. Sept. 11-23", 6-1/8"......	5.00	6.50	8.00
PATROL cast iron cap pistol, HUBLEY 1939, "Made In U.S.A.", 6".........	9.00	12.00	15.00
PAWNEE BILL, circa 1940...........	15.00	25.00	30.00
PEA MATIC pea-shooting steel repeater.	5.00	7.50	10.00
Pea shooter........................	10.00	15.00	20.00
Pea shooter, pewter, highly embossed handle	13.00	20.00	25.00
PEACEMAKER cast iron cap pistol, STEVENS 1940, "Made in U.S.A.", 8½"............................	5.00	6.50	8.00
PERSUADER cast iron cap pistol,			

	G	VG	M
KENTON, 1939, "Made in U.S.A.; Pat. Appld. For", 6-3/8"................	12.00	15.00	18.00
PET, 4¼" HUBLEY..................	1.25	2.00	3.00
Ping-Pong rifle.....................	2.50	3.75	5.00
PIRATE cap pistol, die cast zinc, with cast iron hammers and trigger, HUBLEY 1941, two-barrel, two hammers that cock, 9-3/8"..............	12.00	16.00	20.00
"Pistol Packin' Mama", wood with cardboard sides, circa 1944, four revolving triggers, 8½" long, shoots wooden pegs	3.00	4.50	6.00
PLUCK cast iron cap pistol, STEVENS 1930, "Made in U.S.A.", 3½", early-looking, at least four versions known, one dating to 1895..................	3.00	4.00	5.00
POLICE large steel automatic cap pistol, 8"..............................	5.00	7.00	9.00
POLICE bakelite-framed cap automatic, KILGORE, 1940, 5¼"..............	5.00	6.50	8.00
PONO cast iron cap pistol, KENTON 1936, "Pat. Sept. 11-23", 5-1/8"......	4.50	6.00	7.00
Powder Keg cast iron cap bomb.........	30.00	40.00	50.00
PRESTO cast iron cap automatic, KILGORE, 1940, 5-1/8"............	9.00	12.00	15.00
PUNCH & JUDY cast iron animated cap pistol, 1880, 5" "Patented", IVES, Punch explodes cap with nose, on Judy's back	250.00	325.00	400.00
RANGER cast iron cap pistol, KILGORE, 1939, 8½"......................	12.00	16.00	20.00
RANGER cast iron cap pistol, KILGORE, 1940, 8½", hammer protrudes more than earlier version................	12.00	16.00	20.00
RECORD.......................	2.00	2.50	3.00
RED RANGER steel click pistol, WYANDOTTE, 7¾"....................	5.00	7.50	10.00
RED RANGER steel six shooter repeater with plastic handles, WYANDOTTE, revolving cylinder.................	6.25	9.38	12.50
Repeating Cap Pistol, MARX No.			

"Cowboy guns" or Western six shooter types, embossed with famous names. 1. "LONE RANGER" c.1940. 2. "GENE AUTRY" c.1941. 3. "BILLY THE KID" c.1938. 4. "BUFFALO BILL" c.1940. All of the above are made of cast iron with nos. 1, 2, and 4, having plastic grips.

	G	VG	M
G375, aluminum..................	3.00	4.50	6.00
REX cast iron cap automatic, KILGORE, 1939, 3-7/8".......................	5.00	6.50	8.00
RIP, circa 1909.....................	35.00	50.00	75.00
ROB BOY, circa 1875................	75.00	90.00	110.00
ROY ROGERS cast iron cap pistol, 11"..	12.00	16.00	20.00
ROYAL PISTOL, THE, 1878 cast iron cap mechanical pistol, fires spring-loaded top which is attached to bottom of the barrel, approx. 5", "Pat. Apr. 23 '78"...........................	300.00	350.00	450.00
SAFETY cast iron cap pistol, HUBLEY, 1924, "Pat. Mch 25, '24", 5".........	8.00	10.00	12.00

	G	VG	M
SAFETY FIRST cast iron cap automatic, 1920, "Safe", 3-3/8", maker unknown	16.00	20.00	25.00
SAMBO cast iron cap pistol, hammer hits head, 1887, IVES, "Pat. June 21, 1887", 4-3/8"	70.00	85.00	100.00
SAY I cast iron cap bomb	30.00	40.00	50.00
SCOUT cast iron cap pistol, STEVENS, 1890, "Pat'd. June 17, 1890", 7"	20.00	28.00	35.00
SCOUT cast iron cap pistol, STEVENS, 1935, "Made In U.S.A.", 6¾"	7.00	10.00	12.00
SCOUT cast iron cap pistol, STEVENS, 1940, 6-1/8"	5.00	6.50	8.00
SCOUT cap pistol, tin, 1914, automatic ..	5.00	7.50	10.00
SCOUT JR. cast iron cap pistol, STEVENS, 1935, "Made in U.S.A.", 6"	5.00	6.50	8.00
SENATOR cast iron cap pistol, KILGORE 1925, 7", marked with star and "K"	7.00	10.00	12.00
1776-1876 cast iron cap pistol, STEVENS, 1876, 5¼", produced for America's 100th centennial	40.00	55.00	75.00
SHOO FLY cast iron cap pistol	25.00	35.00	50.00
SHOOT THE HAT cast iron mechanical cap pistol	170.00	240.00	310.00
Shotgun, double-barrel, steel, wood stock 28", both barrels break down, cock and shoot	5.00	7.50	10.00
SIREN SPARKLING AIRPLANE PISTOL, tin litho, MARX No. 182	20.00	28.00	35.00
SIREN SPARKLING PISTOL, tin litho, MARX No. 164	2.50	3.75	5.00
SIX SHOOTER cast iron cap pistol, KILGORE, 1935, 6½"	12.00	16.00	20.00
SIX SHOOTER cast iron cap pistol, with plastic-type grips, KILGORE, 1935, 6½"	12.00	16.00	20.00
SIX SHOOTER cast iron cap pistol, KILGORE, 1938, "Made in U.S.A." on hammer, 6½"	8.00	10.00	12.00

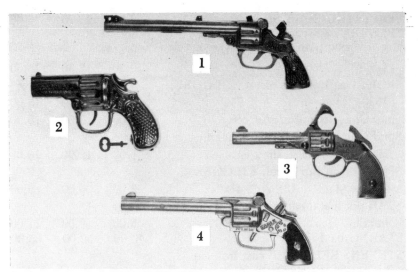

Revolver type pistols. 1. "FOUR WAY" c.1928, cast iron combination pistol that will shoot a cap, rubber band and pea simultaneously. 2. "AIM TO SAVE" c.1909, steel dime bank in shape of a pistol. Pressing the trigger causes an arm to extend from the barrel to receive the coin. 3. "SNAPPY JACK" c.1935, cast iron cap shooter made in England shown with cap holder raised, ready to load. 4. "EAGLE" c.1940, a typical cast iron single shot pistol of the period.

	G	VG	M
SIX SHOOTER cast iron cap pistol, KILGORE, 1938, "Made in U.S.A." on hammer, plastic-type grips, 6½".....	9.00	11.50	14.00
SIX SHOOTER cast iron cap pistol, KILGORE, 1930, 7"...............	10.00	12.50	15.00
SIX SHOOTER AUTOMATIC cast iron cap pistol (not an automatic), KILGORE, 1934, 6½".............	12.00	15.00	18.00
6 SHOT cast iron cap pistol, STEVENS, 1895, "Pat'd. U.S.A., Jan 22, 1895", 6¾"	30.00	40.00	50.00
SLIKO cast iron cap pistol, KENTON, 1930, "Pat. Sept. 11-23", 6¼"........	4.00	5.50	7.00
SNAPPY JACK, circa 1935............	25.00	30.00	40.00
SPARKLING ATOM BUSTER, aluminum, MARX No. 46...............	3.50	5.25	7.00
SPARKLING G-MAN Sub-Machine Gun, MARX No. 2308.................	5.00	7.50	10.00
SPARKLING G-MAN Sub-Machine Gun, MARX No. 2310.................	5.00	7.50	10.00
SPARKLING Pop Gun, MARX No. 198..	2.50	3.75	5.00
SPARKLING Space Gun, MARX.......	5.00	7.50	10.00

SPARKLING SURE SHOT............	2.50	3.75	5.00
SPITFIRE cast iron cap automatic, STEVENS 1940, "Made in U.S.A.", 4-5/8"...........................	10.00	12.50	15.00
SPORT cast iron cap pistol, KILGORE, 1930, "Made in U.S.A.", 7½"........	10.00	12.50	15.00
Spud Gun, tin, automatic, circa 1940....	5.00	7.50	10.00
Spud Gun No. 504, B.J. Cossman, Hollywood, Calif. die-cast...........	8.00	12.00	16.00
SPY cast iron cap pistol, KILGORE, 1936, "Made in U.S.A.", 4¼"........	3.00	4.00	5.00
STAR pot metal cap pistol, steer on handle...........................	6.00	9.00	11.00
STAR, circa 1878....................	40.00	50.00	65.00
STEVENS REPEATER cast iron cap pistol, STEVENS, 1930, 6¼", "Mammoth Cap; Made in U.S.A."..........	10.00	12.50	15.00
STEVENS 6-SHOT RAPID LOAD cast iron cap pistol, 1932, STEVENS "Made in U.S.A.", 6½"..................	12.00	16.00	18.00
STREAMLINE SIREN SPARKLING PISTOL, tin litho, MARX No. 155....	2.50	3.75	5.00
SUN cast iron cap pistol..............	30.00	40.00	50.00
S&W cast iron cap gun, 6"............	9.00	12.00	15.00
SUPER cast iron cap pistol, KENTON 1930, "Pat. Sept. 11-23", 8¾"........	5.00	6.50	8.00
SUPER AUTOMATIC TOM GUN, steel spark automatic....................	5.00	7.50	10.00
SUPER NU-MATIC PAPER BUSTER GUN.............................	5.00	7.50	10.00
SURE SHOT cast iron cap automatic, HUBLEY, 1940, 4¼"...............	9.00	12.00	15.00
TARGET cast iron cap pistol, HUBLEY, 1935, "Pat. 1,488,046", 8"...........	9.00	12.00	15.00
TEDDY cast iron cap pistol, HUBLEY 1938, 5-5/8"......................	5.00	7.50	10.00
TERROR cast iron cap automatic, DENT, 1915, "Pat. Jan. 16'15", 4¼"...........................	5.00	6.50	8.00
TERROR, people embossed, cast iron cap pistol........................	50.00	70.00	90.00

AUTOMATIC type pistols. 1. "G MAN" c.1938, cast iron copy of the German Luger pistol. 2. "TERROR" c.1915, cast iron single shot. 3. "TARGET 25-50" c.1940, an unusual and rare variation of a common cast iron pistol. 4. "25-50" c.1940, same basic pistol as No. 3, above, with standard length barrel. 5. "LIBERTY" c.1912, an early tin pistol with ornate designs. 6. "THE BIG NOISE" c.1922, cast iron pistol with an unusual design.

	G	VG	M
TEXAN cast iron cap pistol, HUBLEY 1940, "Made in U.S.A.", 9¼" long....	15.00	20.00	25.00
TEXAN JR. cast iron cap pistol, HUBLEY 1941, "Made in U.S.A.", 8-1/8".......	6.00	8.50	10.00
TEXAS cast iron cap pistol, KENTON 1936, "Kenton, Pat'd. No. 1993916", 5¾"	6.00	8.50	10.00
TEXAS cast iron cap pistol, KENTON, 1930, "Pat. Sept. 11-23", 6-5/8"......	4.00	5.50	7.00
THE BIG NOISE, circa 1922...........	20.00	25.00	30.00
THE FORTY FIVE cast iron cap pistol, unusual shape, NATIONAL 1928, "Made in U.S.A.", 11-1/8"...........	15.00	20.00	25.00
THE SHERIFF cast iron cap pistol, STEVENS, 1940, 8½"..............	5.00	6.50	8.00
TIGER cast iron cap pistol, STEVENS, 1915, 6¾"........................	6.00	8.50	10.00
TIGER cast iron cap pistol, HUBLEY 1935, 6-7/8".....................	5.00	6.50	8.00
Tin Tin Gun—3x5", turn crank and it makes noise, WOODHAVEN METAL STAMPING CO...................	6.00	9.00	12.00

	G	VG	M
TIP TOP cast iron cap pistol, 1878......	8.00	12.00	16.00
TRAINER..........................	2.00	2.50	3.00
TRAPPER cast iron cap automatic, KILGORE, 1935, 4½", fires only single shot, but roll of caps can be carried in the grip.................	9.00	12.00	15.00
TROOPER cast iron cap pistol, HUBLEY 1938, 5-1/8".....................	3.50	5.00	6.00
TROOPER SAFETY cast iron cap pistol. KILGORE, 1930, "Pat. Pend; Made in U.S.A.", 10", operates either as straight cap pistol, or can be fired with crank..	20.00	25.00	30.00
TROOPER SAFETY cast iron cap pistol, KILGORE, 1925, 10¼".............	10.00	15.00	18.00
25 cast iron cap automatic, STEVENS, 1928, "Pat. Appld. For; made in U.S.A", 4½".....................	5.00	6.50	8.00
25 JR. cast iron cap automatic, STEVENS 1930, "Made in U.S.A.; Patented", 4-1/8"............................	4.00	5.00	6.00
25-50 Cast iron cap automatic, STEVENS 1935, "Made in U.S.A.; Pat. Appld. For", 4½".....................	4.00	5.00	6.00
25-50 Cast iron cap automatic, STEVENS 1935, "Oil Moving Parts; Made in U.S.A.; Patented", 4½".............	4.00	5.00	6.00
25-50 Cast iron cap automatic, can be fired rapidly with crank, hole near muzzle holds removeable crank, STEVENS, 1935, "Oil Moving Parts; Made in U.S.A.; Patented"..........	15.00	20.00	25.00
25-50 TARGET cast iron cap automatic with "silencer" type barrel, STEVENS, 1935, "Oil Moving Parts; Made in U.S.A.; Patented".................	30.00	40.00	50.00
Two Dogs on Bench cap shooter (only two known, one sold, condition unknown, for $3000.			
"2 in 1" cast iron cap pistol, 9¼"........	25.00	30.00	35.00

	G	VG	M
"2 Monkeys", 1882 cast iron animated cap pistol, 4½", maker unknown, monkey butts head against coconut held by another monkey............	100.00	130.00	175.00
TWO TIME cast iron cap and rubber band pistol, 1930, KENTON, "Pat. Appld. For", 9¼".................	6.00	8.50	10.00
UNXLD steel cap automatic, 6½", nickel-plated...........................	4.00	6.00	8.00
U.S.A. LIQUID PISTOL cast iron water pistol, PARKER-STEARNS, 1896, Pat'd. June 30, 1896",4¾"..........	10.00	20.00	25.00
URICA............................	1.50	2.00	3.00
VICTOR cast iron pistol..............	7.00	10.00	12.00
VILLA cast iron cap pistol, DENT, 1934, "Made in U.S.A.", 4¾", "Made in U.S.A."....................	5.00	6.50	8.00
VOLUNTEER cast iron cap pistol, STEVENS, 1873, "Pat'd April 22, '73..	15.00	20.00	25.00
W on one side, S on other, cast iron cap pistol, nickel-plated, normal-size barrel...........................	9.00	12.00	15.00
W on one side, S on other, snub nose, single shot, cast iron nickel-plated.....	6.00	7.50	10.00
WAR cast iron cap pistol, KENTON, 1930, "Pat. Sept 11-23", 4¼"........	4.00	5.50	7.00
WARRIOR cast iron cap pistol, maker unknown, 1926, "Pat Appld. For, 1926", 9"......................	25.00	30.00	40.00
Water Pistol, WYANDOTTE No. 41....	3.50	5.25	7.00
Water Pistol, WYANDOTTE, unmarked.	3.50	5.25	7.00
WESTERN cast iron cap pistol, KENTON, 1935, "Pat Sept 11-23", 7"......	5.00	6.50	8.00
WESTERN cast iron cap pistol, KENTON 1936, "Pat Sept 11-23", 7" has "jewel" over grips.................	6.00	7.50	9.00
WESTERN cast iron cap pistol, KENTON 1939, "Made in U.S.A.", 7½"........	6.00	7.50	10.00
WESTO cast iron cap pistol, KENTON, 1936, "Kenton", 7".................	5.00	6.50	8.00

	G	VG	M
WESTO cast iron pistol (doesn't fire caps), 1938, KENTON, "Kenton", 7"..	3.50	4.50	6.00
WHOOPIE cast iron cap pistol, KENTON, 1932, 5-7/8".............	4.00	5.00	6.00
WILD WEST cast iron cap pistol, NATIONAL, 1930, "Made in U.S.A.", 6½"	6.00	8.50	10.00
WINNER cast iron cap automatic, HUBLEY, 1940, 4-3/8".................	4.50	5.50	7.00
WOODSMAN cast iron cap automatic, STEVENS, 1938, "Patented; Made in U.S.A.", 5¼".....................	12.00	15.00	20.00
XTRA cast iron cap pistol, KENTON, 1936, "Made in U.S.A.", 5" long......	3.50	4.50	6.00
YANK cast iron cap pistol.............	7.00	9.00	12.00
YANKEE cast iron cap pistol, STEVENS, 1895, 5½"........................	12.00	17.00	20.00
YORK cast iron cap pistol, KENTON, 1930, "Pat. Sept. 11-23", 7"..........	5.00	7.00	9.00
YOUNG SPORTSMAN, circa 1868......	60.00	80.00	100.00
ZIP cast iron cap pistol, HUBLEY, 1930, 5".........................	4.00	5.50	7.00
ZIP cast iron cap pistol, HUBLEY, 1938, 6"........................	12.00	15.00	18.00
ZULU cast iron cap pistol, maker unknown, 1890, 6-5/8", has decoration of African warrior with spear pursuing bird...............................	40.00	55.00	75.00

AIRCRAFT

(see also Tin Wind-up, Comic Character, Premiums and Paper)
Early, valuable aircraft turned up infrequently on the lists that served to make up this book. This may be a temporary state, but, as one dealer suggested, it may also be "because so many got thrown out when their wings broke". At any rate, this sampling should be something of a guide to prices on airplanes, dirigibles, etc. Please note that early cast-iron and steel planes seem to be particularly valuable.

CONDITION OF A TOY
AND ITS RELATION TO PRICE

The price of a toy depends not only on its desirability, but on its condition. A toy in mint condition is generally worth twice what that same toy would bring in good condition, with "very good" falling about equally in between good and mint.

"Mint" means just that; the condition in which it was originally issued—perfect, regardless of age, not the slightest blemish. Needless to say this is a fairly rare state of affairs, but enough toys exist in mint condition to make it an employable term. Many people hoping to dispose of items are tempted to call a toy "mint" when it is really "near mint", "very good", or sometimes even just "good". Inevitably this can result in unhappiness all around, and not infrequently, a cancelled sale.

"Very Good" indicates a toy which has obviously seen use, with signs of wear and aging, but in general having a freshness to its appearance that makes it attractive and collectible to all but the most discriminating.

"Good" signals a toy that has seen considerable wear, shows its age, but is basically sound. A collector will collect it, but will often not be wholly satisfied with it as an example of his collection, and thus prices are often drastically below that which the same item in mint can command.

Condition below good results in another drastic drop in price, and toys with missing parts, although otherwise in excellent condition, will usually fall into this lower-priced category. Rust, even small spots of it, can seriously lower the price of a toy. "Near Mint", "Fine", "Very Fine" and similar terms often found in sellers' descriptions denote conditions between Mint and Very Good, and are priced accordingly.

The key to grading is to avoid wishful thinking. Grading can sometimes be a problem for the uninitiated, but common sense will usually prevail, and when possible, a consultation with an expert in the field can often clear up lingering doubts. A toy in its original box is worth up to 10 to 20% more if the box is in mint condition, with the price dropping as condition lessens.

DENT "Lucky Boy" Glider (see page 268).

No. 2007—Buddy "L" Hangar and one Plane. Length 12 ¼ inches, width 8 inches, height 5 inches. Size of plane, length 6 ½ inches, wing spread 10 inches. Packed one set complete in a carton_____ (see page 268)

No. 5000—Buddy "L" Monocoupe. Wing spread 10 inches, length of body 7 inches, height 3 inches. The landing gear is fitted with ⅝ inch aluminum wheels finished in orange and black enamel. Packed one in a carton. Weight ½ lb._____ (see page 268)

AIRCRAFT

	G	VG	M
AIRACUDA, 8½" wingspan, circa 1940, blue pressed steel..................	5.00	7.50	10.00
AIRFORD, small, cast iron, two-passenger, steel wheels, single engine..	14.00	21.00	28.00
AIRPLANE, wood, ride-on............	20.00	30.00	40.00
"ARMY SCOUT PLANE" pedal car, olive-green, metal.................	150.00	225.00	300.00
"ARMY SCOUT PLANE", metal.......	24.00	36.00	48.00
AUBURN RUBBER four-engine Clipper plane, approx. 5" wingspread, USA on port wing, number on starboard wing, circa 1941..................	3.00	4.50	6.00
AUBURN RUBBER ground attack or dive bomber, 4" wingspan, low wing, closed cockpit monoplane, air-cooled engine marked AUB-RUBR under fuselage, circa 1937.......................	3.00	4.50	6.00
AUBURN RUBBER pursuit ship, P-40 type, approx. 4" wingspan, US21755 on wings circa 1941................	3.00	4.50	6.00
AUBURN RUBBER pursuit ship, radial engine, open cockpit, wings marked "Pursuit Ship", "25-P-75", circa 1941	3.00	4.50	6.00
AUBURN RUBBER two-engine transport plane, circa 1937..................	3.00	4.50	6.00
BARCLAY "U.S. Army", small pursuit plane, lead, rubber wheels, circa 1941.	3.00	4.50	6.00
BARCLAY "U.S. Army" single engine transport, Tootsietoy size, white rubber wheels, circa 1940.................	2.50	3.75	5.00
BOMBER, 4-engine pressed steel, two wooden bombs that drop when button pressed, wooden wheels, wingspan approx. 14"................... ..	17.50	26.25	35.00

	G	VG	M
BUDDY "L" triple hangar and three planes No. 5010, 1931, planes are monocoupes	220.00	330.00	440.00
BUDDY "L" Monoplane and Catapult Hangar, 1930-31, No. 2007	34.00	51.00	68.00
BUDDY L single high wing, monoplane, 1929-31 No. 5000	10.00	15.00	20.00
CURTISS TRANSPORT, 9½" wingspan, khaki, pressed steel	4.00	6.00	8.00
DC-3 TRANSPORT, 10" wingspan, pressed steel, circa 1939	5.00	7.50	10.00
DC-4 type, four-motor passenger, circa 1930s, pressed steel	10.00	15.00	20.00
DENT "Air Express", cast iron, 12" wingspread, sample	380.00	570.00	760.00
DENT "Los Angeles" dirigible, 6¾", circa 1932	60.00	90.00	120.00
DENT "Los Angeles" dirigible, 8½" cast iron, circa 1925	100.00	150.00	200.00
DENT "Lucky Boy" glider, wingspread 7½", sample, circa 1932	120.00	180.00	240.00
FIGHTER, tin, circa 1940, single engine, four machine guns mounted on wing	15.00	22.50	30.00
"FLAGSHIP AMERICA" airplane, metal	25.00	37.50	50.00
FORD Tri-Motor, pressed steel, 1930s, 25" wingspan	50.00	75.00	100.00
GIRARD Whiz Skyfighter biplane, early	20.00	30.00	40.00
HELICOPTER, Army, 13" long, tin litho, friction drive, spinning prop	2.50	3.75	5.00
HUBLEY Bremen Junkers, single engine monoplane	140.00	210.00	280.00
HUBLEY P-38, black rubber tires	5.00	7.50	10.00
HUBLEY "U.S. Army" airplane, 8" wingspan, pot metal	6.00	9.00	12.00
HUBLEY "Lindy" single engine monoplane, two pilots in open cockpits, one behind the other	1000.00	1500.00	2000.00
HUBLEY U.S. Navy 3-B-4, two engine	2.50	3.75	5.00
JET, ÚSAF, 5" wingspan, friction-powered, tin litho	2.00	3.00	4.00

BARCLAY single engine "US Army" transport (see page 267).
Photo By Bill Kaufman

	G	VG	M
KEYSTONE Mail Plane, single wing, above fuselage, monoplane 24" long...	30.00	45.00	60.00
KEYSTONE riding plane, seat over tail, steering bar over cabin, single wing, high, one engine, 23½" long.........	40.00	60.00	80.00
KILGORE, Seagull, high wing, pusher prop...........................	100.00	150.00	200.00
MARX bomber, 18" wingspan, tin litho, sparkling mechanism, camouflaged, four-engine......................	10.00	15.00	20.00
MARX "Daredevil Flyer" set, plane, blimp, hangar....................	45.00	67.50	90.00
MARX Friction-powered four-motor transport with whirling propellors, tin litho.............................	9.00	13.50	18.00
MARX friction-powered "Sky-Cruiser", two-motor transport, tin litho........	7.50	11.25	15.00
MARX sparkling Rocket Fighter No. 1425, tin litho....................	9.00	13.50	18.00
P-38 glass candy container.............	15.00	22.50	30.00
P-40 cast ID model (WWII) 6" wing-span, black......................	6.00	9.00	12.00
Passenger Plane, high-wing, four-engine, approx. 9" wingspan, three wooden wheels...........................	9.00	13.50	18.00
Pull-Toy, metal airplane.............	25.00	37.60	50.00
PV-2 two-engine bomber, U.S. Navy identification type, circa WWII, black bakelite.......................	3.00	4.50	6.00
SPIRIT OF ST. LOUIS, 11" wing-spread, cast iron....................	75.00	112.50	150.00
STEELCRAFT "Army Scout Plane", single engine, 22" long, high-wing, 1920s...........................	30.00	45.00	60.00

	G	VG	M
STEELCRAFT "Army Scout Plane", trimotor, single high wing, 1920s.....	30.00	45.00	60.00
STEELCRAFT "Akron" blimp pull toy, 25" long........................	40.00	60.00	80.00
TOOTSIETOY Aero Dawn single motor.	7.50	11.25	15.00
TOOTSIETOY plane, circa 1930s, approx. 5" long, white rubber tires....	9.00	13.50	18.00
TOOTSIETOY Army transport, plane, four-engine	2.50	3.75	5.00
TOOTSIETOY biplane, 1930s, white rubber tires......................	12.50	18.75	25.00
TOOTSIETOY Eastern Airlines plane, two engines, three-blade prop, white rubber tires......................	3.00	4.50	6.00
TOOTSIETOY one and a half-inch metal airplanes from 1930s-early 1940s. Price per each...............	.50	.75	1.00
TOOTSIETOY single-engine with tin wing............................	2.50	3.75	5.00
TOOTSIETOY "U.S. Army" pursuit plane, 4" wingspan.................	5.00	7.50	10.00
TOOTSIETOY U.S. Moon Rocket, three types, all have two wheels to run on string, mid-1960s, replicas of original Buck Rogers spaceships (see Comic Character).......................	3.50	5.25	7.00
TOOTSIETOY "U.S.N. Los Angeles" dirigible, two grooved wheels on top to run on string (also was sold as part of Buck Rogers set).............	12.50	18.75	25.00
TOOTSIETOY "U.S. Navy", white rubber tires, single engine..........	3.00	4.50	6.00
TOOTSIETOY "XOP-1 U.S.N." plane, 2¾" wingspan, runs on pulley along string	7.50	11.25	15.00
TRANSPORT PLANE, pressed steel, approx. 12" wingspan, four-engine....	12.50	18.75	25.00
"UNITED BOEING", two engine cast iron, circa 1941, small.............	12.50	18.75	25.00

	G	VG	M
"UX166" cast iron plane, looks like Lindy's nickeled engine and wheels....	17.00	25.50	34.00
WYANDOTTE Airliner, circa WWII, two engine, wooden wheels..........	4.00	6.00	8.00
WYANDOTTE Bomber, Army, pressed steel, two-engine..................	5.00	7.50	10.00
ZEPPELIN, cast iron, approx. 3" long...	20.00	30.00	40.00
ZEPPELIN, "Akron", MARX, 28" long, 1930s	45.00	67.50	90.00
ZEPPELIN "EPL 1", LEHMANN.......	150.00	225.00	300.00
ZEPPELIN "EPL 2", LEHMANN, circa 1917?	200.00	300.00	400.00
ZEPPELIN, "Graf Zeppelin", small.....	7.00	10.50	14.00
ZEPPELIN, pull-toy, "Little Giant"....	15.00	22.50	30.00
ZEPPELIN, "Los Angeles" cast iron, 12" long........................	125.00	187.50	250.00
ZEPPELIN pull toy, "Macon"..........	15.00	22.50	30.00
ZEPPELIN "Pony DE 107", cast iron, 5½" long........................	30.00	45.00	60.00
ZEPPELIN "U.S. Akron", potmetal, circa 1932, 6" long....................	25.00	37.50	50.00
ZEPPELIN, "ZEP", cast iron, 5" long...	24.00	36.00	48.00
ZEPPELIN, "Goodyear" decals, 25" long, hatch opens......................	80.00	120.00	160.00
ZEPPELIN, metal, 25" long...........	20.00	30.00	40.00
ZEPPELIN, metal, 26½" long.........	20.00	30.00	40.00
ZEPPELIN, metal, 27½" long.........	30.00	45.00	60.00

DENT "Los Angeles" Dirigible (see page 268).

SHIPS

(see also Tin Wind-up, Paper)

Early ships (1920s and earlier) seem to bring the highest prices, and here wood is a much more attractive medium than it is for most toys, well-made early wooden ships often bringing eyebrow-lifting prices. Like aircraft, ships appeared infrequently on the hundreds of lists perused for this book, which could indicate a general scanting of such toys, particularly as this century wore on, and more and more boys were fascinated by vehicles and trains.

CONDITION OF A TOY
AND ITS RELATION TO PRICE

The price of a toy depends not only on its desirability, but on its condition. A toy in mint condition is generally worth twice what that same toy would bring in good condition, with "very good" falling about equally in between good and mint.

"Mint" means just that; the condition in which it was originally issued—perfect, regardless of age, not the slightest blemish. Needless to say this is a fairly rare state of affairs, but enough toys exist in mint condition to make it an employable term. Many people hoping to dispose of toys are tempted to call an item "mint" when it is really "near mint", "very good", or sometimes just "good". Inevitably this can result in unhappiness all around, and not infrequently, a cancelled sale.

"Very Good" indicates a toy which has obviously seen use, with signs of wear and aging, but in general having a freshness to its appearance that makes it attractive and collectible to all but the most discriminating.

"Good" signals a toy that has seen considerable wear, shows its age, but is basically sound. A collector will collect it, but will often not be wholly satisfied with it as an example of his collection, and thus prices are often drastically below that which the same item in mint can command.

Condition below good results in another drastic drop in price, and toys with missing parts, although otherwise in excellent condition, will usually fall into this lower-priced category. Rust, even small spots of it, can seriously lower the price of a toy. "Near Mint", "Fine", "Very Fine" and similar terms often found in sellers' descriptions denote conditions between Mint and Very Good, and are priced accordingly.

The key to grading is to avoid wishful thinking. Grading can sometimes be a problem for the uninitiated, but common sense will usually prevail, and when possible, a consultation with an expert in the field can often clear up lingering doubts. A toy in its original box is worth up to 10 to 20% more if the box is in mint condition, with the price dropping as its condition lessens.

SHIPS

	G	VG	M
AIRCRAFT CARRIER "65", tin litho, large, circa 1950s	10.00	15.00	20.00
AMPHIBIOUS WHEELED VEHICLE, "Army", 9" tin litho by Line Mar, friction motor	4.00	6.00	8.00
"ATOMIC SUBMARINE", remote-controlled, tin litho	10.00	15.00	20.00
AUBURN RUBBER Battleship, 8¼" long, circa 1941	2.00	3.00	4.00
AUBURN RUBBER Freighter, 8" long, circa 1941	2.00	3.00	4.00
AUBURN RUBBER Submarine, 6½" long, circa 1941	2.00	3.00	4.00
BATTLESHIP, cast iron, 14½" long	120.00	180.00	240.00
BATTLESHIP "Columbia", paper and wood, 1882, 36" long	235.00	352.50	470.00
BATTLESHIP, glass, approx. 3" long, candy container	4.00	6.00	8.00
BATTLESHIP "U.S.S. Washington" tin litho, circa 1941	12.50	18.75	25.00
BATTLESHIP "U.S.S. Washington", camouflaged tin litho, circa 1941	12.50	18.75	25.00
"BIG BANG BATTLESHIP", 8¼" long	20.00	30.00	40.00
BIG BANG GUNBOAT, 8" long, cast iron, early	15.00	22.50	30.00
BOAT, pull motor, metal	25.00	37.50	50.00
BOAT, tin friction, lithographed	20.00	30.00	40.00
BOAT, tin friction, painted, early	15.00	22.50	30.00
BOAT, tin friction, painted, early	40.00	60.00	80.00
BOUCHER "Gee Whiz" speedboat, painted sheetmetal, heavy clockwork motor, bronze propellor, 25" long	140.00	210.00	280.00
BUDDY L No. 3000 Tugboat, 1929-30	400.00	600.00	800.00
CHEIN speedboat, 14" long	9.00	13.50	18.00
CRUISE SHIP "Caribbean", tin litho and plastic, circa 1950s	7.50	11.25	15.00

	G	VG	M
CRUISER, glass approx. 3" long, candy container	4.00	6.00	8.00
DAYTON Battleship, 16" long, friction, circa 1920	80.00	120.00	160.00
DESTROYER, on wheels, 12" long, cast iron	700.00	1050.00	1400.00
GUNBOAT, tin friction, large wheel rises above deck' circa early 1920s, smoke-stack	60.00	90.00	120.00
GUNBOAT, two guns, two small stacks, two stories above deck, wheeled, friction, 1920s or earlier	60.00	90.00	120.00

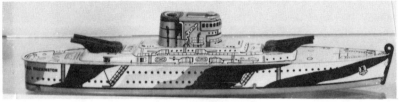

Battleship, "U.S.S. Washington", camouflaged (see page 274).
Photo Courtesy PB84.

	G	VG	M
"JOHNSON'S SEA HORSE" cast iron speedboat with figure, 10½" long	300.00	450.00	600.00
KEYSTONE Battleship, wooden, approx. 2' long with guns, airplanes take off from a spring on deck of ship	9.00	13.50	18.00
KEYSTONE Battleship, under 2' length, early 1940s	3.00	4.50	6.00
KEYSTONE fishing boat, wooden, 12" long, circa 1940s	8.00	12.00	16.00
LIFE BOAT, steel, 11" long by 5¼" wide, simple design, circa late 1930s	12.00	18.00	24.00
MANOIL Submarine, lead alloy	3.50	5.25	7.00
PULL TOY boat by HUSTILAR TOY CORP, STERLING, ILL, wood with some metal parts, oarsmen row in unison	4.00	6.00	8.00
"PURITAN" Sidewheeler, cast iron, approx. 10½" long	200.00	300.00	400.00

TOP, L TO R: "Atomic Submarine" (see page 274); "PT 10" PT boat (see page 129).
MIDDLE, L TO R: Aircraft Carrier, "65" (see page 274); Submarine "575" (see this page).
BOTTOM, L TO R: Battleship "USS Washington", (see page 274); Cruise Ship "Caribbean" (see page 274).

	G	VG	M
ROW BOAT with four men and oars, cast iron, mechanical, 9" long........	350.00	525.00	700.00
SCHIEBEL Battleship, wood stacks and large wood guns and turrets, friction motor, circa 1920..................	75.00	112.50	150.00
SCHIEBEL Battleship, circa 1927, un-powered........................	55.00	82.50	110.00
SIDE WHEELER BOAT, "The Star", tin, height, with stand, 21", length 14½"	1600.00	2400.00	3200.00
"SPEED BOAT", cast iron, with rider, 4¾" long, early....................	30.00	45.00	60.00
SUBMARINE, "575", tin litho, remote-controlled, circa 1960s..............	10.00	15.00	20.00
TOOTSIETOY Aircraft Carrier 6" long..	4.00	6.00	8.00
TOOTSIETOY Battleship, 2½" long....	.50	.75	1.00
TOOTSIETOY Destroyer K880, 4" long.	2.00	3.00	4.00

	G	VG	M
TOOTSIETOY Destroyer or light cruiser with single airplane on launcher......	2.50	3.75	5.00
TOOTSIETOY Freighter.............	2.50	3.75	5.00
TOOTSIETOY Liberty Ship...........	2.00	3.00	4.00
TOOTSIETOY Passenger Liner........	2.50	3.75	5.00
TOOTSIETOY Submarine...........	1.50	2.25	3.00
"U.S. SUBMARINE", 13" long, painted wood, fires torpedo for target set......	5.00	7.50	10.00
U.S. WASP, Carrier 27" long, wood storage under deck for planes.........	12.50	18.75	25.00
WEEDEN Live steam boat, 15" long....	150.00	225.00	300.00
WYANDOTTE Pocket Battleship, 7" long, tin litho, wheeled............	4.00	6.00	8.00
YACHT-TYPE ship, 28" long with spring-wind motor, either IVES or BING.....	650.00	925.00	1300.00

Side Wheeler Boat, tin, "The Star", height, with stand, 21". Length 14½". (see page 276).

MISCELLANEOUS

Probably the biggest news of the year in this category was the sudden boom of interest (and cash) in Schoenhut's toys, sparked by Pennsylvania's Fleetville Auctions on October 10th, 1977. Once again quality had risen to the top, as the photos of Schoenhut toys in this section will attest.

CONDITION OF A TOY
AND ITS RELATION TO PRICE

The price of a toy depends not only on its desirability, but on its condition. A toy in mint condition is generally worth twice what that same toy would bring in good condition, with "very good" falling about equally in between good and mint.

"Mint" means just that; the condition in which it was originally issued—perfect, regardless of age, not the slightest blemish. Needless to say this is a fairly rare state of affairs, but enough toys exist in mint condition to make it an employable term. Many people hoping to dispose of toys are tempted to call an item "mint" when it is really "near mint", "very good", or sometimes even just "good". Inevitably this can result in unhappiness all around, and not infrequently, a cancelled sale.

"Very Good" indicates a toy which has obviously seen use, with signs of wear and aging, but in general having a freshness to its appearance that makes it attractive and collectible to all but the most discriminating.

"Good" signals a toy that has seen considerable wear, shows its age, but is basically sound. A collector will collect it, but will often not be wholly satisfied with it as an example of his collection, and thus prices are often drastically below that which the same item in mint can command.

Condition below good results in another drastic drop in price, and toys with missing parts, although otherwise in excellent condition, will usually fall into this lower-priced category. Rust, even small spots of it, can seriously lower the price of a toy. "Near Mint", "Fine",

"Very Fine" and similar terms often found in sellers' descriptions denote conditions between Mint and Very Good, and are priced accordingly.

The key to grading is to avoid wishful thinking. Grading can sometimes be a problem for the uninitiated, but common sense will usually prevail, and when possible, a consultation with an expert in the field can often clear up lingering doubts. A toy in its original box is worth up to 10 to 20% more if the box is in mint condition, with the price dropping as condition lessens.

MISCELLANEOUS

	G	VG	M
A.C. GILBERT No. 12052 Chemistry Experiment Lab, in three-piece metal box	10.00	15.00	20.00
A.C. GILBERT Erector Set No. 2, 1919, "Patented Jan. 16th 1917, Patented May 6th 1918" includes box	22.50	33.75	45.00
A.C. GILBERT Erector Set No. 4, 1919, price includes box	22.50	33.75	45.00
A.C. GILBERT Erector Set No. 7, builds steam shovel, price includes wood box	8.00	12.00	16.00
A.C. GILBERT Erector Set No. 9, price includes wood box	25.00	37.50	50.00
A.C. GILBERT Erector Set No. 10, giant delux set, includes box approx. 30x30", makes zeppelin (fabric included), Hudson and Tender, White Truck, etc	900.00	1350.00	1800.00
A.C. GILBERT Erector Set No. 217, makes train engine and tender, price includes wood box	55.00	82.50	110.00
A.C. GILBERT Erector Set "The New Erector, World's Greatest Toy, Copy. 1928", "A.C Gilbert Co., New Haven Conn. USA", complete set with box and directions	12.50	18.75	25.00
A.C.GILBERT Erector How To Make 'Em Book, 1938, tells how to make various projects with Erector Set	5.00	7.50	10.00
A.C. GILBERT Erector Hudson Locomotive	237.50	356.25	475.00
A.C. GILBERT Erector Set Manual of Instructions for set Number 4, 1928, illustrated	2.50	3.75	5.00
A.C. GILBERT Erector, very large set, comes with big white truck, trains, crane	90.00	135.00	180.00

	G	**VG**	**M**
A.C. GILBERT Wood tool box and tools.	6.00	9.00	12.00
Air Raid Warden Junior Kit, felt hat, arm band, gas mask, whistle, window sign, forms and street-plan sheets, stethoscope, book of instructions, WW II era	15.00	22.50	30.00
ALL-NU jockey on horse, circa 1941	3.00	4.50	6.00
Alligator, cast iron, 9"	10.00	15.00	20.00
Alligator, cast iron, two-part, 9" long	20.00	30.00	40.00
American Badge ring, circa 1930s or 1940s, heavy metal, may have been premium	4.00	6.00	8.00
AMERICAN LOGS—similar to Lincoln Logs, circa WW II, price includes box.	2.25	3.38	4.50
"Anti-Aircraft Rapid-Fire Machine Gun", cast iron, on wheels	30.00	45.00	60.00
ARCADE Farm Wagon, "Whitehead & Kales Co.", 6½"	70.00	105.00	140.00
ARCADE tools, cast iron No. 779N, small, nickel finish, screwdriver, hammer, monkey wrench, pipe wrench, crescent wrench and S wrench, came in set of 6, 1938. Price per each	.90	1.00	1.10
ARCADE weapons, cast iron, No. 778N, small, nickel finish, cutlass, pistol, automatic, aerial bomb, tommy gun, airplane, came in set of six, 1938. Price per each	.90	1.00	1.10
ARCADE Pump and Tub	25.00	37.50	50.00
Archie sparkler toy, "Archie, a RONSON Toy Pat. 1918", uses flints, both eyes sparkle	40.00	60.00	80.00
AUBURN RUBBER Calf, circa 1937	1.00	1.50	2.00
AUBURN RUBBER Chicken, circa 1937.	1.00	1.50	2.00
AUBURN RUBBER Collie, circa 1937	2.00	3.00	4.00
AUBURN RUBBER Colt, circa 1937	2.00	3.00	4.00
AUBURN RUBBER Cow, circa 1937	1.50	2.25	3.00
AUBURN RUBBER Duck, circa 1937	1.00	1.50	2.00
AUBURN RUBBER Fence Section, circa 1937	1.00	1.50	2.00

	G	VG	M
AUBURN RUBBER Horse, circa 1937...	2.00	3.00	4.00
AUBURN RUBBER Pig, circa 1937......	1.50	2.25	3.00
AUBURN RUBBER Piglet, circa 1937....	1.00	1.50	2.00
Baby Buggy, cast iron, 4¼" high.......	14.00	21.00	28.00
Baby Carriage, tin, with folding cloth top, 7¾" long....................	26.00	39.00	52.00
Badge, "Dick Steel News Service".......	2.00	3.00	4.00
Badge, Jet Ranger...................	5.00	7.50	10.00
Badge, "Junior Detective", heavy six-pointed star badge with copper insert, nickel badge......................	7.50	11.25	15.00
Badge, Junior G-Man, circa late 1930s, brass, shield-shaped, eagle on top.....	4.00	6.00	8.00
Badge, Junior Secret Agent, metal......	4.00	6.00	8.00
Badge, "The Purple Mask" detective badge..........................	6.50	9.75	13.00
Badge, "Sheriff", six-pointed star, black oval insert and word "Oklahoma", nickeled metal.....................	8.00	12.00	16.00
Badge, Wyatt Earp Marshall, six-pointed	6.50	9.75	13.00
BALDWIN Toy hens, pair. Lay marble eggs and cluck, 4½"................	26.00	39.00	52.00
Barbed Wire (Army), 8" long, for toy soldiers...........................	2.50	3.75	5.00
Barbed Wire, mesh, for toy soldiers.....	1.00	1.50	2.00
Bear and Black Boy with hammers, mechanical, 13" long...............	240.00	360.00	480.00
Bee, tin, with propellor, "Brevete S.G.D.G.", 8" long................	18.00	27.00	36.00
Bell Toy, cast iron, 6" long, 7" high Spanish-American era, soldier pivots to tinkle two bells...................	95.00	142.50	190.00
Bell Ring Pull Toy, boys eating bananas, cast iron..........................	70.00	105.00	140.00
Bell Ringer, bird and bell, tin and iron, 6" long...........................	160.00	240.00	320.00
Bell Ringer, Boy Scouts, iron, rest pressed steel, heart-shaped tin wheels, 13½" long........................	120.00	180.00	240.00

	G	VG	M
Bell Ringer with chimes, tin horse, 5¾" long	150.00	225.00	300.00
Bell Ringer, "Eskimo & Bear", pressed steel body and iron figures	250.00	375.00	500.00
Bell Ringer, heart-shaped tin wheels, iron figures, clown and black man	220.00	330.00	440.00
Bell Ringer, horse with rider, cast iron and tin, tin heart-shaped wheels	30.00	45.00	60.00
Bell Ringer, horse and rider, heart-shaped wheels, 9" long, tin	360.00	540.00	720.00
Bell Ringer, horse and rider, iron and pressed steel, iron heart-shaped wheels, 6¼" long	40.00	60.00	80.00
Bell Ringer, "Monkey and Dog", heart wheels, cast iron and tin, 7" long	54.00	81.00	108.00
Bell Ringer, tin and cast iron, horse and rider	24.00	36.00	48.00
Bell Ringer, two comic characters, pressed steel and iron, three bells, pierced heart wheels	225.00	337.50	450.00
Bell Ringer, two heads hit bell, heart wheels, cast iron	60.00	90.00	120.00
Bell Toy, bear on tricycle, 4" long	66.00	99.00	132.00
Bell Toy, cast iron, heads ring bells	14.00	21.00	28.00
Bell Toy, cast iron, in the form of Victory, in a shell-form chariot, mounted with bell and eagle	1500.00	2250.00	3000.00
Bell Toy, clown and black man on see-saw, circa 1905, 6½" long, six colors, WATRESS, cast iron	95.00	142.50	190.00

Bell Toy, cast iron, in the form of Victory in a shell-form chariot, mounted with bell and eagle. (see this page).
Photo Courtesy PB84

	G	VG	M

Bell Toy, figure moves and rings bell,
cast iron and pressed steel, 5¾" long.. | 50.00 | 75.00 | 100.00

	G	VG	M
Bell Toy, figure moves and rings bell, cast iron and pressed steel, 5¾" long..	50.00	75.00	100.00
Bicycle, early, wood-spoked, 67" long...	100.00	150.00	200.00
Bicycle, Wheeler, red-painted..........	500.00	750.00	1000.00
Blocks, nested, 6, paper litho on cardboard, picturing children and animals, 1920, CRAMER PUBLISHING CO...	9.00	13.50	18.00
Blocks, 16, embossed, wooden, 1¾" square, red and blue, alphabet and pictures, 7½" square box, Dutch scene on cover, THE EMBOSSING COMPANY'S TOY BLOCKS, USA, price includes box......................	6.25	9.38	12.50
Blocks, 64, wooden, 1¼" square, very colorful, letters and numbers on sides, box 6" square, price includes box......	11.00	16.50	22.00

Bicycle, early, wood-spoked. 67" long. (see this page).
Photo Courtesy PB84

	G	VG	M
Boy on Sled friction toy, rear wheels have spokes	70.00	105.00	140.00
Boy on Velocipede, papier mache, cloth and cast iron, wind-up, STEVENS & BROWN or ALTHORP & BERGMANN, circa 1870-1880, 10¾" long	250.00	375.00	500.00
Boy Scout Five-In-One Mystery Hidden Compass	20.00	30.00	40.00
Brochure, framed, illustrating mechanical banks, cap pistols, cannon, etc., J.E. STEVENS, CONN	55.00	82.50	110.00
BUDDY L tool chests, 1927-28, four different, per each	50.00	75.00	100.00
Bulldog, kid-covered wind-up, walks and turns head, 7½" long	94.00	141.00	188.00
Cackling Hen, cardboard, drum, 2¼x3½", with brown plaster chicken standing on top of drum, metal side handle activates cackling, dated 1936	7.00	10.50	14.00
Camel, jointed	25.00	37.50	50.00
Candy Container, Stop and Go, glass, etc., traffic signal	25.00	37.50	50.00
Candy Container, tin, shaped like cannon, candy comes out barrel when crank is turned, "WEST BROS. CO. Grapeville, Pa.", 7½" long	40.00	60.00	80.00
Candy Container shaped like a desk phone, glass base with cast pewter mouthpiece and wooden receiver, paper labels "lines busy", 4¼" high	7.00	10.50	14.00
Cannon, ARCADE howitzer, 4" long, circa 1941	8.00	12.00	16.00
Cannon, AUBURN RUBBER (AUB-RUBR), 6½" long	8.00	12.00	16.00
Cannon, BARCLAY, 4½" long	4.00	6.00	8.00
Cannon, BARCLAY, shoots, approx. 5½" long	4.00	6.00	8.00
Cannon, BIG BANG 13"	9.00	13.50	18.00
Cannon, BIG BANG 23" long	14.00	21.00	28.00
Cannon, BIG BANG 24" long	14.00	21.00	28.00

	G	VG	M
Cannon, "Boy Scout Machine Gun", 19" with 8¼" wheels.............	20.00	30.00	40.00
Cannon, brass, with wood base, 9" long..	20.00	30.00	40.00
Cannon, carbide, 9" long, wheels.......	5.00	7.50	10.00
Cannon, cast iron, 5" long.............	3.00	4.50	6.00
Cannon, cast iron on wood base, 5½" long	3.00	4.50	6.00
Cannon, cast iron, 6" long.............	9.00	13.50	18.00
Cannon, cast iron, 6½" long...........	10.00	15.00	20.00
Cannon, cast iron, 7" long.............	7.00	10.50	14.00
Cannon, cast iron, 7" long, gold paint...	3.00	4.50	6.00
Cannon, cast iron, 7" long, pat. 1894....	10.00	15.00	20.00
Cannon, cast iron, 8" long, unusual design............................	14.00	21.00	28.00
Cannon, cast iron with turned barrel, "Hotchkiss", 9½" long.............	10.00	15.00	20.00
Cannon, cast iron, 9¾"..............	9.00	13.50	18.00
Cannon, cast iron, 10" long, black......	14.00	21.00	28.00
Cannon, Army, cast iron with brass barrel, 10½" long, mechanically elevated barrel............................	16.00	24.00	32.00
Cannon, cast iron, 11" long............	14.00	21.00	28.00
Cannon, cast iron, 15½"...............	22.50	33.75	45.00
Cannon, cast iron, 15½", "Young America", "Rapid Fire Gun".........	10.00	15.00	20.00
Cannon, cast iron, fires caps, mounted on wood base.....................	3.00	4.50	6.00
Cannon, Coast Defense Gun, 5" long, camouflaged, litho tin.............	5.00	7.50	10.00
Cannon, "Dainty" cast iron, on wood base, 10" long....................	94.00	141.50	188.00
Cannon, die cast, approx. 5½" long, old type, shoots......................	3.00	4.50	6.00
Cannon "Disappearing Coast Defense Gun", THOMAS & SKINNER, Indianapolis, 15" wood and steel, fires.......	20.00	30.00	40.00
Cannon, field, World War I, cast iron, 15¾"	24.00	36.00	48.00
Cannon, firecracker, cast iron, 4" long, "Pat Apr. 23 1895"................	14.00	21.00	28.00

	G	VG	M
Cannon, howitzer type, die cast, shoots, approx. 5" long, spring mechanism, pre WW II........................	3.00	4.50	6.00
Cannon, IVES, cast iron, brass barrel...	14.00	21.00	28.00
Cannon, IVES, red wheels, brass cannon, 7" long...........................	26.00	39.00	52.00
Cannon, KENTON, firecracker type....	14.00	21.00	28.00
Cannon, LINE MAR, 17" long, elevates with wheel.......................	7.00	10.50	14.00
Cannon, MANOIL howitzer, several similar versions, die cast............	3.00	4.50	6.00
Cannon, MARX Anti-Aircraft Gun, No. 617.............................	5.00	7.50	10.00
Cannon, PREMIER, large thick barrel, large wheels, cast iron..............	12.00	18.00	24.00
Cannon, pressed steel base 9½"........	3.00	4.50	6.00
Cannon, RANGER JR. cast iron, 10" long	34.00	51.00	68.00
Cannon, rapid fire, cast iron, embossed eagle............................	106.00	159.00	212.00
Cannon, sheetmetal, shoots small marbles, 14" long, blue with red wheels...........................	8.00	12.00	16.00
Cannon, silver, with red wooden wheels, approx. 3" long...................	1.75	2.63	3.50
Cannon, tin, pull lever for corks.........	10.00	15.00	20.00
Cannon, tin, striped spring-loaded barrel with lever........................	16.00	24.00	32.00
Cannon, tinplate, 7" long, spring action.	5.00	7.50	10.00
Cannon, TOOTSIETOY, approx. 3¾" long, pre WW II, shoots............	2.50	3.75	5.00
Cannon, TOOTSIETOY, 40MM AA gun, pre WW II.......................	5.00	7.50	10.00
Cannon, TOOTSIETOY, 155 MM gun, pre WW II.......................	5.00	7.50	10.00
Cannon, TOOTSIETOY, 155 MM self-propelled howitzer, 1950s..........	3.00	4.50	6.00
Cannon, TOOTSIETOY, 1930s, approx. 5½" long, shoots..................	5.00	7.50	10.00

	G	**VG**	**M**
Carousel Horse, hand-carved, American-made, with jeweled eyes and man and eagle saddle, 64" high, 55" long	2600.00	3900.00	5200.00
Cat, cardboard, standing on piece of wood, circa 1900	1.50	2.25	3.00
Catalog: AUBURN RUBBER, 1941, toy soldiers etc	2.50	3.75	5.00
Catalog: Baltimore Price Reducer, 1928, illustrated with toys, games, etc	7.00	10.50	14.00
Catalog: Butler Bros. 1889, tin toys, squeak toys, etc	10.00	15.00	20.00
Catalog: Butler Bros. 1891, illustrated with mechanical banks, toys, dolls, etc	10.00	15.00	20.00
Catalog: Butler Bros. 1930, illustrated with toys, banks, etc	14.00	21.00	28.00
Catalog: DENT Hardware Co	5.00	7.50	10.00
Catalog: DENT Hardware Co., Fullerton, Pa., undated	7.00	10.50	14.00
Catalog: DENT Hardware Co., Fullerton, Pa., iron toys	7.00	10.50	14.00
Catalog: "Dunham", Buckley & Co., New York, 1895, toys, etc	20.00	30.00	40.00
Catalog: Ehrich Bros., New York, 1892, illos of banks, toys, dolls, etc	20.00	30.00	40.00
Catalog: A.J. Fisher, N.Y. 1877, illustrating cap pistols, etc	14.00	21.00	28.00
Catalog: Illustrated brochure of cap pistols and animated cap pistols by IVES and WILLIAMS	7.00	10.50	14.00
Catalog: KENTON HARDWARE CO., 1934, illus in color	90.00	135.00	180.00
Catalog: "McCadden & Bros." Philadelphia, illustrated iron and tin toys, banks, mechanical toys, dolls, games, etc	40.00	60.00	80.00
Catalog: Mickey Mouse Merchandise Catalog, 1935, by Kay Kamen Co., 80 pages, hundreds of illustrations of Mickey Mouse items	130.00	195.00	260.00

	G	VG	M
Catalog: Nicol & Co. 1895, illustrating banks, etc.	5.00	7.50	10.00
Catalog: Popsicle Pete Radio News and Premium catalog, early	27.50	41.25	55.00
Catalog: Popsicle Pete's 1949 four-page gift list	3.00	4.50	6.00
Catalog: SCHOENHUT Circus	14.00	21.00	28.00
Catalog: SCHOENHUT Humpty Dumpty Circus Toys (other toys as well), circa 1915, many illustrations	30.00	45.00	60.00
Catalog: SELCHOW & RIGHTER, 1894-5, games and toys, illustrated trains, boats, bell toys, mechanical banks, etc.	90.00	135.00	180.00
Catalog: State, Adams & Dearborn Sts., Chicago, illustrated	3.00	4.50	6.00
Catalog: Carl P. Stern, illustrating cap pistols, etc.	14.00	21.00	28.00
Catalog: J.E. STEVENS CO. 1906, illustrations of iron toys and mechanical banks	24.00	36.00	48.00
Catalog: Thorsen & Cassady, 1894, guns, etc.	16.00	24.00	32.00
Catalog: Tom Mix 1936 Premium Catalog	17.50	26.25	35.00
Catalog: A.C. WILLIAMS CO., Ohio, illustrating still banks, cast iron toys, airplanes, etc.	74.00	111.00	148.00
Cathedral Music Box, tin litho, of organ pipes and cherubs, plays loud or soft according to speed of cranking, 5x5x7", no markings	20.00	30.00	40.00
CHEIN Easter Egg with chicken on top, opens up to hold candy, circa 1938, tin, 5½"	5.00	7.50	10.00
CHEIN Musical Church, tin, circa 1937	15.00	22.50	30.00
CHICAGO Printing Press, No. 15	16.00	24.00	32.00
Children's Telephone (set of two), 1920	9.00	13.50	18.00
Chimes Bell-Ringer with Elephant, 7" long	34.00	51.00	68.00

Climbing Monkey brings coconuts down from palm tree, tin, 18" high, "Monkey

	G	VG	M
Shines, Emporium Specialists"....	44.00	66.00	88.00
Clock, tin, transfer scene of coach and four, works with small pendulum, "Lux Clock Mfg. Co., Waterbury, Conn. USA", 7" high....	30.00	45.00	60.00
Clockwork Dancers, pair, with melting cloth costumes on wood base, 9½" high	240.00	360.00	480.00
Clown, balancing, copper, clown holding arched balancing pole weighted at both ends with lead balls, standing on one leg on small round platform on stationary metal ladder 6½" high. Move clown in any direction and he won't fall off platform....	10.00	15.00	20.00
Clown, wind-up, papier mache and cardboard, 43" high....	50.00	75.00	100.00
Coffee Grinder, cast iron, 4" high....	26.00	39.00	52.00
Composition Toy with tin wheels. Little man in driver's uniform goggles and steering wheel with weighted base, 3¾" high....	50.00	75.00	100.00
"Consul", the educated monkey, tin hand toy, monkey automatically adds, subtracts, multiplies, and divides, 5½x6", dated June 27, 1916....	9.00	13.50	18.00
Conveyor Belt, wood....	14.00	21.00	28.00
Cot, Army, canvas with steel frame, circa early 1940s....	1.75	2.63	3.50
Cow, papier mache, 44" long....	46.00	69.00	92.00
CRACKERJACK Prizes—Metal toys from 1930s, includes binoculars, screwdriver, fish, trolley car, trowel, battleship, monkeywrench, cat, horsedrawn hansom cab, deer, mason's hammer, doll, lady's old-fashioned shoe, police badge, dog, rabbit, overshoe, cow, old-fashioned men's shoes, rooster, fancy pitcher, thimble, full dimension fancy dining room chair. Price per each....	.60	.80	1.00

	G	VG	M
Crackle (KELLOGG'S RICE KRISPIES) handpuppet	3.00	4.50	6.00
Cupboard, cast iron, open work iron has diamond and heart pattern, two doors and one drawer	26.00	39.00	52.00
Dancing Figure, mechanical, on wood base, in clothing	100.00	150.00	200.00
Dog Cart, wood and metal	66.00	99.00	132.00
Dog on Turntable, two different, one sold at $200 in very good, the other at $100 in very good			
Dog pulling girl in cart, cloth covered, tin, 9" long	20.00	30.00	40.00
Donkey, cast iron, 4¼"	3.00	4.50	6.00
Drum, metal body, litho, red white and blue design, varnished wooden hoops, leather "ears", sheepskin head and fiber bottom, with wooden drumsticks, circa 1910	8.00	12.00	16.00
Drum, about 1920	8.00	12.00	16.00
Dump Wagon, pressed steel, cast iron wheels, 13" long, bottom opens	24.00	36.00	48.00
Egyptian Figure, brass. When button in base is pushed, sides fly open, revealing naked women in gilt brass. Signed by "B" in a double handle vase, 5¼" high .	40.00	60.00	80.00
Electric Stove, works, 1930s	16.00	24.00	32.00
Farm Wagon with figure, cast iron, 14½" long	40.00	60.00	80.00
Flagpole, wooden, with flag that raises and lowers, approx. 8" high	2.00	3.00	4.00
Flying Propellor Ring, heavy metal, circa 1930s-40s, could have been a premium .	4.00	6.00	8.00
Fort, RICH TOYS, Clinton, Iowa, 9X11X21, wood, pressed wood and metal with moveable drawbridge circa 1940	20.00	30.00	40.00
Froggie, rubber squeeze toy, REMPEL, 1940s	9.00	13.50	18.00

	G	VG	M
G-MAN siren pocket signal, metal, oval-shaped, WALT REACH TOYS, turn metal crank on side and makes siren sound	3.00	4.50	6.00
George Washington on horseback, bisque, 19th century	440.00	660.00	880.00
Giraffe, 97" high, stuffed cloth	166.00	249.00	332.00
Glass candy container shaped like train engine, 3" long	3.00	4.50	6.00
Glass candy container shaped like a train lantern, 3½" high	3.00	4.50	6.00
Glass candy container shaped like a train lantern, tin top and base, "Victory Glass Inc.", 3½" high	3.00	4.50	6.00
Glass perfume container shaped like lantern, "Tappan's Famous Sweet Bye and Bye", 3½" high	8.00	12.00	16.00
Grandfather's Clock, tin, has weights that make hands rotate and pendulum swing, but is not a working clock, transfer decorated, 8¾" high	20.00	30.00	40.00
Grasshopper Mechanical Pull Toy, HUBLEY	220.00	330.00	440.00
H.K. Electric Engine, patented 1908, uses D.C. current	40.00	60.00	80.00
Hand Washing Machine with wringer	5.00	7.50	10.00
HESS Dynamobil	160.00	240.00	320.00
Hitch, DENT, two-horse, cast iron 14¼"	12.50	18.75	25.00
Hitch, front, for goat cart, two goats	180.00	270.00	360.00
Hitch, two-horse for caisson, 9½" with figure	15.00	22.50	30.00
Hitch for log wagon, two-oxen, HUBLEY, 10¼"	54.00	81.00	108.00
Hitch, HUBLEY, three-horse, for large fire engine, 9" horses	26.00	39.00	52.00
Hitch, back, cast iron, for log, KENTON	16.00	24.00	32.00
Hitch, KENTON, cast iron, two-horse, with driver, 9"	11.00	16.50	22.00
Hitch, three-horse, cast iron, 5¼"	3.00	4.50	6.00

	G	VG	M
Hitch, three-horse, cast iron, 7¼"......	3.00	4.50	6.00
Hitch, three-horse, large front-end, 9" horses.........................	34.00	51.00	68.00
Hitch, three-horse, cast iron, 11½" long.	20.00	30.00	40.00
Hitch, three-horse, cast iron, 15".......	36.00	54.00	72.00
Horse and Rider, tin, on tin rockers, with bell, 6" long.................	45.00	67.50	90.00
Horse, cast iron.....................	.66	.99	1.32
Horse, cast iron, 5"..................	1.50	2.25	3.00
Horse, cast iron, standing, 10" high.....	11.00	16.50	22.00
Horse, sheet metal, with cast iron jointed legs, full form, 10¾" long, 11" high...	100.00	150.00	200.00
Horse Race, circular track within rectangular box, circa 1900, lever-activated...	50.00	75.00	100.00
HUBLEY grasshopper pull toy, cast iron.	80.00	120.00	160.00
Hurdy-Gurdy, turn crank and play tune, shows animal playing cello..........	14.00	21.00	28.00

IVES "Fire Engine House" circa 1890, cast iron and wood. 16" long. (see page 294).
Photo Courtesy PB84

	G	VG	M
"I Hear A Call", dog with knapsack.....	34.00	51.00	68.00
Ice Box, "Alaska", cast iron, has glass cube of ice in top, 5" high...........	25.00	37.50	50.00
Iron and Trivet, cast iron.............	7.00	10.50	14.00
Iron, tin, 5" high....................	5.00	7.50	10.00
Iron, tin, 3½" high..................	9.00	13.50	18.00
IVES Boy smoking cigar and holding stomach, cast iron.................	45.00	67.50	90.00
IVES Fire Engine House, circa 1890, cast iron and wood, 16" long........	400.00	600.00	800.00
IVES Struktiron, 1916, non-motorized, with box........................	50.00	75.00	100.00
IVES Struktiron, building set, 1916, motorized, with box...............	75.00	112.50	150.00
Jockey, small, on very large horse, on base, tin, 14½" high, wheeled.....	250.00	375.00	500.00
"Jolly Jungleers", MILTON BRADLEY, 1932, derringer type pistol shoots over animal targets.....................	22.50	33.75	45.00
Kangaroo, cast iron, 6¼" long, "Jumps".	114.00	171.00	228.00
KENTON Dray Wagon, lithographed paper on sides, driver, 15½" long.....	26.00	39.00	52.00
KENTON Driver, small size...........	1.50	2.25	3.00
KENTON Driver with high hat for pleasure vehicle......................	5.00	7.50	10.00
KENTON Musicians, 8, for Kenton Band Wagon..........................	17.50	26.25	35.00
KENTON Polar Bear, cast iron........	3.00	4.50	6.00
KENTON Stove, cast iron, marked "Oak" on door........................	12.00	18.00	24.00
KENTON Stove, with warming shelves and stove plates, high back for smokestack, "Royal" on door and shelves, 10" high........................	20.00	30.00	40.00
Kingpin Bowling Game, "BALDWIN MFG. CO. Brooklyn NY No. 300", circa 1940.......................	15.00	22.50	30.00
"Knockout Target Shooting Gallery", lithographed tin with rifle, many targets..........................	25.00	37.50	50.00

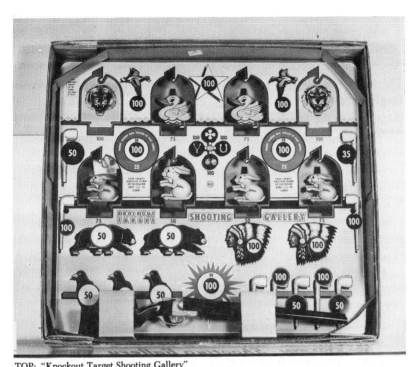

TOP: "Knockout Target Shooting Gallery"
(see page 294).

	G	VG	M
Ladder for fire trucks, cast iron.........	1.00	1.50	2.00
Ladders, stamped steel, from HUBLEY and ARCADE trucks................	8.00	12.00	16.00
Lady Pulling Cart, tin friction, marked "Depose, R.F.", feet rotate as she walks, 5" long....................	67.50	101.25	135.00
Lamb, tin, 2¼" long................	18.00	27.00	36.00
LEHMANN "Express" tin friction of man pulling wagon.....................	46.00	69.00	92.00
LEHMANN "Mechanical Flying Bird", paper wings......................	225.00	337.50	450.00
LEHMANN Peking, two chinese carrying chest, tin friction toy................	320.00	480.00	640.00
LINCOLN TIMBERS, pre WW II, price includes box......................	1.75	2.25	3.50
LINCOLN LOGS, per WW II, large set, price includes box.................	20.00	30.00	40.00
Lion in Hoop, tin 6¼" high............	80.00	120.00	160.00
LIONEL Science Kit, circa 1960........	17.50	26.25	35.00

	G	VG	M
Log Wagon, cast iron and wooden, 14" long	7.00	10.50	14.00
Machine Gun, wood and steel, gravity feed, wooden bullets	5.00	7.50	10.00
Magic Lantern	10.00	15.00	20.00
Magic Lantern, KEYSTONE, "Radioptocin"	26.00	39.00	52.00
Magic Lantern Projector, tin, embossed deer on door and side, 8" long	7.00	10.50	14.00
Man on Bicycle, animated, tin, high wheel bike, bell on top of bicycle, 10½" high	360.00	540.00	720.00
Man, smoking, clockwork mechanism	500.00	750.00	1000.00
Marbles, with sulphide animal centers, price per each marble	15.00	22.50	30.00
Marbles, glass, with spiral swirls, up to $10 apiece in mint			
Marionette Show, electrically operated, Santa Claus' workshop with 23 moving figures and four moving animals making presents, 46" high, 72" long, 24" deep	630.00	945.00	1260.00
Marky Maypo rubber squeeze toy, 1960s	3.00	4.50	6.00
MARX Air-Sea Power game	7.50	11.25	15.00
MARX Air-Sea Power Bombing Set	7.50	11.25	15.00
MARX Army and Navy Mechanical Target NO. G169	7.50	11.25	15.00
MARX Army Code Sender, 9½" Morse key and phone, pressed steel	6.00	9.00	12.00
MARX Bust 'Em Target Game No. G38	7.50	11.25	15.00
MARX Co. A Barracks, tin litho building, 6x8x12"	7.00	10.50	14.00
MARX Colonial Doll House No. 4052	5.00	7.50	10.00
MARX Deluxe Dial Typewriter, 1930s	17.50	26.25	35.00
MARX Dial Typewriter No. 1000A, 1930s	15.00	22.50	30.00
MARX Dishwasher K54, circa 1950s	4.00	6.00	8.00
MARX Doll House No. 4021	5.00	7.50	10.00
MARX Doll House No. 4030	7.50	11.25	15.00
MARX Headquarters, tin litho, U.S. Army Training Center, 5x8x11"	12.50	18.75	25.00

	G	VG	M
MARX Junior Dial Typewriter No. 2109, circa 1930s	17.50	26.25	35.00
MARX Kitchen Sink K47, circa 1950s	4.00	6.00	8.00
MARX Medieval Castle Fort No. 4709	7.50	11.25	15.00
MARX Refrigerator, K42, circa 1950s	4.00	6.00	8.00
MARX Rex Mars Planet Patrol Set, 1950s	17.50	26.25	35.00
MARX Searchlight, tin litho, 3½" high	8.00	12.00	16.00
MARX Stove K39, circa 1950s	4.00	6.00	8.00
MARX Swinging Arm Target Game No. G52	3.75	5.25	7.50
MARX Swinging Arm Target Game No. G55	3.75	5.25	7.50
MARX Suburban Colonial Dollhouse, metal	5.00	7.50	10.00
MARX Typewriter No. 1110, metal and plastic, circa 1950s-1960s	7.50	11.25	15.00
MARX U.S. Army Training Center No. 4133	7.50	11.25	15.00
MARX Zippo Monkey, climbs string	15.00	22.50	30.00
MATTEL Jack in the Music Box, circa 1950s	2.50	3.75	5.00
Meat Grinder with clamp, die cast	2.50	3.75	5.00
MECCANO Microscope Set, 1933	5.00	7.50	10.00
Merry-Go-Round, wind-up, lithographed paper and wood, with four bisque figures riding fur-skinned papier mache horses	466.00	699.00	932.00
Merry-Go-Round, wood and lithographed paper Jenny musical wind-up with five horse-form seats	166.00	249.00	332.00
METALCRAFT Build-A-Zep, builds 21 different 18" zeppelins	64.00	96.00	128.00
Monkey, mechanical, in red pants, red-checked shirt, squeeze metal lever attached to 34" spiral wire and monkey jumps alongside you, hitting cymbals, 10" high	14.00	21.00	28.00
Monkey, stuffed, cloth	50.00	75.00	100.00

MERRY-GO-ROUND, wind-up, lithographed paper and wood, with four bisque figures riding fur-skinned papier mache horses (see page 297).
Photo Courtesy PB84

	G	VG	M
Monkey, stuffed, red felt cap and jacket, glass eyes, moveable arms and legs, move his tail and head moves from side to side, and up and down, circa 1910, 9½" high	14.00	21.00	28.00
Monkey, stuffed, with red hat and shirt, short pants, circa 1939	3.00	4.50	6.00
Mound of Earth, tin litho, 4" long (for toy soldiers)	2.00	3.00	4.00
Movie Projector, "Flip Movies", turn crank and flip cards from "Midgette" movies, with film, circa early 1930s	56.00	84.00	112.00

MERRY-GO-ROUND, wood and lithographed paper Jenny musical wind-up with five horse-form seats. (see page 297).
Photo Courtesy PB84

	G	VG	M
Movie Projector, "Uncle Sam", hand cranks, circa 1930s	25.00	37.50	50.00
Music Box, tin, shaped like coffee grinder, 3" high	22.50	33.75	45.00
Musical Spinner Toy, hand-carved bear, spin with hand and hear music box play	64.00	96.00	128.00
Noise Maker, tin, shaped like old-fashioned phone mouthpiece, 2¼" high	5.00	7.50	10.00
"Old Kentucky Home" wood litho action toy, six dancers, singer-musicians, moved by hand crank, 15½" long	366.00	549.00	732.00
Paddle Wheel and Tower on base, tin, 14" high	20.00	30.00	40.00
"Paris Coaster", wood-wheeled cart	26.00	39.00	52.00
Phonograph, "Bing Pigmyphone", early, with sound horn, decorated with black musicians on sides, toy	180.00	270.00	360.00
Phonograph, toy, GENOLA, cranks, with sound horn	144.00	216.00	288.00
Phonograph, toy, NERONA, cranks, sound comes from horn connected to needle, early	110.00	165.00	220.00
Pig and Piglet in cage, wood, cloth and lithographed paper, spring-loaded squeak toy	50.00	75.00	100.00

	G	VG	M
PLAROLA CORPORATION Organ, tin lithographed, with six organ rolls	35.00	52.50	70.00
"Play Store Register", tin and brass, DURABLE TOY AND NOVELTY CO., 4" high	6.00	9.00	12.00
Player Toy Saxophone, "Q.R.S. Playasax, Q.R.S. DeVry Corp.", comes with three rolls, 11½" long	24.00	36.00	48.00
Pool Table, two men shooting pool	50.00	75.00	100.00
Pop (KELLOGG'S RICE KRISPIES) hand puppet	3.00	4.50	6.00
Pram, four-wheel painted wood with leather canopy and wood wheels	66.00	99.00	132.00

Pram, four-wheel painted wood with leather canopy and wood wheels. (see this page).
Photo Courtesy PB84

	G	VG	M
"Preacher In The Pulpit" mechanical toy, all wood........................	300.00	450.00	600.00
Pull Bell Toy, tin dog standing on platform with bell mechanism on back, 14" long........................	116.00	174.00	232.00
Pull Toy, cast iron horsewoman riding sidesaddle on pony................	66.00	99.00	132.00
Pull Toy, turtle with frog and bell on his shell, 6¾" long, cast iron........	36.00	54.00	72.00
Pull Toy, man and woman on seesaw, with bell, cast iron and tin, 7¼"......	1000.00	1500.00	2000.00
Pull Toy, cloth and wood horse mounted on a rocking base..................	40.00	60.00	80.00
Pull Toy, stuffed rabbit, legs outstretched on wheels........................	2.50	3.75	5.00
Pull Toy, elephant, tin, with blanket, iron wheels, 4½" long.............	25.00	37.50	50.00
Pull Toy, elephant with saddle, tin. Iron wheels, 4½" high.............	35.00	52.50	70.00
Pull Toy, four race horses and riders, tin with cast iron wheels, 8¼" long....	134.00	201.00	268.00

TOP, L TO R: MARX Junior Dial Typewriter No. 2109; MARX Typewriter No. 1110.
BOTTOM, L TO R: MARX Dial Typewriter No. 1000A; MARX Deluxe Dial Typewriter. (see pages 296-297).
Photo Courtesy PB84

	G	VG	M
Pull Toy, galloping horse, tin, 7" long...	40.00	60.00	80.00
Pull Toy, horse, white, pulling water wagon, tin, 6¾" long...............	175.00	262.50	350.00
Pull Toy, horse, dark, pulling water wagon, tin, 7¼" long..............	75.00	112.50	150.00
Pull Toy, tin horse, iron wheels, 9" long..	75.00	112.50	150.00
Pull Toy, horse and cart with chicken-shaped sides, iron wheels, tin 5¼" long	28.00	42.00	56.00
Pull Toy, horse and covered delivery wagon, tin, 5¼" long...............	25.00	37.50	50.00
Pull Toy, tin horse and wheels, wooden platform and animated figure with composition head and tin arms playing tin drum and cymbal, 13½" long.....	155.00	232.50	310.00
Pull Toy, horse and rider, tin, iron wheels, 4½" long.................	42.50	63.75	85.00
Pull Toy, horse and rider, tin, iron wheels, 11" long.................	75.00	112.50	150.00
Pull Toy, horse and wagon, tin, 9¼" long	50.00	75.00	100.00
Pull Toy, polo player on horse, tin, 4¼" long.........................	35.00	52.50	70.00
Pull Toy, race horse in car, tin "Moxie", 8½" long.........................	54.00	81.00	108.00
Pull Toy, rooster, tin, 3¼" long........	22.00	33.00	44.00
Pull Toy, sheep, tin, 7" long...........	60.00	90.00	120.00
Pull Toy, tin horse and cart with iron wheels, friction toy?, 7½" long.......	22.00	33.00	44.00
Pull Toy, two ponies ridden by children, animated, tin, 9" long..............	180.00	270.00	360.00
Pull Toy, horse on wheels, wooden, very small wheels, horse is dappled........	2.50	3.75	5.00
Pump, cast iron.....................	4.00	6.00	8.00
Pump, tin, with round trough, transfer of puppies, 7" high.................	14.00	21.00	28.00
Push Toy, clown on log, bell toy, cast iron.............................	100.00	150.00	200.00
Push Toy, large running horses, tin, cast iron wheels, 14" high by 14½", horses' size........................	234.00	351.00	468.00
Rabbit, moves ears, small.............	110.00	165.00	220.00

	G	VG	M
Rabbits, two, mashing ingredients in small bowl, tin, animated by squeezing, 6" high	12.00	18.00	24.00
Ripley's Believe It Or Not Disk-O-Knowledge, round piece of cardboard with another piece attached on top, turn to reveal questions and answers, 1932, 9½" diameter	2.50	3.75	5.00
Road Signs, cast iron, two bases and four signs, read "R.R. Crossing", "Stop", "Hill", "US 30", ARCADE, price per set	8.00	10.00	12.00
Rocking Chair, two-horse, wood and wicker	26.00	39.00	52.00
Rocking Horse, cloth and wood	26.00	39.00	52.00
Rocking Horse, tin, horse with rider, 6" long	140.00	210.00	280.00
Rocking Horse, hand carved, all wood	26.00	39.00	52.00
Rocking Horse, painted wood	66.00	99.00	132.00
Rocking Horse, wood	40.00	60.00	80.00
Rocking Toy, tin, girl on horse, 3¾" long	34.00	51.00	68.00
Roller Skates, early, metal	7.00	10.50	14.00
Rolmonica, harmonica that plays rolls of tunes, "Blow, crank and play", with three songs, 1930s	60.00	90.00	120.00

ROLMONICA (see this page).

TOP: SCHOENHUT Elephant, jointed; SCHOENHUT Rhinoceros, jointed.
MIDDLE: SCHOENHUT Zebra, jointed; SCHOENHUT Giraffe, jointed.
BOTTOM: SCHOENHUT Lion, jointed; SCHOENHUT Horse, jointed, with circus rider saddle.
(see this page and next).
Photo Courtesy PB84

	G	VG	M
Sandbags, variously marked, for toy soldiers	.75	1.13	1.50
Sand Pail, tin litho, circa 1940	2.50	3.75	5.00
Scales, cast iron, tin tray and four brass weights, 5¾" long	26.00	39.00	52.00
Scales, cast iron, "DAYTON", 3½" high	18.00	27.00	36.00
SCHOENHUT Camel, two-humped	460.00	690.00	920.00
SCHOENHUT Elephant, jointed	57.50	86.25	115.00

	G	VG	M
SCHOENHUT Gazelle	350.00	525.00	700.00
SCHOENHUT Giraffe, jointed	50.00	75.00	100.00
SCHOENHUT Girl Bareback rider, bisque head, wood-jointed body	130.00	205.00	260.00
SCHOENHUT Golfer in Knickers	180.00	270.00	360.00
SCHOENHUT Golfer in Skirt	200.00	300.00	400.00
SCHOENHUT Hippopotamus	150.00	225.00	300.00
SCHOENHUT Hollywood Home buildings, set of six homes, 1928	150.00	225.00	300.00
SCHOENHUT Horse, jointed, with circus rider saddle	25.00	37.50	50.00
SCHOENHUT Lion, jointed	45.00	67.50	90.00
SCHOENHUT Monkey	50.00	75.00	100.00
SCHOENHUT Ostrich	150.00	225.00	300.00
SCHOENHUT Piano	20.00	30.00	40.00
SCHOENHUT Piano, brass-mounted	30.00	45.00	60.00
SCHOENHUT Reindeer	300.00	450.00	600.00
SCHOENHUT Rhinoceros, jointed	57.50	86.25	115.00
SCHOENHUT Side-show circus tent	1200.00	1800.00	2400.00
SCHOENHUT Wild Animal Cage	180.00	270.00	360.00
SCHOENHUT Zebra, jointed	45.00	67.50	90.00
See-Saw, boy and girl, tin, works by pouring water or sand onto board, 1930s	8.00	12.00	16.00
SEIBERLING LATEX PROD. Panda, rubber squeak toy	2.00	3.00	4.00
Shooting Gallery chickens, cast iron, 10¼" long	11.00	16.50	22.00
Signal Jr. R-70 Twin Wireless Practice Set, two beginner's sending keys, and one advanced key, circa 1920	17.50	26.25	35.00
Sled, hand-operated mechanical, early, 56" long	100.00	150.00	200.00
Sled, push-type, wood and metal, red-painted	90.00	120.00	180.00
Sled, push-type, wood, upholstered	54.00	81.00	108.00
Sled, "Star", wood and metal, painted, 71" long	66.00	99.00	132.00
Snap (KELLOGG'S RICE KRISPIES) hand puppet	3.00	4.50	6.00

SLED, push-type, wood, upholstered. (see page 305).
Photo Courtesy PB84

	G	VG	M
Sparkler, push-down mechanism to make sparks, circa 1940, tin..............	2.50	3.75	5.00
Spinner Toy, old man, small...........	9.00	13.50	18.00
Sprinkling Can, color litho, tin, 1930s...	5.00	7.50	10.00
Squeak Toy, cat and mouse, in clothing, 8½" high......................	34.00	51.00	68.00
Steam Engine Accessory—blacksmith with bellows.....................	34.00	51.00	68.00
Steam Engine Accessory—man pumping water...........................	24.00	36.00	48.00
Steam Engine that generates electricity, old	75.00	112.50	150.00

L TO R: Wheelbarrow, cast iron, 6½" long (see page 312); Baby Buggy, cast iron, 4¼" high (see page 282); Scales, cast iron, tin tray and four brass weights, 5¾" long (see page 304); Iron, tin, 3½" high (see page 294); Stove, "Daisy," cast white metal, 4¼" high (see page 308).
Photo Courtesy Garth's Auctions Inc.

ARCADE Tools, cast iron
No. 779N, 1938 (see page 281).

	G	VG	M
Steam Engine with horizontal boiler tank, burner, twin pistons, two flywheels and revolving boiler, rectangular base measures 6¾" by 14"	7.00	10.50	14.00
Steam Engine, Electric, EMPIRE, chrome-plated, 1930s	15.00	22.50	30.00
Steam Engine, "Mamod", horizontal brass boiler, whistle and flywheels, base is 7¼" by 8"	30.00	45.00	60.00
Steam Engine, vertical, with whistle, burner, water gauge, two flywheels and piston-operated water pump, 9¼" high	24.00	36.00	48.00
Steam Engine, vertical, with burner, whistle, flywheel and shaft running through boiler tank 11¼" high	14.00	21.00	28.00
Steam Engine, "Empire", cast iron base . .	20.00	30.00	40.00
Steam Engine, IVES, 1870, with cardboard accessories	700.00	1050.00	1400.00
Steam Engine, tin, with bell, marked "Union", 11½" long	200.00	300.00	400.00
Steam Engine, WEEDEN No. 648, iron and brass	20.00	30.00	40.00
Steam Engine, "WEEDEN", vertical with whistle, flywheel and revolving governor, 9½" high	15.00	22.50	30.00
Steam Engine, "WEEDEN", vertical, with burner, whistle and flywheel, 11½" high	14.00	21.00	28.00

SEE MISCELLANEOUS:
TOP, L TO R: MARX Sink K-47; MARX Dishwasher K-54.
BOTTOM, L TO R: MARX Stove K-39; MARX Refrigerator K-42. (see pages 296-297).
Photo Courtesy PB84

	G	VG	M
Stichwell Sewing Machine, child's floor model, circa 1920s..................	44.00	66.00	88.00
Stove, cast iron, "American"...........	60.00	90.00	120.00
Stove, "Daisy", cast white metal, 4¼" high.............................	7.00	10.50	14.00
Stove, "Eagle", cast iron, 4¼" high.....	20.00	30.00	40.00
Stove, electric, one burner, two ovens, chrome-finished steel, procelain on oven doors, 16" wide, 14" tall........	44.00	66.00	88.00
Stove, "Lancaster", "Eagle" on door and shelf, 10¾", cast iron...........	22.00	33.00	44.00
Stove, wood-burning cast iron, "The Queen"...........................	55.00	82.50	110.00

	G	VG	M
Stove, wood-burning cast iron, "The Triumph Range"	45.00	67.50	90.00
Stove, tin, with four plate covers, four pans and one skillet, 5" high	34.00	51.00	68.00
Stretcher for 3" toy soldiers, pre-WW II	1.50	2.25	3.00
Sulky, cast iron, single casting	24.00	36.00	48.00
Swing, animated, cast iron and pressed steel, for doll, with eagle, wheel	400.00	600.00	800.00
Swinging Clown, tin, base marked "C.D. KENNY CO.", 4¼" high	54.00	81.00	108.00
"The Symmetroscope", wood and tin type of kaleidoscope, 6¼" high, F.P. IRVING, Troy, N.Y.	22.00	33.00	44.00
Tea Kettle, cast iron, 3¼" long	18.00	27.00	36.00
Tent, Army, two pole, two flags on top, approx. 5" long	2.00	3.00	4.00
Tent, canvas, white, 9" long	4.00	6.00	8.00
Tent, Army, "Field Hangar, U.S. Aviation Corp Squadron 1", two flags atop tent, approx. 9" long	5.00	7.50	10.00

Bicycle, wheeler, red-painted. (see page 284).   Photo Courtesy PB84

Tricycle, wood and metal, 50" long (see page 311).
Photo Courtesy PB84

	G	VG	M
Tent, Army, "U.S. Battery B. Coast Artillery", two poles, two flags on top.	4.00	6.00	8.00
Tent, "Guard Tent Co. A" 4¼" high....	3.00	4.50	6.00
Tent, "U.S. Infantry Co. A", 4½" high, two flags on top.....................	4.00	6.00	8.00
Tent, "U.S. Infantry Co. B"............	4.00	6.00	8.00
Tent, paper, 5" high, "State Camp Co. A"...........................	1.50	2.25	3.00
Tiger, jointed.......................	37.50	56.25	75.00
Tin dog with boy rider, 13½" long, on wheeled platform.................	360.00	540.00	720.00
Toledo Scales, 4x4", cast iron...........	14.00	21.00	28.00
"Tom Thumb" cast register, metal, 6½"x7½"x7¼" by WESTERN STAMP-ING CO..........................	6.00	9.00	12.00

	G	VG	M
TOOTSIETOY furniture, six chairs, moveable bar, two side tables and a dining table......................	25.00	37.50	50.00
TOOTSIETOY living room set, two chairs, lamp, gramophone, sofa, secretaire, table...................	25.00	37.50	50.00
TOOTSIETOY metal kitchen and bathroom furniture, sink, bathtub, toilet, stove, table and cupboard...........	15.00	22.50	30.00
Top, wooden, circa 1940..............	2.00	3.00	4.00
TRANSWORLD AIRLINES Jr. Pilot Wings...........................	3.00	4.50	6.00
Tricycle, iron........................	34.00	51.00	68.00
Tricycle, "Overland", wood and metal...	26.00	39.00	52.00
Tricycle, small metal................	14.00	21.00	28.00
Tricycle, wood and metal articulated horseform, 44" long................	100.00	150.00	200.00
Tricycle, wood and metal, 50" long.....	120.00	180.00	240.00
Tricycle, wood, painted, 38" long.......	46.00	69.00	92.00
"Trinity Chimes" tone player toy, early..	54.00	81.00	108.00
TURNER Garage, heavy sheet metal, one window on each side, divided into four panes	3.50	5.25	7.00
Upside Down Toy, circa 1910, two figures on tall towered see-saw.............	44.00	66.00	88.00
Velocipede, wood, hand-operated, with horse-head motif, painted in blue and yellow, approx. 31" long...........	160.00	240.00	320.00
Velocipede, black-painted iron, 37" long.	100.00	150.00	200.00
Velocipede, 44" long.................	66.00	99.00	132.00
Velocipede, L. GOULD & CO., iron, three-wheeled	74.00	111.00	148.00
Waffle Iron, cast iron, WAGNER.......	2.50	3.75	5.00
Wagon, wood, for child, 1900.........	30.00	45.00	60.00
Walking Horse, metal and papier mache wind-up, early, 8¼"...............	150.00	225.00	300.00
Washing Machine, 1900, salesman's sample	46.00	69.00	92.00
Washing Machine, tin, works, circa 1940, seashore scene on side..............	3.00	4.50	6.00

Velocipede, black-painted iron. 37" long (see page 311).
Photo Courtesy PB84

	G	VG	M
Wheelbarrow, cast iron, approx. 5½"...	8.00	12.00	16.00
Wheelbarrow, cast iron, 6½" long......	9.00	13.50	18.00
Windmill, metal, with pumping apparatus.........................	7.00	10.50	14.00
WOLVERINE "Automatic Sand Crane", tin...............................	14.00	21.00	28.00
WOLVERINE Organ, tin, turn crank to make organ-like sounds.............	30.00	45.00	60.00
WOLVERINE Sunny Andy "Kiddie Kampers" action toy, 5-5/8" by 3½",' color litho, three boy scouts and two girl scouts in backdrop camp setting, boys chop and saw wood and girls signal with flags, marbles drop down chute, circa 1929...................	22.50	33.75	45.00
WOLVERINE Sandy Andy sand loader, 1912............................	25.00	37.50	50.00
WOLVERINE Sand Loader, tin beach toy, lithographed, circa 1950s........	5.00	7.50	10.00
Woman chasing duck, early tin friction..	26.00	39.00	52.00
Wood Cage with horse, when gate is open horse pops out and whinnies.........	66.00	99.00	132.00

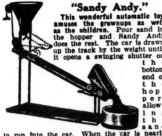

"Sandy Andy."

This wonderful automatic toy amuses the grownups as well as the children. Pour sand in the hopper and Sandy Andy does the rest. The car is drawn up the track by the weight until it opens a swinging shutter on the bottom end of the hopper, allowing the sand to run into the car. When the car is nearly full the added weight of the sand causes the car to run down the track and automatically dump the sand. The weight then again pulls the car up for another load and this operation is automatically continued as long as there is sand in the hopper. Great fun for the children. Size, 20½x18 inches. Shipping weight, 4½ pounds.

No. 49K1409

Zoetrope (see this page).
Photo Courtesy Milton Bradley

WOLVERINE "Sandy Andy"
(see page 312).

	G	VG	M
Wood Cage, mechanical, rooster flies out when door is open..................	7.00	10.50	14.00
Wood Mechanical Dancing Figure, clockwork, on box base..................	60.00	90.00	120.00
Wooden Music Maker, "Auto Phone Co. H.B. Horton's, Ithaca, N.Y.", 9½" high, uses player rolls..............	56.00	84.00	112.00
WYANDOTTE Hen, chubby, tin, lays egg when body pressed down, 8½" long, with eight eggs...............	10.00	15.00	20.00
"Zoetrope", wood and cardboard, illustration of motion game, MILTON BRADLEY.......................	100.00	150.00	200.00

BIBLIOGRAPHY

(A number of the publications listed here, if not available locally, can be purchased through Antique Toy World, listed below)

ANTIQUE TOY WORLD—$8.00 for one-year subscription, payable to Dale Kelley, 3941 Belle Plaine, Chicago, Illinois, 60618

A CELEBRATION OF COMIC ART AND MEMORABILIA by Robert Lesser, HAWTHORN

CAST IRON TOY PISTOLS by Charles W. Best, ROCKY MOUNTAIN ARMS & ANTIQUES

DISNEYANA by Cecil Munsey, HAWTHORN

JIM HARMON'S NOSTALGIA CATALOGUE by Jim Harmon, TARCHER/HAWTHORN

AMERICAN DIMESTORE SOLDIERS, Volume 1 by Don Pielin, available at $6.00 from Don Pielin, 1009 Kenilworth, Wheeling, Illinois, 60090

OLD TOY SOLDIER NEWSLETTER, $8.00 for one-year subscription, payable to Steve Sommers, 209 North Lombard, Oak Park, Illinois, 60302

IT'S ALL IN THE GAME, Biography of Milton Bradley, by James J. Shea, PUTNAM

"The Grey Iron Casting Company of Mount Joy, Pa." by Karl Zipple, published in GUIDON Vol. 30 No. 4, 1972, Vol. 31 No. 2, 1973, and Vol. 32 No. 1, 1974

CAVALCADE OF TOYS by Ruth and Larry Freeman, 1942, CENTURY HOUSE

TOYS IN AMERICA by Inez and Marshall McClintock, 1961, PUBLIC AFFAIRS PRESS, WASHINGTON, D.C.

THE TOY COLLECTOR by Louis H. Hertz, 1969, FUNK & WAGNALLS

ANTIQUE TOYS by Gwen White, 1971, ARCO

THE BUYER'S GUIDE—Comics, Premiums, Disney items and other toys, Single Copies $1.00 Dynapubs, 15800 Route 84 North East Moline, Illinois, 61244

TOY MUSEUMS
AND MUSEUMS THAT FEATURE TOYS

American Museum of Automotive Miniatures
  Andover, Massachusetts
Auburn-Cord-Duesenberg Museum
  Auburn, Indiana, 46706
  (AUBURN toys and Cord and Duesenberg
  automobiles)
Museum of the City of New York
  5th Avenue and 103rd Street
  New York, New York
Smithsonian
  Washington, D.C.
Daisy Gun Museum
  U.S. 71 South
  Rogers, Arkansas
  (The world's most complete collection of air
  rifles, dating from the 18th century)

AUCTIONEERS

These are reputable firms experienced in disposing of large collections of toys by auction.

PB84 (A Division of Sotheby Parke Bernet Inc. New York)
171 East 84th Street
New York, New York
(212) 472-3584

Sotheby Parke Bernet, Los Angeles
7660 Beverly Boulevard
Los Angeles, California, 90036
(213) 937-5130

Garth's Auctions Inc.
2690 Stratford Road
Delaware, Ohio, 43015
(614) 362-4771

Ted Maurer
Pottstown, Pennsylvania
(215) 323-1573

Gene Harris Antique Center
P.O. Box 294-203 So. 18th Avenue
Marshalltown, Iowa, 50158
(515) 752-0600

Butterfield & Butterfield
1244 Sutter Street
San Francisco, California, 94109
(415) 673-1362

Fleetville Auctions, Route 407
Fleetville, Pennsylvania, 18420
(717) 945-3277

Ken Gooch
Dexter, Iowa, 50070
(515) 789-4406

Phillip B. Robinson
1010 Gray Street
St. Charles, Illinois, 60174
(312) 584-0383

LEADING COLLECTORS AND DEALERS

JIM HARMON—Radio premiums and tapes, comic books and strips
P.O. Box 38612
Hollywood, California, 90038

RAY FUNK—Bronze trains, comic books, toys
Funk's Trains
826 East 8th Street
Upland, California, 91786

BARBARA & JONATHAN NEWMAN—Paper toys, old and new
The Paper Soldier
8 McIntosh Lane
Clifton Park, New York, 12065

CHARLES W. BEST—Old toy pistols, etc.
6288 South Pontiac
Englewood, Colorado, 80110

AL RIZZOLO—Vehicles, soldiers, all other old toys
The Red Pony
216 Bloomfield Avenue
Bloomfield, New Jersey, 07003

ALAN LEVINE—Premiums, Big Little Books, Movie Material,
Comics, Toys
P.O. Box 1577
Bloomfield, New Jersey, 07003

C.B.C. LEE—Automotive toys, toys by HUBLEY, ARCADE
and TOOTSIETOY
P.O. Box 8
Shawsheen Village, Massachusetts, 01810

THOMAS W. SEFTON—Standard Gauge Trains, BUDDY L,
other toys
San Diego Trust & Savings Bank
Box 1871
San Diego, California

EDWARD K. POOLE—Toy soldiers, 1/36 scale ID vehicles and
old wooden military vehicle kits
926 Terrace Mt. Drive
Austin, Texas, 78746

DON PIELIN—Toy soldiers
1009 Kenilworth
Wheeling, Illinois, 60090

ED & ELAINE LEVIN—Comic and Celebrity toys
Nickelodeon Antiques
13826 Ventura Blvd.
Sherman Oaks, California, 91403

OLD FRIENDS—Disney toys, etc.
202 East 31st Street
New York, New York

SECOND CHILDHOOD—Antique toys
283 Bleecker Street
New York, New York

SPEAKEASY ANTIQUES—Antique toys, etc.
799 Broadway
New York, New York

RON LOWDEN, JR.—Antique toys, etc.
The Time Machine
Ardmart No. 37
44 Greenfield Ave.
Ardmore, Pennsylvania

ALBERT W. McCOLLOUGH—BUDDY "L" Trains and vehicles
c/o Copydesk
Newsweek
444 Madison Avenue
New York, New York, 10022

KARL ZIPPLE—GreyKlip Toy Soldiers
3514 Devonshire
Kalamazoo, Michigan, 49007

MEMORABLE THINGS—American and foreign toy soldiers,
vehicles, etc.
P.O. Box 166
Riderwood, Maryland, 21139
(Shop Address: 31 W. Allegheny Avenue, Towson, Maryland,
Room 250)

DON & JEAN PORTER—Soldiers, Repros of MANOIL & BARCLAY
figures
DJ's Miniatures
7609 Grandview
Arvada, Colorado, 80002

ATTIC TREASURES—Tin Wind-Ups, etc.
6106 Ashley Place
Springfield, Virginia, 22150

THE GRENADIER GUARD—Foreign and American toy soldiers
115 East 69th Street
New York, New York, 10021

GOOD OLD DAYS STORE—All types of old toys
148 Merrick Road
Amityville, New York, 11701

AMERICANA NOSTALGIA—Toys, comic books
P.O. Box 10150 Hackberry Sta.
San Antonio, Texas, 78210
(Shop Address: 3520 S. New Braunfels Road)

BUD READ—Toys and trains
1348 S.W. 20th Terrace
Fort Lauderdale, Florida, 33312

DAVISON BOOKS—Toy books and toy catalogs
14 Boxwood Drive
Stamford, Connecticut, 06906

ECCLES BROTHERS—Barclay soldiers from original molds, and tin helmets
902 Summer Street
Burlington, Iowa, 52601

TERRY SELLS—Hollow cast, hand-painted soldiers, etc., from the original Manoil molds.
1196 N. Decatur Road
Atlanta, Georgia, 30306